A
CHRONICA BOTANICA
PUBLICATION

Consulting Editor, Frans Verdoorn

PLANT TAXONOMY

Methods and Principles

LYMAN BENSON

Pomona College

THE RONALD PRESS COMPANY • NEW YORK

To

HARVEY MONROE HALL

(1874–1932)

Harvey Monroe Hall in America and G. Turesson in Europe introduced a new era in taxonomy of plants. Hall sought to reflect the evolution of species in formulation of systems for their classification. He believed evolution to be based upon the physiological adjustment of the organism, the measurable result of which is seen in morphological and histological adaptations, and he argued that the taxonomist of the future would think in terms of evolutionary processes, treating morphological criteria as dynamic rather than static. To this end he adapted experimental methods, particularly those of ecology, to research in taxonomy and, collaborating with his

iii

Timber-line experimental station established by H. M. Hall for the Carnegie Institution of Washington, at 10,000 feet elevation in the Sierra Nevada. The Harvey Monroe Hall Natural Area is in the background.

colleague, E. B. Babcock, employed the data and techniques of the new field of cytogenetics. He died in 1932 when he was only fifty-eight, but his work was carried forward brilliantly, augmented, and published by his younger colleagues, Jens Clausen, David D. Keck, and William M. Hiesey.

Dr. Hall was an active member of the faculty of the University of California at Berkeley, in charge of the herbarium and the botanical garden from 1903 to 1919, and an honorary professor both there and at Stanford afterward. After 1919 he developed for the Carnegie Institution of Washington a program of experimental taxonomy and established laboratories in various ecological habitats.

Dr. Hall's range of interests is shown by (1) his surveys of areas, such as the exceedingly rugged San Jacinto Mountains and Yosemite National Park; (2) his monographic studies of genera so difficult that others avoided them—*Atriplex, Potentilla, Artemisia, Chrysothamnus, Haplopappus,* and various genera in the Madinae (or Madieae); (3) his studies of ecological zonation of plants (in collaboration with Joseph Grinnell); (4) his studies of hayfever plants; (5) his classical studies, with T. H. Goodspeed and Frances L. Long, of the rubber content of North American plants; (6) his interest in international aspects of botany, as exemplified by securing Rockefeller Foundation funds for a new building for the Muséum d'Historie Naturelle in Paris and financial aid for the Conservatoire et Jardin Botanique in Geneva, as well as his proposal of an international bureau for plant taxonomy (carried out after his death).

Preface

Since the little-known writings of Gregor Mendel were brought to light, as the twentieth century began, the field of plant classification, or taxonomy, has matured into a thorough study of natural population systems and of their evolution in relation to past and present environments. Like all other fields of knowledge, taxonomy has deep roots in related and even in seemingly unrelated areas of investigation. Because the factors to be taken into account have changed, and because the underlying principles are now better understood, the entire field of taxonomy requires thoughtful reevaluation. It is hoped that this book is a contribution toward that end.

The chapters which follow place primary emphasis upon the dynamic application of taxonomic methods and principles, and the rules of nomenclature. The reader is shown how to explore for data in herbaria and in published studies. He is made aware that much can be contributed to his search by data from the sciences of microscopic morphology, paleobotany, biogeography, chemistry, ecology, physiology, cytology, and genetics. By experimental studies, he comes to grips with the methodology of constructing a taxonomic system and the rules which govern the choice of valid scientific names. He also learns how taxa should be described and how to supply proper documentation for his research. The orientation of the book is toward research, and the final chapters deal with the preparation of treatises and monographs for publication.

Although primarily written as a textbook for students who have already acquired some familiarity with plant classification, this volume will, it is believed, also find reference use by students in conjunction with other course work; by teachers, in the preparation of lectures and laboratories in taxonomy or other fields; and by research workers in taxonomy and in fields which bear kinship to this discipline.

The gratitude of the author is expressed to many individuals, particularly to those who have read all or parts of the manuscript. For their contributions, the author is especially indebted to Dr.

Verne Grant, Rancho Santa Ana Botanic Garden; Drs. Norman H. Boke and George J. Goodman, University of Oklahoma; Dr. Hugh Iltis, University of Wisconsin; Dr. Earl E. Sherff, Hastings, Michigan; Dr. G. Ledyard Stebbins, Jr., University of California, at Davis; and Dr. Robert E. Woodson, Jr., Washington University and the Missouri Botanical Garden.

Much of the field work described in Chapter 3 was carried out with advanced classes at Pomona College. In recent academic years this has been in collaboration with Dr. Edwin A. Phillips of Pomona College and students who were supported in their research work by the National Science Foundation Undergraduate Research Participation Program. Their help is gratefully acknowledged.

Two research grants for the study of the cacti of the United States and Canada have been made by the National Science Foundation, one by the Society of Sigma Xi, and several by the Claremont Graduate School. Many of the examples in this book are based upon this otherwise unpublished research, and the writer is grateful for this support.

Dr. Frank Salisbury of Colorado State University developed and printed nearly all of the films used as halftone illustrations. For his excellent work, the author is deeply indebted.

LYMAN BENSON

Claremont, California
    February, 1962

Contents

Part II

Classification

Part III

Choice of Names

Part IV

Description and Documentation

Part V

Treatises and Monographs

INTRODUCTION

Research in Taxonomy

THE PROBLEM OF CLASSIFICATION

In ancient times the Mediterranean Sea was a Roman lake. The galleys of the Caesars patrolled it from one end to the other. But west of the Mediterranean was a great ocean which the Romans found void, and they wrote on the rocks at the Strait of Gibraltar, *"Ne plus ultra!"*

Several years ago a college student of botany and one of mathematics compared notes. The botany student was amazed to learn of research in mathematics. In high school he had been fascinated by the subject, but he had supposed it to be finished and its study to consist merely of working out problems solved by every academic generation since Greek and Roman times. The mathematics student was equally amazed at the thought of research in plant classification. He liked the out-of-doors, and in high school he had enjoyed making a collection of pressed plants, but he had supposed all taxonomy to be merely identifying dried specimens according to authoritative books. Each had labeled the other's field *ne plus ultra.*

Collecting and identifying specimens is only the beginning of taxonomy, for plant specimens are significant to research only insofar as they may reveal the existence of problems or may fit into patterns leading toward their solution. The problem of classification is not identification of plants according to an established system, but devising or revising of the taxonomic system itself.

Classification of living plants is complex partly because species vary from individual to individual and from race to race as do human beings. The plants composing a species may include tens,

3

hundreds, or even thousands of gene combinations, and, unless there has been asexual reproduction, two individuals alike may be as rare as identical human fingerprints or faces. Consequently, determination of the characters marking the species is difficult.

Furthermore, species are continually in a state of flux, and the boundaries between them are not clear. A species may include several short lines of evolution ranging from budding new ones to remnants of nearly extinct ones. As one generation dies its members, like the people in a town, are replaced by others similar to, but not identical with, themselves. As the environment changes gradually through geologic time, the individual plants best adapted to new conditions are likely to survive and reproduce while others die out. If different groups of members of the natural plant populations within a species tend to be favored by changing local environments, in time some groups may become gradually differentiated from each other, thus raising the question of whether all belong to one species. Ultimately all the intermediate populations may die, and two or more clear-cut species may result. Even after clear differentiation has occurred, another shift of conditions in at least some geographic areas may permit hybrids to survive in competition with these species. Breeding of the hybrids back to one of the parental species may permit transfer of genes characteristic of one species into some individuals of the other, again complicating classification.

When the intergradation of major population systems is so nearly complete that it is difficult to tell where one begins and another ends, it may be practical to define and name only the extreme forms as species, or it may be better to describe the entire group as a single variable species. In other cases the plastic mass of related forms may include two or more groups having fewer intermediates than extremes, and these may be classified as relatively distinct species or varieties. Thus, species and other recognized taxa [1] are not necessarily always of the same degree of distinctness.

There can be no final answer to classification problems, because, although species and other taxonomic units are real entities, their composition is irregular, their boundaries are not fixed, and one shades into the next. The plant taxonomist may develop a better, more readily understandable explanation of the nature and status of taxa, but he can only revise and improve, never complete, the taxonomic system. No matter how long he may search or how many

---

[1] Singular, **taxon**: a category used in classification, as, for example, a variety, species, genus, family, etc. (See discussion in Chapter 9.) The term was proposed originally as a convenience in nomenclature, but its scope has been expanded with use.

experiments he may conduct, he still does not discover all that can be learned about the classification of any taxon. He must draw tentative conclusions from incomplete data or draw none at all. He is forever approaching the truth but he never reaches it in all particulars.

THE SIGNIFICANCE OF EVOLUTION IN CLASSIFICATION

In the eighteenth century, Linnaeus organized data from the earlier literature of plant classification on the basis of his own extensive study of species. The results were best summarized in two of his books which are the official starting points for the naming of vascular plants, *Species Plantarum* (1st ed., 1753) and *Genera Plantarum* (5th ed., 1754). This was before the proposal of the theory of evolution, and a century before Darwin's *Origin of Species* . . . , published in 1859. Linnaeus proposed for practical use in identifying plants an **artificial system** of classification, emphasizing especially the number of stamens in the flower. This was an arbitrary device for pigeonholing plants according to categories not reflecting their relationships. However, Linnaeus thought the great goal of botany to be that of devising a **natural system** which would reflect these relationships, placing the plants in categories indicating their affinities. He made an attempt in this direction, describing 68 "orders," approximately the equivalents of modern families, but he knew the information available in his day was inadequate for fulfillment of this objective.

In the time of Linnaeus and for a century afterward an attempt to discover a natural system of classification meant trying to learn the plan of Creation. The passage of another century since the revolutionary proposals of Darwin and others has shifted this concept to discovery of the course of evolution. If there is a "key" to classification, it is determination of the factors which have influenced the appearance of certain characters in one taxon and not another. Often minute structural or obscure physiological features may be responsible for the differentiation of taxa. The following is an example:

In the flowers of many Ranales, including *Magnolia* (Fig. 1–1) and *Ranunculus* (buttercup), there is no special pathway which a visiting insect must follow, and many potential pollinators may be ineffective because they touch only the numerous stamens or only the many pistils. However, the insects do carry pollen and leave some of it here and there. The accumulated pollen in the flower is partly its own and partly from other flowers. Since flowers of

Fig. 1–1. See next page for legend.

many species are self-fertile, pollen from either source may be effective, provided it can reach the stigma.

In some species of *Ranunculus* the pollen may be floated to the stigmas by rain water (Hagerup, 1950). Hagerup tested the effect of the water upon the pollen, and the effectiveness of rain pollination, as follows:

1. Some flowers out of reach of insects were exposed to rain for one hour; others were not. Only those exposed to rain set fruit normally; the others were pollinated in only a few cases in which the innermost anthers touched the outermost stigmas.
2. Pollen which had been soaked for three hours in rain water in a flower was placed in a sugar solution; germination was normal.
3. Some of the pollen was placed on the pistils on one side of a flower otherwise excluded from pollination; only this side developed fruits.

Floating of the pollen to the level of the stigmas is governed in *Ranunculus bulbosus* (Figs. 1–2 and 1–3) by a coordinated system of minute structures, including (1) the glossy and non-glossy portions of the upper surfaces of the petals and (2) passageways formed by the bases of the petals and sepals, the grooves on the pedicels, and two types of hairlike structures (trichomes) (Hagerup, 1950). The height of the water in the upturned flower is determined in part by the texture of the surfaces of the basal and apical parts of the upper sides of the petals (Fig. 1–4). Because water does not adhere to the distal glossy areas of the petals, the surfaces determine the height of the collected water in the center of the flower. This is just sufficient to float pollen grains above the pistils and, as the water recedes, to leave pollen stranded on the stigmas, as also in *Ranunculus Flammula* (Fig. 1–5).

Microscopic examination of sections of petals of *Ranunculus* provides an explanation of the surface glossiness appearing in the petals of some species and not others (Parkin, 1928, 1935). The gloss is

---

Fig. 1–1. The Ranalian flower (*Magnolia grandiflora*, representing the order Ranales, which retains more primitive features than the flower of any other order of the flowering plants): (1) flower open the first morning, with a small insect on the stigmas and another on the stamens, no structural feature compelling the same insect to visit both; (2) flower open the second morning, the stamens, except two, having fallen from the receptacle of the flower and two stamens having lodged in the concavities of two of the six petals (actually seven, there being an extra small one in this flower). Ordinarily in this species many stamens lodge in the concavities of the petals, and they are visited there by insects. However, this flower was tilted too much to retain the stamens.

due to a layer of cells filled with starch, a factor making buttercup petals a delicacy in the eyes of herbarium beetles as well as those in the field. The glossy area occurs on the distal portions of the petals, extending varying distances from the tips toward the bases, in some species more than half way, in some less.

Fig. 1–2. *Ranunculus bulbosus,* a European species introduced widely but usually occurring rather sparingly in eastern North America. Specimen from Milton, Massachusetts.

The starch-filled cells imparting glossiness to the petals are only part of an interlocking system of minute structures. This system includes obscure features of the flower and associated parts and of their minute appendages. Most of the water entering the flower of rain-pollinated species does not carry the pollen away from the flower by overflowing the cup or bowl formed by the lower non-glossy portions of the petals and occupied by the stamens and pistils; the excess is drained off through minute passageways beginning with

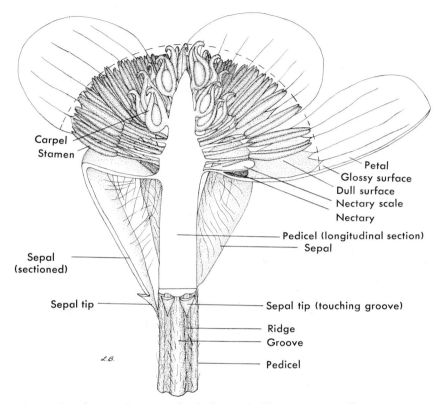

Fig. 1–3. Flower of *Ranunculus bulbosus*, half cut away. Pollen, as in many flowers of the Ranales (Fig. 1–1), is not necessarily transferred from the stamens to the stigma of the same or a different flower, pollination being haphazard because there is no structural mechanism controlling the pathway of a visiting insect. Pollen accumulating in the flower is floated above the stigmas by rain water, and when the water recedes some pollen is left stranded on the stigmatic surfaces. The approximate water level is indicated by the dotted line, and it is limited by inability to adhere to the glossy distal portions of the petals. Most of the excess water does not run off the top of the drop in the flower but is drained away between the basal stalks (claws) of the petals into chambers formed by the backs of the reflexed sepals, where it is enclosed also partly by the long marginal hairs. Water drains from the pointed tip of each sepal into a groove running along the pedicel, being held in the groove by hairs on the adjacent ridges. The fluid is removed from the flower by a slow steady flow like ink from a fountain pen. Thus, many structures are coordinated in a system contributing to pollination, and these structures have been important in the evolution of the species. Therefore they are a basis for taxonomic segregation from other species.

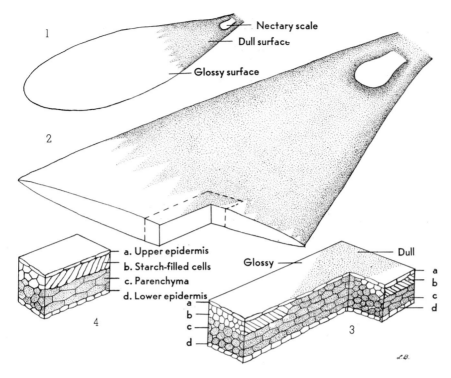

Fig. 1–4. The dull and glossy surfaces of the petal of *Ranunculus*: (1) petal of *Ranunculus Ficaria,* a European species introduced along the North American Atlantic seaboard; (2) enlargement of the basal and middle portions of the petal, showing sectional views; (3) enlargement of a segment of the petal, showing cellular layers, as labeled—the starch-filled cells beneath the upper epidermis imparting the gloss to the surface of the distal portion of the petal; (4) section of the glossy part of the petal of *Ranunculus bulbosus,* showing similar structure but the starch-filled cells slanted in the opposite direction. (Based partly on living material and partly on John Parkin, Annals of Botany 44: 285, 1935. Used by permission.)

the narrow openings between the bases of the sepals and petals. For *Ranunculus bulbosus* (Figs. 1–2 and 1–3) a long-recognized key character distinguishing the species from its nearest relatives, *Ranunculus acris* and *Ranunculus repens,*[2] is the reflexed habit of the sepals. This feature occurs also in several other species, particularly in the *Ranunculus occidentalis* complex (western North

[2] These three species are European, but all are introduced in (especially southern) Canada and the northern and eastern parts of the United States.

America; Chapter 9). The reflexed sepals form triangular chambers against the upper portion of the pedicel, and water collects between long stiff hairs of a type occurring only at this point. From this reservoir the water proceeds slowly to the tips of the sepals, which touch grooves on the stem. Each groove is bordered by short appressed hairs, and thus a narrow passageway is formed. Excess water flows slowly and evenly from the flower through this series of channels, as ink flows from a fountain pen.

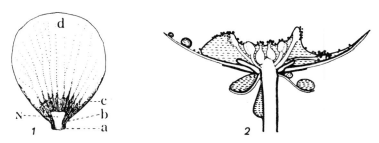

Fig. 1–5. Rain pollination in *Ranunculus*: (1) petal of *Ranunculus repens*, a European species introduced widely in North America—(a) attachment, (b) claw, dull surface, (c) middle and upper portion of the blade, glossy surface, (N) nectary scale, arching above the nectar gland or nectary; (2) longitudinal section of the flower of *Ranunculus Flammula* var. *Flammula*, primarily an Old World plant very rare in eastern North America (Newfoundland, St. Pierre, Miquelon, and Nova Scotia), showing accumulation of rain water not arising above the level of the dull portions of the petals and being drained away over the surfaces of the spreading sepals, where large drops accumulate before falling off. The pollen floats on the surface of the water, and it is left stranded on the stigmas. Greater specialization favoring rain pollination is shown by *Ranunculus bulbosus* (Fig. 1–3). (From O. Hagerup, Det Kongelige Danske Videnskabernes Selskab 18: 4, 1950. Used by permission.)

The carpels of some species are so close together that in misty weather small quantities of water may effect pollination. The water tends to rise by capillarity through the minute passageways between pistils. Thus the spacing of the carpels is another character in the system connected with rain pollination. Other species of the same genus have evolved in different ways correlated with development of differing structures, and as in the following example:

Ranunculus acris, a near relative of *Ranunculus bulbosus*, is pollinated by flies (Hagerup, 1950), and its flower structure differs accordingly. The flower of this species (Fig. 1–6) does not remain erect in rainy weather. Instead, it turns downward, and the combination of long curving (instead of reflexed) sepals and large over-lapping petals forms an umbrella under which flies take refuge from rain and effect pollination. In the Faeroe Islands, *Ranunculus acris*, probably introduced in prehistoric times from the European main-land, is restricted to areas about villages. Away from human habita-

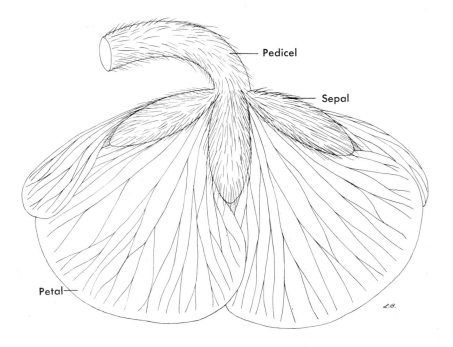

Fig. 1–6. Flower of *Ranunculus acris*, a European species naturalized in northern North America, chiefly from Alaska to Greenland, Washington, Iowa, and New Jersey. In rainy weather the flower turns downward, forming an "umbrella" in which flies take refuge, effecting pollination. The broad, over-lapping petals and the spreading sepals with forward-directed hairs prevent entry of water into the flower. These features have formed the basis for an evolutionary history different from that of *Ranunculus bulbosus* (Fig. 1–3), and they are a basis for taxonomic segregation.

tions, where in these islands there are no flies, the species dis-appears.

Thus the apparently minor internal and external features of the *Ranunculus* flower and pedicel may be correlated with wholly differ-ent methods of pollination, and they may represent the reasons for divergence of the species they characterize.

In *Narthecium* Hagerup (1950) found that pollen is floated to the stigmas in the same way as in some species of *Ranunculus*, but the cup holding the water is formed by the long hairs on the filaments of the stamens surrounding the pistils (Fig. 1–7). On one of the rare occasions in the Faeroe Islands when there was no rain for two weeks, the flowers of plants sprinkled artificially developed into the young fruiting stage, while those not sprinkled were still fresh and unpollinated. In this instance, as in *Ranunculus bulbosus*, characters of the hairlike trichomes are significant in pollination.

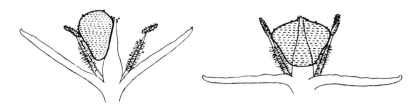

Fig. 1–7. Rain pollination in *Narthecium ossifragum* (lily family, Liliaceae, of the Monocotyledoneae, as opposed to *Ranunculus* [Figs. 1–2 through 1–6], which is of the Dicotyledoneae): longitudinal sections of the flowers, showing water drops on the surface of which the pollen floats across from the stamens to the stigmas. (From O. Hagerup, Kongelige Danske Videnskabernes Selskab 18: 17, 1950. Used by permission.)

Most members of the cactus family (Cactaceae) are adapted to rapid absorption and storage of water from the infrequent rains of dry regions. This is possible because of (1) a widely spreading root system just below the surface of the soil in a position favorable for absorption of water after even a light rain, (2) a heavy cuticle resistant to evaporation, (3) either no leaves or ephemeral ones disappearing after the growing season in which each branch is formed, and (4) presence in the stem of large quantities of fleshy water-storage tissue. The succulence of the stems invites rodents or other animals seeking water or food, but spines are a defense against these animals. In some species of cacti, many of the longest spines are directed downward (Fig. 1–8). This not only makes the stems more difficult for rodents to climb but also concentrates the water from light rains or mists into droplets large enough to fall off and soak the soil beneath the plant. Thus, even the direction of the spines may determine survival of some cacti and not others and so determine the course of evolution and provide the distinctions between species.

Fig. 1–8. See next page for legend.

14

Characters present only seasonally or not seen by the naked eye may determine the course of evolution and therefore the classification of species. For example, the Californian coast redwood (*Sequoia sempervirens*) and the Chinese redwood (*Metasequoia glyptostroboides*) have similar foliage. In fossils the twigs are nearly enough alike not to have been distinguished for many years as the remains of the two plants were found together in many parts of the Northern Hemisphere. Recently the segregation of the two genera was made on the basis of fossils, and soon afterward *Metasequoia* was found growing in a limited area deep in the interior of China. The twigs and attached leaves of *Sequoia* fall a few at a time throughout the year, and the trees are evergreen. The twigs of *Metasequoia* and their attached leaves fall in the autumn, leaving the tree bare through the winter—a characteristic of plants growing where seasonal water retention may be necessary because the winter is cold and water may not be available from the soil. The twigs of the two species photographed for Fig. 1–9 illustrate a difference in response of the two trees to dry summer air—those of *Sequoia* being little changed after exposure for six hours to summer heat averaging 100° F. and accompanied by a relative humidity averaging approximately 25 per cent, but those of *Metasequoia* being close to desiccation. Probably these are among the factors permitting localized survival of relics of these two species, both widespread in Tertiary times. Now they are restricted to limited areas in different continents, where each persists in a favorable local habitat.

THE ACTIVITIES OF THE TAXONOMIST

In advanced taxonomy the chief concern is the biological basis for classification of taxa on any level from the lowest to the highest rank. The goal of taxonomic botany is **organization,** arrangement of the myriads of living plants into a readily understandable classification system made up according to the available evidence of phylogenetic relationships. To achieve the nearest possible approx-

---

Fig. 1–8. Water concentration by downward-directed cactus spines: (1) a hedgehog cactus, *Echinocereus* (natural hybrid from near El Paso, Texas); (2) a prickly pear (*Opuntia Nicholii*). Water accumulates at the tip of the spine until the drop is large enough to fall off. The larger drops soak into the soil, and the shallow root system of the cactus absorbs them. Most cacti are dependent upon absorption of water from even light rains and upon its retention in the fleshy storage areas of the stems. Downward direction of spines may determine survival of some plants and not others.

Fig. 1–9. Redwoods: (1) the Californian coast redwood (*Sequoia semper-virens*); (2) the Chinese redwood (*Metasequoia glyptostroboides*)—both in culti-vation. They occurred together through much of the Northern Hemisphere in Tertiary times as part of the Arctotertiary Geoflora (Fig. 5–13), the forerunner of the Pacific Northwestern Flora. Today each species is relict, one in extreme southwestern Oregon and in northwestern California, the other in a limited area in the interior of China. *Metasequoia* was known first from fossils. (3–6) Resist-ance to desiccation of the leaves of (3), (5) Californian coast redwood (*Sequoia sempervirens*) and (4), (6) Chinese redwood; (3), (4) branches just taken from the trees; (5), (6) the same branches after six hours in the shade at an average of 100° F. and a relative humidity averaging approximately 25 per cent. Char-acters such as this, affecting the physiology of the plant, are of primary impor-tance in the evolution and segregation of species.

16

imation to this organization the botanist engages in the following activities: (1) *exploration for data*, (2) *classification* of what he finds and of what others have found, (3) *choice of names* for the taxa he considers worthy of naming, (4) *description and documentation* of these taxa so that others may distinguish them, and (5) synthesis of the whole into a *treatise* or a *monograph*.

Part I

EXPLORATION
FOR DATA

Herbarium Studies

The existence of classification problems may be detected in the herbarium or in the field. For example, their presence is indicated by plants which do not combine consistently the characters used for identification in the keys of a manual. The consistency of association of characters may be tested first in the field, but often a more comprehensive and rapid preliminary check in the herbarium [1] (Fig. 2–1) reveals the nature of the problems involved and the geographical areas critical to their study. An ultimate solution requires study by as many methods as possible.

SIGNIFICANCE OF THE HERBARIUM

One professor of plant physiology commonly referred to the herbarium in his own department as "the hay mow." Nevertheless he knew that scientifically the dry hay retained the breath of life, for it portrayed the natural populations of the complex living flora of three large states and, more irregularly, most of the vegetation of a continent. In part it was a vast body of raw data related to the classification and distribution of many plant groups and in part carefully organized information about taxa which had received special study.

Before development of the theory of evolution, one full specimen was considered adequate to represent each specially created species. Linnaeus (circa 1753) gave his extra collections to his students, not

[1] Procedures for starting a research project are described and discussed in Chapter 16; procedures for using a herbarium are presented in Chapter 17.

Fig. 2–1. A herbarium: (1) herbarium cabinet, showing the folders in which the specimen sheets are filed according to families, genera, species, varieties, and other taxa. The wire-screen pockets on the door are filled with naphthalene flakes to repel and kill insects, which may eat the specimens. (2) herbarium cabinets arranged in rows, Herbarium of Pomona College. (Photographs by Frank Salisbury. From Lyman Benson, *Plant Classification*, D. C. Heath & Co., 1959, p. 399. Used by permission.)

supposing this material necessary to his own herbarium (Fig. 12–1). However, a single specimen represents only imperfectly the natural population of which it was a part, for it depicts only one of many character combinations. One collection stands for a complex species only as well as a single dog skin stuffed and placed in a museum represents all the breeds and mongrels of *Canis familiaris*.

As the complexity of species has become better understood, the necessity for many specimens has become apparent. Ideally, the herbarium is hoped to include the complete range of geographical, ecological, and other forms within each species, in order to reveal either the constancy or the instability of the characters thought to distinguish taxa from each other.

Monographers of genera or of other taxa study not only the specimens in their "home" herbaria but also those in as many others as possible. The herbaria pool the results of research and travel of many individuals, supplementing the necessarily limited field studies of a single person. From both a taxonomic and a geographical viewpoint, the combined herbaria provide a broad overview of problems.

By study of collections a considerable degree of accuracy in taxonomy may be achieved, and usually, as in several of the examples given below, the areas of weakness of evidence may be determined and marked for further study by other methods. Fortunately, the herbarium gives clues not only to the necessity for additional research but also to where and how it may be carried out.

From the herbarium a preliminary treatment of each species group may be worked out. Concurrently or subsequently an extensive study may be made in the field, where numerous individuals growing together may be analyzed, as with the cacti and the oaks used as examples in Chapter 3. This information may be correlated with data from other fields of study, as shown in Chapters 4 to 8.

USE OF THE HERBARIUM

Examples of the herbarium as a source of data for taxonomic research are chosen from studies of *Ranunculus*. Although most of the herbarium research has been correlated with field studies, the latter are not emphasized in this chapter. The Ranunculi of North America have been studied in the collections of more than 60 herbaria.

The specimens of *Ranunculus* in the herbaria have indicated the natural population systems they represent to constitute taxonomic groups of varying degrees of distinctness in classification. These, in order of increasing difficulty, are as follows: *a relatively stable spe-*

Fig. 2-2. Herbarium specimens of *Ranunculus pensylvanicus*.

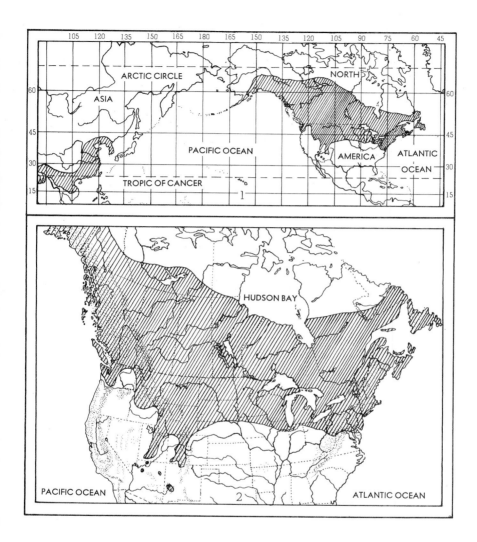

Fig. 2–3. Distributional maps showing general but not detailed geographical locations: (1) *Ranunculus pensylvanicus,* including the possible Asiatic segregate species or variety known as *Ranunculus chinensis;* (2) *Ranunculus pensylvanicus* in North America, showing more detail (Cf. Figs. 2–4, 2–5). (Base maps copyright by Denoyer-Geppert Co., Chicago. Used by permission.)

cies, vicarious species,[2] *vicarious varieties,* and the members of a *species complex.*

A Relatively Stable Species: Ranunculus pensylvanicus. Most wide-ranging species are composed of local races or varieties, but *Ranunculus pensylvanicus* (Fig. 2–2) is unusual. It has appeared to be so nearly stable in its character combinations that, since the

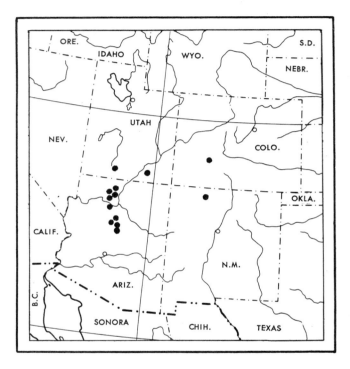

Fig. 2–4. Distributional map showing by black dots all the known localities of occurrence of a rare species, *Ranunculus oreogenes,* growing only in western yellow pine (*Pinus ponderosa*) forest (Rocky Mountain Montane Forest) on the Colorado Plateau. (Base map, Goode Map Series, copyright by the University of Chicago. Used by permission.)

species was discovered and named in 1781, no American botanist has attempted to segregate from it either species or subordinate taxa. The evidence in the herbarium confirms this point of view, indicating the populations to be members of a single species and not separable into satisfactory units of even a lower rank. Although there is some variation in combinations of characters from individual to indi-

---

[2] A **vicarious** species is one which stands in place of a similar one occurring in a different geographical range.

vidual, the herbaria show no evidence of any clear and constant association of groups of characters according to any special geographical range, ecological habitat, or other factor.

The herbaria record evidence of the geographical distribution of *Ranunculus pensylvanicus* through a vast North American area—a range which could be established otherwise only by years of field work and many thousands of miles of travel. The species is shown by the specimen labels to be common in meadows and along the

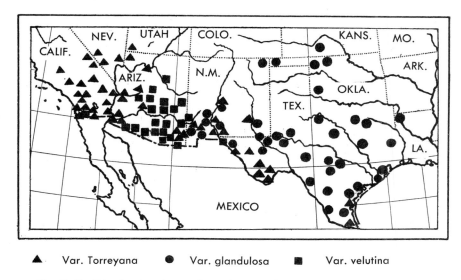

▲ Var. Torreyana   ● Var. glandulosa   ■ Var. velutina

Fig. 2–5. Distributional map based upon many, but not all, of the known specimens of the three varieties of *Prosopis juliflora*, mesquite, native in the United States. (Modified from Lyman Benson, American Journal of Botany 28: 750, 1941. Used by permission.)

edges of forests from Alaska to Washington and eastward across Canada and the two northernmost tiers of states to Newfoundland and New Jersey. It is occasional in occurrence southward in the Rocky Mountain system as far as the highlands of northern Arizona and western New Mexico. (For maps of the distribution of species, see Figs. 2–3, 2–4, and 2–5.)

The ecological relationships of the species can be tentatively established by bringing together the data recorded on many of the specimen labels. Some labels include altitudes, and these are indicative of plant associations, as are statements concerning the type of forest or other vegetation in which the species grows [Fig. 2–9 (3)]. More detailed ecological information such as soil types, underlying geological formations, and direction of slope appears on some her-

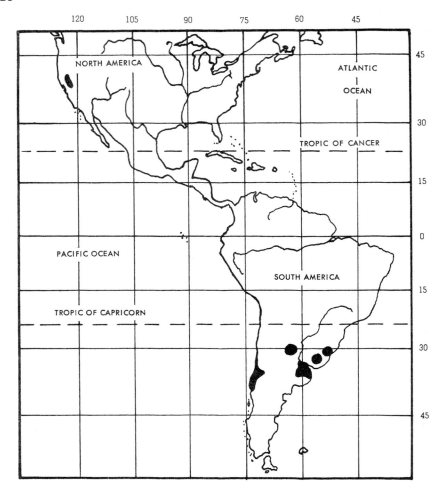

Fig. 2–6. Distribution of *Ranunculus bonariensis* var. *trisepalus,* a species occurring in both North and South American warm temperate regions but unknown in the intervening areas. (Base map copyright by Denoyer-Geppert Co., Chicago. Used by permission.)

barium labels. A research worker familiar with various parts of the country can determine the approximate conditions under which many of the plants represented in the herbarium lived.

Studies of herbarium specimens from other continents often result in reorganization of species on a world-wide basis. For example, they show the presence of plants similar to *Ranunculus pensylvanicus* in Siberia, Burma, China, and Korea, these having been named *Ranunculus chinensis* (Fig. 2–3). If, after further study, the populations of the Orient and North America prove to be identical, both must be known under the older name, *Ranunculus pensylvanicus.* However, the Asiatic populations appear to compose either a distinct species or another variety of this one. Thus specimens in the North American herbaria point out the existence of a problem which they do not solve, and those examined so far in European herbaria do not provide a conclusive answer. Additional specimens and data of other types are needed.

A problem similar to that of the intercontinental distribution of *Ranunculus pensylvanicus* is revealed by recent study in European herbaria. The supposedly rare Californian endemic known as *Ranunculus alveolatus* appears to be nearly identical with *Ranunculus bonariensis* var. *trisepalus,* long thought to be restricted to Chile, Brazil, Uruguay, and Argentina. (Fig. 2–6; see also Figs. 12–3 and 14–3.)

Vicarious Species: Ranunculus ambigens and Ranunculus Lingua. Ranunculus ambigens (Fig. 2–7) grows on wet clay soil at low altitudes in the American Northern Forest and the Deciduous Forests (for vegetation types, see Table 2–1) from Minnesota to

TABLE 2–1
The North American Floras and Their Subdivisions *

The Boreal Flora	3. The California Chaparral
1. The Arctic Tundra	4. The Pacific Grassland
2. The West American Alpine Tundra	5. The Juniper-Pinyon Woodland
	6. The Sagebrush Desert
The Northern Forest Flora	
1. The American Northern Forest	The Mexican Desert Flora
	1. The Mojavean Desert
The Rocky Mountain Forest Flora	2. The Sonoran (Colorado and
1. The Rocky Mountain Subalpine Forest	Arizona) Deserts
2. The Rocky Mountain Montane Forest	3. The Chihuahuan Desert
	The Plains and Prairie Flora
The Pacific Northwestern Flora	1. The Great Plains Grassland
1. The Pacific Forest	2. The Desert Grassland
2. The Sierran Subalpine Forest	3. The Prairie
3. The Sierran Montane Forest	
4. The Palouse Prairie	The Eastern Forest Flora
	1. The Deciduous Forests
The Sierra Madrean Flora	The American Subtropical Flora
1. The Southwestern Oak Woodland and Chaparral	1. The Caribbean Subtropical Flora
2. The California Oak Woodland	

* Based on Lyman Benson, *Plant Classification.* Chaps. 24–25. 1957. D. C. Heath, Boston.

Fig. 2–7. Vicarious species occurring in North America and Eurasia: (1) *Ranunculus ambigens*, eastern North America (in the Deciduous Forest) (specimen from east Lake George, New York); (2–3) *Ranunculus Lingua* of Eurasia (specimens from East Prussia and Austria).

Maine and southward to Louisiana, Tennessee, southeastern Virginia, and perhaps Georgia (Fig. 2–8). Herbarium specimens indicate no significant correlation of special character combinations with particular areas or habitats. A related taxon known as *Ranunculus Lingua* occurs in similar habitats through much of Western

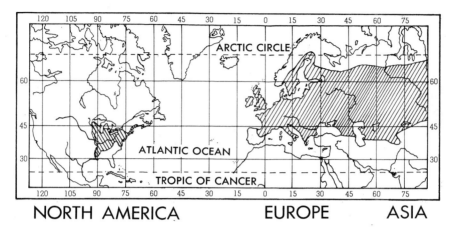

NORTH AMERICA   EUROPE   ASIA

Fig. 2–8. Distributional map, showing the vicarious species *Ranunculus ambigens,* the Deciduous Forests, eastern North America, and *Ranunculus Lingua,* Eurasia. (Base map copyright by Denoyer-Geppert Co., Chicago. Used by permission.)

Europe and Asia. Examination of herbarium specimens indicates relative constancy of the characters of *Ranunculus Lingua* in Eurasia, as is the case with those of *Ranunculus ambigens* in North America. It differs from *Ranunculus ambigens* in the characters summarized in Table 2–2. Tabulation of these characters is the

TABLE 2–2

Characters of *Ranunculus ambigens* and *Ranunculus Lingua*

Character	*Ranunculus ambigens*	*Ranunculus Lingua*
Pubescence	Glabrous	Markedly appressed—pubescent, especially on the pedicels and calyces
Leaf length	2–12 cm.	15–25 cm.
Leaf breadth	0.4–2 or 3 cm.	1.5–2.5 cm.
Petal shape	Broadly oblanceolate	Obdeltoid-orbiculate
Petal length	5–7 mm.	13–22 mm.
Achene beak	Subulate	More slender

Fig. 2–9. Ranunculi and their habitats: (1) *Ranunculus pedatifidus* var. *pedatifidus,* common in Arctic and subarctic regions of Eurasia but rare in North America—the type specimen, the original collection to which the name of the species was first applied, in the herbarium of Sir James Edward Smith, Linnaean Society of London (from M. L. Fernald, Rhodora 36: pl. 279 [opposite p. 100], 1936. Used by permission); (2) North American habitat of var. *pedatifidus,* tundra near Nome, Alaska; (3) typical habitat of *Ranunculus pensylvanicus,* spruce forest (American Northern Forest) along the Tanana River, near Fairbanks, Alaska.

Fig. 2–10. *Ranunculus pedatifidus* var. *affinis,* the widely distributed North American variety of the species (specimen from Frobischer Bay, Baffin Island).

result of examination of many herbarium specimens, and correlation of the combinations of characters with geographical distribution.

The differences between the two populations, as in most such cases, are quantitative, that is, they are matters of degree such as size of parts, proportion of length and width of organs, or abundance and distribution of hairs. The mode of inheritance of quantitative characters is explained in Chapter 7.

Because the North American and European plants have many characters in common, an ancient origin from a common stock is almost certain. Since the two do not occur naturally together and

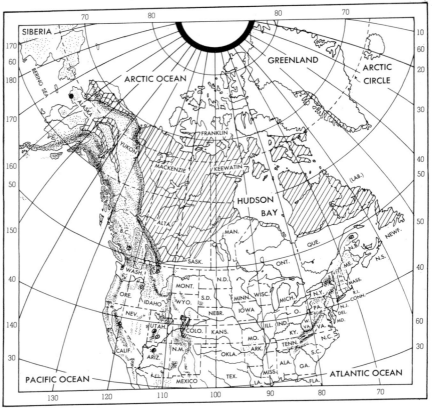

Fig. 2–11. North American distribution of the vicarious varieties of *Ranunculis pedatifidus* var. *pedatifidus* (dark dot near Nome, Alaska) and var. *affinis* (cross-hatching). (Base map copyright by Denoyer-Geppert Co., Chicago. Used by permission.)

since breeding experiments have not been attempted, the presence or absence of isolating mechanisms other than the geographic one has not been established. Inasmuch as the two population systems are isolated geographically and are clearly differentiated by several quantitative characters, they are considered tentatively, on the basis of herbarium study alone, to be two distinct species. This decision, however, is subject to revision according to the results of further study in the field or by other methods. Thus the herbarium reveals the existence of a problem and furnishes a tentative answer, but the data it provides are not conclusive by themselves.

Vicarious Varieties: Ranunculus pedatifidus. A more difficult research problem is presented by *Ranunculus pedatifidus.* Plants of this group occur in both central and eastern Asia and northwestern North America. They are common in the southern portions of the Arctic Tundra and in the boreal and mountain forests of both continents. Study of herbarium specimens indicates the presence of two major population systems. According to some authors, these are distinct species; according to others, they are varieties composing a single species. One population system (*pedatifidus*) occurs in Asia and in a somewhat modified form on the Alaskan shore of the Bering Sea [Fig. 2–9 (1), (2)], where it shades off into the widespread North American system (*affinis,* Fig. 2–10; see also Fig. 2–11). Local forms occur in various American subboreal and Rocky Mountain populations, but, according to specimens, these are nowhere consistent in association of character patterns.

TABLE 2–3

Characters of the Varieties of *Ranunculus pedatifidus*

Character	Var. *pedatifidus*	Var. *affinis*
Plant size and aspect	Small, slender, delicate	Larger and more robust
Root thickness	Filiform, less than 0.5 mm. in diameter	Stout, 0.6–1 mm. in diameter
Stem length	1–2 dm.	2–4 dm.
Stem diameter	1–2 mm.	2–3 or sometimes 4 mm.
Basal leaf blade shape	Orbiculate	Cordate to cordate-orbiculate
Basal leaf blade size	1.5–2.5 cm. in diameter	1.5–3.5 cm. long, 1.5–3 or rarely 4 cm. broad
Leaf dissection	Finely twice or more dissected into very narrowly linear segments no more than 1.5–2.5 mm. broad	Usually divided into 5–7 relatively broad linear segments 2–4 mm. broad (some of these once more lobed)

The quantitative differences detected in the herbaria and summarized in Table 2–3 are as numerous as those between *Ranunculus ambigens* and *Ranunculus Lingua,* but either the gaps between measurements for one population and those for the other are not great or there is overlapping of measurements. Because, according

Fig. 2–12. Two eastern North American species of the *Ranunculus septentrionalis* group or complex: (1–2) *Ranunculus septentrionalis*, (2) showing a stolon (specimens from Bolton Pass, Quebec, and Stokes Bay, Ontario); (3) *Ranunculus carolinianus* (specimen from Allen, Texas) (See achenes in Fig. 2–13).

to herbarium data, the characters segregating the Old World and New World populations are not convincingly differentiated and because even geographical isolation is incomplete, the two population systems occurring largely on different continents are accorded tentative varietal status instead of specific rank. As in the other cases, the data from the herbaria point up the problems to be studied but provide only a conditional classification. Nevertheless, they make possible preliminary study of specimens representing populations covering nearly one-quarter of the land mass of the earth.

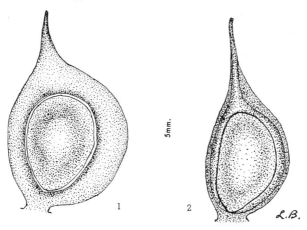

Fig. 2–13. Two eastern North American species of the *Ranunculus septentrionalis* group or complex: (1) the strongly winged achene of *Ranunculus carolinianus;* (2) the slightly winged achene of *Ranunculus septentrionalis.*

A Species Complex: The Ranunculus septentrionalis Group. Far greater difficulty is encountered in classifying the *Ranunculus septentrionalis* complex, a group of common species native in eastern North America. For many years, two of these buttercups (Figs. 2–12 and 2–13) were confused and known as a single unit given the name *Ranunculus septentrionalis.* The northern plants, known commonly now as *Ranunculus septentrionalis,* occur (map, Fig. 2–14) on marshy ground at low elevations in the American Northern Forest and more especially in the northern phases of the Deciduous Forests from the eastern edge of the Dakotas and Nebraska to Battle Harbour in Labrador and southward to Missouri and northern Virginia, and to outposts in Georgia and North Carolina. The related southern plants, known now as *Ranunculus carolinianus,* occur in similar habitats from the eastern edge of Kansas and southern Minnesota eastward to southern Michigan and southward to eastern Texas,

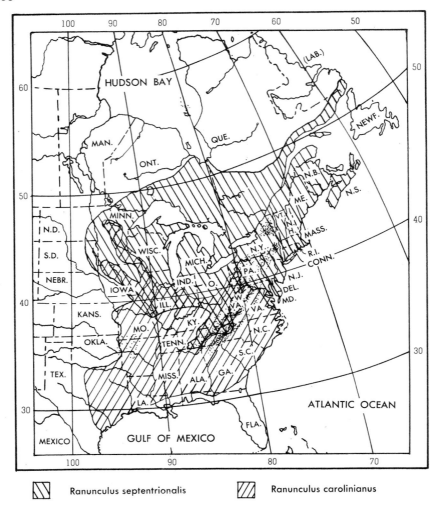

Fig. 2–14. Distributional map of two eastern North American species of the *Ranunculus septentrionalis* group or complex, as indicated. (Base map copyright by Denoyer-Geppert Co., Chicago. Used by permission.)

Arkansas, Kentucky, and Alabama, as well as on the Atlantic Coastal Plain from Maryland to Georgia and northern Florida.

Classification of the two population systems is not absolute. Inconsistency in correlation of characters leaves the possibility that these plants should be considered two varieties of the same species.

If this classification should prove to be correct, the southern plants should be known as *Ranunculus septentrionalis* var. *pterocarpus* instead of as *Ranunculus carolinianus*.

After study of herbarium specimens, nearly all the collections from the southern portion of the geographical range have been assigned to *Ranunculus carolinianus* (or, according to preference, *Ranunculus septentrionalis* var. *pterocarpus*). The vegetative parts of *Ranunculus carolinianus* are subglabrous instead of hispid as in *Ranunculus septentrionalis*, but all except perhaps one of the reinforcing characters are less consistent in occurrence. In every fruiting southern subglabrous specimen the wing of the achene, an expansion of the margin of both the dorsal and the ventral sides of the fruit, is remarkably broad (Fig. 2–13). Because Ranunculi flower conspicuously in early spring, many collections are made before the appearance of fruits (achenes); consequently, a complete correlation with other characters cannot be made in the herbarium. If this character of the achenes is found in the field to be constant in association with the other differentiating characters, the distinction of species will be clarified.

A third major population system in the *Ranunculus septentrionalis* complex is known as *Ranunculus hispidus*. This is an exceedingly difficult group composed of several important secondary population systems (Figs. 2–15 and 2–16). Classification of all the varieties on the basis of herbarium specimens is uncertain and indicative of need for field study, especially in the southern states and in New York and Pennsylvania where geographic ranges overlap, as well as for study by the methods described in Chapters 4 to 8.

The populations known as the typical variety, *hispidus*, occur (map, Fig. 2–17) in moist places, mostly in rich woods at low elevations in the Deciduous Forests intermittently from eastern North Dakota and eastern Nebraska to Ontario, southernmost New York, and westernmost Massachusetts, and abundantly from Missouri and Arkansas to southern Ohio and northwestern Alabama. They are less common and often modified in characters in the Shenandoah Valley and from New York City southward along the Coastal Plain to South Carolina and Georgia, where they grow in mixed and intergrading populations with other varieties. Three other varieties occupy somewhat more limited geographic ranges as follows:

Variety *falsus* occurs in dry or rocky woodlands at low elevations in the Deciduous Forests from Iowa and southern Wisconsin to southern Ontario, southeastern Vermont, Massachusetts, and New Jersey. Especially in the eastern part of this range, it intergrades

Fig. 2–15. The *Ranunculus septentrionalis* group or complex, varieties of *Ranunculus hispidus*: (1) var. *hispidus* (specimen from Knoxville, Tennessee); (2) var. *falsus* (from Ithaca, New York); (3) var. *eurylobus* (from Marlboro, Maryland) (Cf. Fig. 2–16).

Fig. 2-16. The *Ranunculus septentrionalis* group or complex: (1) *Ranunculus hispidus* var. *eurylobus* (type specimen from Augusta, Georgia); (2–3) var. *Greenmanii* (specimens from eastern Tennessee) (cf. Fig. 2–15).

with var. *hispidus*. It is rare and in special local forms at Toledo, Ohio, and in northeastern Kentucky. In the Appalachian region and on the Atlantic Coastal Plain, where the variety occurs sparingly as far south as South Carolina, distinction from var. *hispidus* is not clear.

Variety *eurylobus* was represented in European herbaria as early as 1804, but it was not distinguished until 1941. By chance, specimens were almost absent from the Gray Herbarium of Harvard University, and therefore the taxon had been overlooked by many

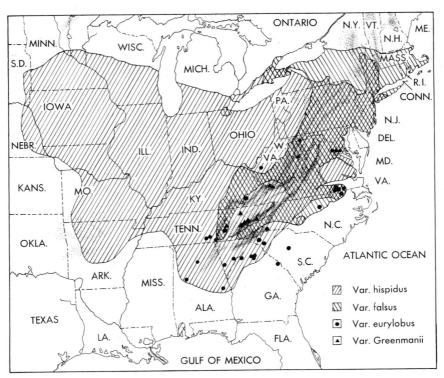

Fig. 2–17. Distributional map: varieties of *Ranunculus hispidus,* as indicated.

botanists. Although a dozen specimens were in the Herbarium of the New York Botanical Garden, these were scattered through several folders, the plants having been identified under various species. Bringing together the solitary specimens in each of several other herbaria revealed the relative consistency of the association of characters of a population occurring in the hill country toward the interior from West Virginia and Maryland to Georgia and

Alabama, and the presence of a somewhat modified form ranging into the hills of southeastern Kentucky and eastern Tennessee. Isolated specimens had passed for many years as representing freakish individuals of each of several species. Thus, assembling of herbarium collections called attention to the presence of an extensive natural population system overlooked by numerous field botanists.

Variety *Greenmanii* is a localized variety occurring in mountain woods in West Virginia, Tennessee, Maryland, and North Carolina at elevations somewhat above those at which the other varieties occur. The validity of var. *Greenmanii* is indicated by the herbarium record, but only tentatively. It is known from several collections—three from a small area in West Virginia being in one herbarium, two from Maryland and North Carolina in a second, and several from Tennessee in a third. Study of the material in only one of the three herbaria would have been unconvincing. Most of the field collectors of plants from single colonies did not recognize the possible significance of the populations they had found, and further field studies made in the light of the data from the herbaria may determine more accurately the relationships of plants like those represented by specimens to population systems of living plants.

Both *Ranunculus septentrionalis* and *Ranunculus carolinianus* are stoloniferous (Fig. 2–12), but many specimens of both have been collected early in the season when the first flowers appeared; at this time the plants, resuming growth after the winter dormant season, had not yet produced new stolons. Even later in the season, collectors, selecting material for pressing, frequently have overlooked the presence or absence of stolons. Therefore, many herbarium specimens do not indicate either the ability of the plant to produce stolons or the lack of it. Although the capacity for adventitious rooting may be the most reliable means of distinction of these two species from *Ranunculus hispidus*, which, so far as is known, never produces stolons, the taxonomic validity of the character cannot be proved from pressed collections. Resort to other characters is not necessarily satisfactory, because there is some inconsistency about all other distinguishing features. Usually, however, specimens of *Ranunculus hispidus* can be segregated by their narrower leaf bases (Fig. 2–18).

Thus, as in the previous instances, herbarium collections give an over-all view of the species and reveal the existence of problems for which they provide only incomplete solutions. They point the way for further study.

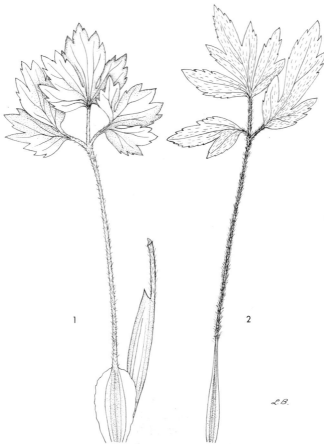

Fig. 2–18. A diagnostic character in the *Ranunculus septentrionalis* group or complex—the expansion of the leaf base: (1) *Ranunculus septentrionalis;* (2) *Ranunculus hispidus.*

THE HERBARIUM AND PLANT DISTRIBUTION

Studies in the herbarium provide at least a rough outline of the geographical occurrence of individual species and varieties. The ecological requirements reflected in the distribution of these taxa represent patterns significant in determining the broader outlines of plant geography, of association of species in natural vegetation, and of the interrelationships of the species in natural communities of living organisms. Although, as in strictly taxonomic research, not all the data are to be found in the herbarium, pressed specimens indicate promising areas for further investigation.

The following examples include herbarium study of a single species of *Ranunculus* and of a large group of related species.

A Single Species: Ranunculus gelidus. Among the 60 herbaria investigated, 12 included one to three specimens of a small northern alpine species. These were filed, even when identified correctly, under names applied in different regions. Those from the Rocky Mountain system in Alaska, British Columbia, Alberta, and Colorado were named either *Ranunculus Hookeri* or *Ranunculus Drummondii;* those from Swiftcurrent Pass in Glacier National Park, Montana, had received the name *Ranunculus ramulosus;* those from the Altai

Fig. 2–19. *Ranunculus gelidus,* a species occurring from central Asia to the Bering Strait and thence along the Rocky Mountain System from the Brooks Range, Alaska, to the high peaks of Colorado: (1) habitat in Glacier National Park, Montana (the Garden Wall); (2) specimen from Mount Lincoln, Colorado.

Range in central Siberia had been named earlier than the rest as *Ranunculus gelidus.* Since studies in many herbaria show all to be one species, the name *Ranunculus gelidus* is correct for the North American as well as the Asiatic populations (Fig. 2–19). The collections of no one institution could have been adequate for understanding the nature of this obscure and relatively rare species, which is known to occur in only a few localities ranging from central Siberia to the high mountains of Colorado.

Although distribution is partly disjunct, it may not be as markedly so as is indicated by the herbarium collections. The small number of the Siberian and Alaskan specimens, for example, must be due to lack of exploration of many of the remote mountain ranges of eastern Asia and of the American Arctic.

In North America, distribution (Fig. 2–20) follows a pattern of occurrence in or near the Rocky Mountain system, including the Brooks Range in north-central Alaska, the nearby Richardson Mountains west of the mouth of the Mackenzie River, the Marble Mountains in British Columbia, the Continental Divide in Alberta and in Glacier National Park, and the high peaks of central Colorado.

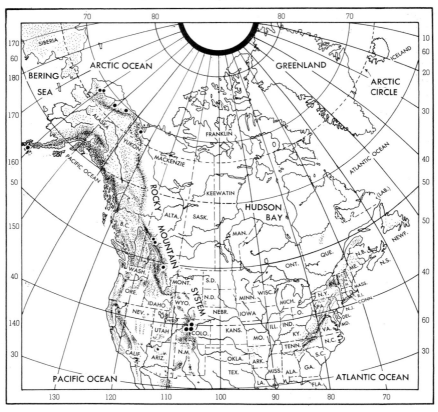

Fig. 2–20. Distributional map for *Ranunculus gelidus* in North America. (Base map copyright by Denoyer-Geppert Co., Chicago. Used by permission.)

Both this species and the (in part) similarly distributed *Ranunculus glacialis* var. *Chamissonis* occur in the northern mountains of Alaska and not the southern ones, which offer probably equally suitable alpine habitats. During the Pleistocene glaciations large areas in southern Alaska and Canada were under four successive ice sheets, but, because of low precipitation, the eastern side of the Bering Strait, the Alaskan Arctic coast, and areas in the Brooks

Range were not glaciated. These species appear to have survived the glacial periods in a northern Alaskan refugium beyond the ice sheets (Fig. 2–21; see also pages 200–202).

The circumpolar occurrence of these and ten other species of *Ranunculus* occurring on both sides of the Bering Sea raises the question of the time and mode of their dispersal. Migration across

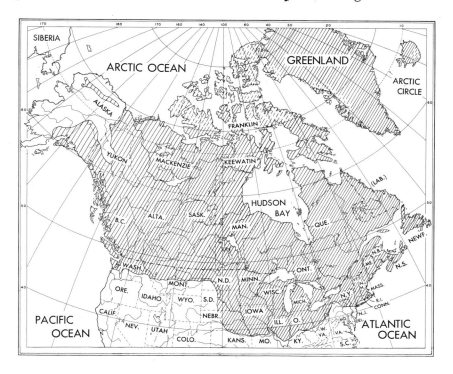

Fig. 2–21. North American Pleistocene glaciation by solid ice sheets. Local glaciation in mountains has been omitted. Glaciation of areas indicated by broken lines has been disputed by some authors. Concerning the vegetation of the unglaciated areas in the Canadian Arctic Archipelago, see Savile (1961). (Base map, Goode Map Series, copyright by the University of Chicago. Used by permission.)

land has not been possible since at least Pleistocene and perhaps Tertiary or Mesozoic times (Table 2–4). Either these species (and others; see Hultén, 1958) have persisted for a long period on both continents, most of them without any noticeable divergence in characteristics, or else they have had some means of recent seed dispersal, by water currents, birds, or other agencies, across bodies of

TABLE 2–4

Geological Time Scale

Era	Period	Epoch	Dominant Organisms	
			Land Plants	Animals
CENOZOIC Began about 60 or 70 million years ago	QUARTER-NARY	RECENT PLEISTO-CENE	Flowering plants	Insects and mammals (large mammals dying out in Pleistocene and recent time)
	TERTIARY	PLIOCENE MIOCENE OLIGOCENE EOCENE PALEOCENE		
MESOZOIC Began about 200 million years ago	CRETACE-OUS		Ascendency of flowering plants, following climax of upland gymnosperms	Ascendency of insects in Cretaceous. Mesozoic the age of large reptiles (dinosaurs)
	JURASSIC			
	TRIASSIC			
PALEO-ZOIC Began about 500 million years ago	PERMIAN (cold, dry)		Decline of swamp pteridophytes and gymnosperms	Rise of reptiles
	CARBON-IFEROUS (warm, moist)		Abundance of pteridophytes and gymnosperms	Amphibians
	DEVONIAN		Ascendency of pteridophytes and gymnosperms	Fishes
	SILURIAN		Early pteridophytes	
	ORDOVI-CIAN		Early pteridophytes	Early chordates
	CAMBRIAN		Early pteridophytes	Invertebrates
Precambrian time is in the process of being reclassified. The plants and animals were simple, and the record is poor.				

water such as the Bering Sea. According to Hultén (1937, pp. 33–34; see also Hopkins, 1959) the level of the oceans was lowered sufficiently by withdrawal of water bound up in the Pleistocene ice sheets to allow a broad land connection between continents across the present site of the shallow northern Bering Sea (Fig. 5–8). Thus there may have been a land connection between Asia and North America within the last one million years, but this has not been proved.

The Arctic and alpine *Ranunculus gelidus* occurs on both continents, and, as shown by herbarium specimens, is restricted in North America essentially to the Rocky Mountain system. This may or may not be correlated with its occurrence upon related geological formations in Asia. This question can be detected but not settled by study of herbarium specimens.

A Large Group of Related Species: The Section Epirotes. In North America the species and varieties of *Ranunculus* show a marked correlation of some major taxonomic groups with geographical distribution. For example, *Epirotes,* one section of the genus, is restricted almost completely to Arctic regions (beyond the timber line in the Far North); alpine areas (above the timber line in the mountains of the West); and the forests of the Rocky Mountain system, including those of its continuation in western Mexico, the Sierra Madre Occidental (Fig. 2–22). Thus the species of *Epirotes* are confined to boreal regions and essentially to a north-south band along the Continental Divide from Alaska and Canada far into Mexico. The section is almost unknown elsewhere on this continent. Although the forests and woodlands of the Cascade–Sierra Nevada axis and the Pacific Slope and the eastern half of North America appear to be ecologically favorable for species of *Epirotes,* the section is almost unrepresented in either region. The only exceptions are one highly specialized and aberrant small group of species almost endemic in the Deciduous Forests east of the Great Plains, a single species occurring in parts of the Sagebrush Desert, and one growing on the northern Great Plains and in the Prairie. This is summarized in Table 2–5, which is based upon study of thousands of herbarium specimens.

The species of *Epirotes* occurring in the Arctic, above the timber line in all the western mountains, in the forests of the Rocky Mountains, and in the Sierra Madre Occidental are, of course, related, but different. As is shown in Table 2–6, each of the four regions includes its own characteristic and largely endemic species within the section *Epirotes.*

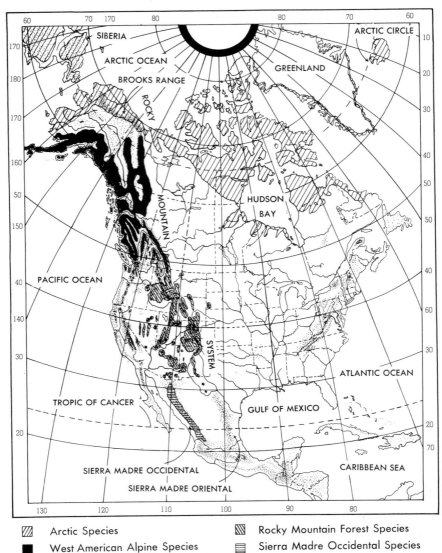

☐ Arctic Species   ☒ Rocky Mountain Forest Species
■ West American Alpine Species   ≡ Sierra Madre Occidental Species

Fig. 2–22. Distribution of four groups of species of the section *Epirotes* of *Ranunculus,* one group being endemic to the Arctic, one to alpine regions of western North America, one to the forests of the Continental Divide in the Rocky Mountains of Canada and the United States, and one to forests of the Continental Divide in the Sierra Madre Occidental of Mexico. (Base map copyright by Denoyer-Geppert Co., Chicago. Used by permission.)

TABLE 2–5

Distribution of Species and Varieties of the Section *Epirotes*
in North America

	Characteristic Ranunculi [*]	*Epirotes*	Endemics	*Epirotes* Endemics
Boreal, Alpine, Rocky Mt. For., and Sierra Madre Occidental .	53	40	34	29
Pacific Northwestern Flora	34	1 [†]	26	0
Sierra Madrean Flora	18	1 [†]	11	0
Eastern Forests	21	6 [‡]	20	5 [‡]

[*] Ranunculi well represented within the vegetation type, excluding species occurring rarely or only barely within a border zone.
[†] Aberrant species occurring in and just above the Sagebrush Desert.
[‡] Aberrant small group of mostly local species and varieties.

TABLE 2–6

Summary of Species and Varieties of the Section *Epirotes* in Arctic and
Western North America

	Characteristic Ranunculi	*Epirotes*	Endemics	*Epirotes* Endemics
Arctic	11	9	4	4 [*]
Western alpine	13	12	10	10
Rocky Mt. For.	17	12	12	9
Sierra M. Occ.	12	7	8	6
Totals	53	40	34	29

[*] American endemics. Three more are endemic in the Arctic Tundra, in the Eastern Hemisphere as well as in the Western.

The contrast in relationships of the species occurring in forests of the Rocky Mountain system with those of the mountains near the Pacific Ocean is particularly striking. On some ecological grounds and especially on the basis of a few species of trees occurring and dominant in both mountain systems, these forests have been classified ecologically according to altitude rather than mountain range. However, as is indicated by herbarium studies of *Ranunculus* correlated with field investigation, they differ in floristic composition primarily according to the mountain system. Similar studies of other genera are needed to check the general validity of this proposition.

Thus, correlation of data from the herbarium may raise a host of questions significant not only in taxonomic botany but in ecology, paleontology, and other sciences as well, and it may contribute some evidence toward solution of these problems.

SUMMARY

Pressed plants provide an opportunity for comparing specimens from many places; for determining the scope and frequency of variation within families, genera, species, and varieties; and for ascertaining the geographical range and something of the ecological relationships of each major or minor natural population or population system. They furnish data forming the basis for tentative conclusions and generate the stimulus for further study of questions which specimens may raise but do not answer. They are a permanent record of the factors upon which investigations have been based.

SUGGESTED READING

HOPKINS, DAVID M. 1959. Review of the history of the northern Bering Sea, which probably was submerged in middle Eocene times, was land through most of the Tertiary period, was submerged again in late Pliocene times, and was alternately land during glaciations and sea between glaciations, in Pleistocene times.

HULTÉN, ERIC. 1937. Note especially the following: (1) resumé of the history of floras and the associated faunas of Arctic and adjacent regions during the Pleistocene glacial periods, (2) postulate of refugia in which species survived the glaciations, (3) theory of connections of North America and Eurasia across the shallow northern Bering Sea because of withdrawal of ocean water in formation of ice sheets.

SAUER, JONATHAN D. 1951. Study of latitudinal strains of a species grown under uniform conditions and exhibiting striking differences, these being significant but not quite discontinuous. Discussion of quantitative differences not preserved in herbarium specimens derived from fragments of large weedy plants.

Field Observations

The living plant in the field is the ultimate source of taxonomic data. Out-of-doors, natural populations may be used to test herbarium studies, and living plants may be secured for experiments or for investigation by the methods described in Chapters 4 to 8.

FIELD STUDIES AND THE HERBARIUM

Field research contributes specimens to the herbarium, and these record the basis for the investigation. Proper representation of the associated variants in a given local population requires specimens made from individuals, which, taken together, represent all the discernible character combinations. These collections from many plants are known as *mass collections.* A *population sample,* a type of mass collection consisting of selected representative fragments from each individual, is easier to collect and requires less storage space. With these and other additions, the herbarium becomes even more valuable for use in the future, and its collections represent more fully the populations occurring in nature (Fig. 3–35).

VARIATION OF PHENOTYPES WITHIN SPECIES

Frequently, two individuals commonly assigned to the same species may differ so much as to seem obviously of different species. Study of other plants in the vicinity usually reveals individuals with character combinations combining selections from the first two. Observation of twenty or thirty individuals may reveal a continuum from one of the first extremes to the other and usually to still other phases of the population.

Fig. 3–1. The scrub oak (*Quercus dumosa*) of the California Chaparral: (1) a large, evergreen shrub, about 12 feet high and 20 feet in diameter; (2) a twig from each of 19 individuals, selected at random. The species grows on hot, dry, south-facing slopes with shallow soil. (Plants from Ganesha Hills, Pomona, California.)

For example, the common scrub oak (*Quercus dumosa*) (Fig. 3–1) of the chaparral, or brushland, of California varies amazingly in phenotypic combinations and degrees of sizes and shapes of parts. The leaves have many degrees of size, shape, toothing, color, texture, thickness, pubescence, and convexity above and concavity beneath; the acorns range from short and stout to elongated and slender; the bark, twigs, flowers, and acorn cups vary, too.

Strong trends toward segregation of well-differentiated local secondary populations of *Quercus dumosa* are not evident in coastal California, but locally there may be an abundance of special gene combinations or of individual genes. In particular, on the islands off the southern California coast there are both the usual mainland combinations and others perhaps derived from ancient or recent hybridization with other species. These insular character combinations, or others approaching them, are few and rare on the mainland.

Not only is there great variation among individuals, but also there is considerable difference in foliar and other characters on the same plant (Fig. 3–2). It is necessary only to pick a large number of leaves from a single shrub of *Quercus dumosa* and to arrange them in a row to see the large number of character patterns which may occur on a single individual. On young shoots grown late in the season, the leaves may be sharply serrate. Farther down the same branch, the persistent spring leaves often are entire or differently toothed. Such seasonal variation within the organs of an individual of any plant species may lead to confusion in classification. One author is reported to have named three species from herbarium specimens obtained by another collector from the same individual.

INTERGRADATION OF PHENOTYPES

Observation in the field is necessarily of genetic phenotypes; genotypes may be studied only by experimentation (see Chapter 7). The phenotypes reflect both the genetic variability within each species and the phenomenon of *intergradation* between species and between their component populations.

The Explanation of Intergradation. Intergradation usually is explained by **hybridization** and the formation of **hybrid swarms** derived by the crossing of two species, followed by free interbreeding of the derivatives of hybridization with each other and by backcrosses to the parental types. The following is an example of a field population which appears to represent a hybrid swarm:

Although areas of California Oak Woodland are the dominant features of the lowlands of northern California, they are few and small in southern California and are being replaced gradually in

Fig. 3–2. Variation in the leaves of a single individual, the scrub oak (*Quercus dumosa*): (1) twigs and leaves from one individual; (2) leaves from the twigs above.

many situations by the prevailing more drought- and fire-resistant California Chaparral (brushland) species (Figs. 3–12, 3–13, and 5–15). The relict patches of oak woodland occurring along the foothills of the higher mountain ranges from Pasadena to San Diego County are dominated by the Englemann oak (*Quercus Engelmannii*) (Fig. 3–3), a deciduous tree usually thirty or forty feet high. The plants are in marked contrast to the scrub oak (*Quercus dumosa*), one of the dominants in the adjacent chaparral. The scrub oak is a clump- or thicket-forming evergreen shrub only five or ten feet high.

Along the zones of geographical contact between the small patches of oak woodland and the surrounding or adjoining chaparral, individual oaks display all conceivable combinations of the distinguishing features of the Engelmann oak and the scrub oak, together with quantitative characters intermediate between the extremes common in the two species (Fig. 3–4). Usually recombination or intermediate types occur some distance into the surrounding chaparral, and some trees growing several hundred yards or much farther into the oak woodland have at least some of the characters of the scrub oak.

Although this discussion is based on the hybrid swarm as an explanation, an alternative may be based on *incomplete divergence* in evolution. The term *hybrid swarm* carries the connotation of past complete divergence of the two stocks, later followed by hybridizing. Instead, divergence may never have been complete, and local swarms of intermediate individuals may have occurred at all times since it began (Fig. 3–5).

Taxa segregated by a mountain barrier may still interbreed through the lower passes at elevations within the tolerance of both, as do the scrub oak and the California desert scrub oak (Fig. 3–20). Thus there may be a flow of genes from one population into the other. One may speculate upon whether the scrub oak populations were once distinct but are now merging, or whether they long have been diverging but never were wholly separate. Uplift of the passes by 2,000 feet or so would put an end to interbreeding; depressing them would result in a merging of populations. Reduction by erosion of the mountains to a peneplane (base level) would result in a widespread inland extension across the present desert area of a variable population of the scrub oak. Characters now common in the desert scrub oak would be evident in the drier interior areas, but probably with the mountains removed there could be no clear segregation even of varieties.

Regardless of whether populations are merging or diverging, the present taxonomic situation is the same, and classification of the

Fig. 3–3. The Engelmann oak (*Quercus Engelmannii*) of the California Oak Woodland: (1) a tardily deciduous tree about 30 feet high; (2) a twig from each of 13 individuals, selected at random. The species grows on the deep soils of valleys. (Plants from Arcadia, California.)

Fig. 3–4. Arborescent plants characteristic of presumed hybrid swarms of the scrub oak (*Quercus dumosa*) and the Engelmann oak (*Quercus Engelmannii*): (1) individuals in the hybrid swarm on Canyon Drive, Monrovia, California, the hybrids occupying varying ecological niches in the lower foothills between the chaparral and the oak woodland; (2) a twig from each of 19 individuals, selected at random (Monrovia).

current population systems offers exactly the same complications. The bearing of evolutionary history in past geologic time upon classification of living plants is discussed in the first pages of Chapter 6 and in Chapter 10.

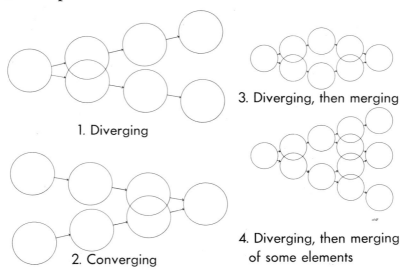

Fig. 3–5. Evolution: genetically diverging and merging populations.

Isolating Mechanisms and Intergradation. Delimitation of species or other taxa is dependent partly upon finding complete or incomplete discontinuities between population systems. These are correlated with the presence of isolating mechanisms, which may exist in any degree of effectiveness (see Chapter 9). Some mechanisms tending to reduce intergradation are too subtle to be detected by ordinary field observation; these may require microscopic or experimental study. Others may be determined at least tentatively or in part by field examination.

GENETIC ISOLATION. Regardless of the effects of external factors, hereditary characters within the organisms may prevent or reduce interbreeding of population systems. For example, although many species of white oaks [Fig. 3–6 (2), (3)] may interbreed with each other and many black oaks [Figs. 3–6 (1) and 3–7] may interbreed among themselves, crossing of these two major groups of oaks never has been observed in the field or produced experimentally. The acorns of the eastern white oaks mature one season after flowering; those of the eastern black oaks require two seasons. According to

Fig. 3-6. Black and white oaks (subgenera *Erythrobalanus* and *Lepidobalanus*): (1) the red oak (*Quercus rubra*), one of the black oak group, southern Minnesota to southern Quebec, New Brunswick, Oklahoma, and Georgia (specimen from Ithaca, New York); (2) the white oak, one of a group of oaks known by the same name, *Quercus alba*, Minnesota to southern Quebec, Texas, and Florida (specimen from Williamsburg, Virginia); (3) the blue oak (*Quercus Douglasii*), showing the warty scales typical of the acorn cups of white oaks (specimen from Upper Lake, California). Note the smooth thin scales of the black oak type (cf. Fig. 3-25).

Fig. 3–7. A member of the black oak group (subgenus *Erythrobalanus*), the California black oak (*Quercus Kelloggii*): (1) branches collected in rather early spring, bearing young leaves and, on the new growth (see arrows), the pistillate flowers of the current season and the staminate flowers, in catkins on the year-old wood, Cold Creek Canyon, Ukiah, California; (2) branch collected in early summer, bearing the acorns to be matured in the fall and (see arrows) the matured pistillate flowers to develop into acorns in the autumn of the next year, Chat, California.

Allard (1932), in the white oaks the growth of the pollen tube from the stigma to the ovary occurs without an evident pause. In the black oaks the tube grows the first year only to the lower coherent basal portions of the styles; there it suspends growth through the winter, effecting fertilization the next season. These sequences of development doubtless are controlled by genetic factors. They must have arisen early in the evolution of *Quercus*, in the forerunners of the two phylogenetic lines of development which gave rise to the present white and black oaks. A firm breeding barrier of this sort was necessary to maintain the two lines; without it, they would have merged.

Delay of pollen-tube growth, however, is not wholly constant among the black oaks, and even this genetic barrier may not be absolute. For example, in California the acorns of the coast live oak (*Quercus agrifolia*) mature the first year; those of the other species of black oaks (Fig. 3–7), the second. Some individuals of the coast live oak and the interior live oak (*Quercus Wislizenii*) show evidence of possible interbreeding. For example, a population near the Ridge Route (U.S. 99) between Los Angeles and Bakersfield suggests occurrence of hybridization.

Genetic factors may affect any phase of the life histories of plants, and interbreeding may be eliminated or restricted in many ways. The Californian holly-leaved cherry and Catalina cherry hybridize freely in cultivation, but neither interbreeds with the related Carolina cherry commonly cultivated with them. The Californian plants bloom in April and May; the Carolina cherry blooms in late February or March. Whether or not other genetic isolating mechanisms exist in nature, the difference in flowering seasons prevents hybridization, and *Prunus caroliniana* remains completely distinct in horticulture.

GEOGRAPHICAL ISOLATION. When *Quercus Robur*, the English oak, is cultivated in eastern North America it spreads locally, becoming established along roadsides and on the borders of woods. There it hybridizes with the native white oak (*Quercus alba*), producing the hybrid named as *Quercus* ×*bimundorum*, and with the native chestnut oak (*Quercus Prinus*), producing the hybrid named as *Quercus* ×*Sargentii* (Fig. 3–8). Thus genetic isolation is wanting or incomplete, and these species have been kept distinct for a long period of geologic time perhaps only through geographic separation. Each has evolved in its own way, but its independence has been due, at least in part, to the intervening Atlantic Ocean.

The two Californian cherries mentioned above (Fig. 3–9) are maintained in nature perhaps only through geographic isolation.

Fig. 3–8. Hybridization of introduced and native species: (1) the English oak (*Quercus Robur* [*Quercus pedunculata*]), a northern-European species closely related to the American white oak (*Quercus alba*) and commonly planted in eastern North America, where it is frequently naturalized along roadsides and the edges of woods, hybridizing there with native species; (2) hybrid of *Quercus Robur* and *Quercus alba* (specimen from Jamaica Plain, Massachusetts, the type of *Quercus × bimundorum*); (3) hybrid of *Quercus Robur* and *Quercus Prinus* (the chestnut oak) (specimen from Massachusetts, the type of *Quercus × Sargentii*).

Fig. 3–9. Evergreen cherries: (1) the holly-leaved cherry (*Prunus ilicifolia*), growing in the California Chaparral near Fontana; (2) the holly-leaved cherry; (3) the Catalina cherry (*Prunus ilicifolia* var. *occidentalis* or *Prunus Lyonii*); (4) the Carolina cherry (*Prunus caroliniana*).

The holly-leaved cherry (*Prunus ilicifolia*) (Fig. 3–10) occurs along the mainland coast from the San Francisco Bay region southward. The Catalina cherry (*Prunus ilicifolia* var. *occidentalis* or *Prunus Lyonii*) is restricted to the islands off the coast of southern California; it grows on Santa Cruz, Anacapa, Santa Catalina, and San Clemente islands. The holly-leaved cherry is reported to occur on some of the islands; otherwise in nature the taxa are segregated by an ocean barrier which has existed since Tertiary times.

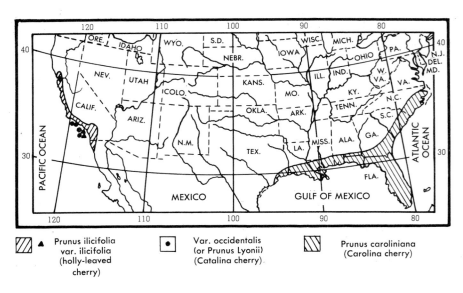

Fig. 3–10. Map showing the approximate distribution of three evergreen cherries, the holly-leaved, Catalina, and Carolina cherries, as indicated. At some points on the Gulf and Atlantic coastal plains the Carolina cherry is native, at others it is introduced from cultivation. (Base map copyright by Denoyer-Geppert Co., Chicago. Used by permission.)

In cultivation in nurseries and in towns, the cherries form complex hybrid swarms. Nurseries sell plants approaching one extreme or the other as "holly-leaved" or "Catalina" cherry, but many intermediates are sold, and many more come up as volunteer seedlings after the shrubs or trees bear fruit (Fig. 3–11). In cultivation, the geographical barrier is removed and pollination occurs at random. Whatever ecological or other factors may occur in nature also are removed, and the seeds germinate in a neutral habitat which probably does not favor one type much more than another. Consequently, plants with all character combinations and all intermediate characters may persist.

Fig. 3–11. Hybridization of the holly-leaved cherry *(Prunus ilicifolia)* and the Catalina cherry *(Prunus ilicifolia* var. *occidentalis* or *Prunus Lyonii)*: (1) seedlings growing where the two cherries were planted together and where in the course of about 30 years they formed a hybrid swarm of surviving large individuals, the plants toward the left with characters mostly of the Catalina cherry and those toward the right mostly of the holly-leaved cherry; (2) branches from the older plants arranged similarly.

Fig. 3–12. Genetic constitution of species in relation to the effect of fire—I: (1) an "island" of California Oak Woodland dominated by the blue oak (*Quercus Douglasii*) (background), surrounded by California Chaparral dominated by the scrub oak (*Quercus dumosa*) (foreground), photographed in 1957; (2) the same area following a chaparral fire which in 1960 surrounded the "island" of oak woodland, the scrub oaks (foreground) killed above ground but capable of sprouting from below, the outermost blue oaks killed outright or singed, the others practically unharmed (all points verified in September, 1961); (3) a chaparral area cleared of its typical species, including the scrub oak, for an oil pipeline, the young trees coming up (in 1957) being blue oaks, as in the oak woodland 50 feet away, rather than scrub oaks, indicating ecological conditions favorable to the blue oak so long as fire does not interfere; (4) typical sharply defined border zone between oak woodland with blue oaks (left) and chaparral with scrub oaks (right). Along this zone no hybrids have been found, indicating either genetic factors preventing hybridization or incapability of the hybrids to withstand fire, or both [cf., in Fig. 3–13 (1), exactly the same spot after fire].

Fig. 3–13. Genetic constitution of species in relation to the effect of fire
—II: (1) the exact spot shown in Fig. 3–12 (4), following a chaparral fire in
1960, the scrub oaks in the chaparral killed above ground level but capable of
sprouting from below ground, the blue oaks in the woodland at the left scorched,
with those nearest the chaparral probably killed, the line between chaparral
and oak woodland being sharpened probably through both the incapability
of the oaks to interbreed and the ability of only the scrub oak to resist a hot
fire, the encroachment therefore being only from chaparral to woodland and
not the reverse; (2) view to the left into the oak woodland from the central
area of (1), the interior trees of the woodland being only lightly scorched by
grass fire.

69

For classification of these cherries as natural species or varieties one vital piece of information is missing. This is the reproductive behavior of the taxa with respect to each other if, as reported, they do occur together in nature on some of the islands. There they may or may not be segregated by effective barriers which do not exist in cultivation.

ECOLOGICAL ISOLATION. Ecological isolation is dependent upon genetic differences, for if these did not exist the reaction of one organism to the environment would be the same as that of another. For example, the unlike reactions of taxa to low temperature depend upon differences in their genotypes.

The reactions of species of oaks to fire demonstrate the interrelationship of a genetic isolating mechanism and an ecological factor. *Quercus Douglasii* (the blue oak) [Fig. 3–6 (3)] is a characteristic tree of the oak woodland of northern California. South of Tejon Pass, which marks the division between northern and southern California, the species occurs only in "islands" surrounded by a sea of the chaparral typical of southern California, this being dominated by *Quercus dumosa* (the scrub oak). The boundary between vegetation types is sharp, and in the zone of contact no intergradation of the blue oak and the scrub oak has been found. No ecological factors except the probable effects of fire show correlation with the boundaries of the two contiguous vegetation types. The line of demarcation between species and between the vegetation types must be due primarily to genetic factors preventing interbreeding of the oaks.

However, the boundary is sharpened because of the different effects of fire upon the two oaks (Figs. 3–12 and 3–13). Although the blue oaks can survive grass fires beneath them in the oak woodland, they are killed outright by a hot brush fire, so they are unable to invade the chaparral. The scrub oaks are adapted to periodic burning of the chaparral, for after a fire they sprout up from below ground level. As the scrub oaks invade the oak woodland they carry fire which kills the outposts of the blue oak. Thus the demarcation between the blue oaks and the chaparral is sharp, following the line where the brush enables fire to kill the blue oaks. This line is determined by genetic isolating mechanisms in combination with fire as an ecological factor.

Farther south the Engelmann oaks, like the blue oaks near Tejon Pass, often are surrounded by chaparral in which the scrub oak is predominant (Figs. 3–1, 3–2, 3–3, and 3–4). The effects of fire upon the Englemann oak are similar to those upon the blue oak. The recent trend toward decrease of rainfall in southern California has favored the chaparral, and the islands of oak woodland are contracting, and in some areas only hybrids and no Englemann oaks survive. The effect of drought was demonstrated clearly in 1961, when, following an exceedingly dry winter, some of the hybrids in an oak hybrid swarm at the Webb School, near Claremont, died. Just above them, on thinner soils of a hot south slope, the scrub oak population survived. Fire aids in the encroachment of chaparral upon the oak woodland, but the line of demarcation between the dominant oaks is not sharp, because separation of the species is according to ecological factors, including soil moisture, and not according to genetic isolating mechanisms. Consequently each species tends to hold its own within a suitable environmental niche, and the intermediate habitats are occupied by hybrids of varying degrees of size and shrubbiness and of resistance to fire by means of sprouting from underground. With a decrease in the availability of moisture, fire enables *Quercus dumosa* to move into the oak woodland much more rapidly than, with an increase in rainfall, *Quercus Engelmannii* could move in the opposite direction, but no matter which way the climate changes there is always a buffer zone of intermediate habitats and of hybrids.

Individual factors such as water, temperature, soil type, or direction of slope may determine the isolation or intergradation of species, but usually a combination of factors is involved. Although the relative significance of each may be learned only by experiment, the features determining the areas which may be occupied by one taxon and not by another and the amount of intergradation occurring where ecological isolation breaks down may be observed in the field.

Opuntia compressa (*Opuntia humifusa* of *Gray's Manual*) (Figs. 3–14 and 3–15) is a wide-ranging eastern North American species of prickly pear occupying special ecological niches in a habitat generally unfavorable to cacti. In northern and median areas most cactus genotypes have been ruled out by low temperature, dampness, soil type, or some other factor or combination of factors. In most of the range of *Opuntia compressa*, from the eastern edge of the Great Plains to southern Ontario, Massachusetts, and Virginia, there are no other cacti. In this area there is some variation from individual to individual, and there is even a possibility of division of the species into a largely Middle Western variety (*microsperma*) and an eastern coastal variety (*compressa*), but classification presents no unusually difficult problems.

Fig. 3–14. Prickly pears: the common small prickly pear of the Middle West East, and South, *Opuntia compressa*—(1) plant from Warren, Arkansas; (2) from Norfolk, Virginia; (3) from Pensacola, Florida. The common juicy-fruited prickly pear of the Great Plains, *Opuntia macrorhiza*—(4) plant from Alva, Oklahoma (5) from Elkhart, Kansas; (6) from near the Grand Canyon, Arizona.

On the western and southern edges of its range *Opuntia compressa* is in contact with other species, and both greater internal variation and intergradation with other species make classification more complex. The areas of contact with other species are favorable to cacti, and the ecological factors are less critical. Consequently, intermediate plants may live in competition with the typical forms of the species, which would crowd them out in areas with more rigorous natural selection.

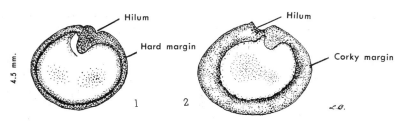

Fig. 3–15. Differences in the seeds of two juicy fruited small prickly pears: (1) *Opuntia compressa,* of the Middle West, East, and South; (2) *Opuntia macrorhiza,* mostly of the Great Plains. The character of the borders of the seeds, added to other characters known previously, may establish a means of distinction of these cacti as species rather than varieties.

On the eastern edge of the Great Plains, *Opuntia compressa* grows near or with its western relative, *Opuntia macrorhiza* (Figs. 3–14, 3–15) or *Opuntia compressa* var. *macrorhiza* (including *Opuntia tortispina of Gray's Manual*) (Fig. 3–16), which is characteristic of the dry highlands of Arizona and New Mexico and of the Great Plains, and is occasional in occurrence eastward as far as Wisconsin, Ohio, and northern Kentucky. Drought resistance must be a major factor enabling *Opuntia macrorhiza* to occur through most of its range. Lack of this ability may restrict *Opuntia compressa* to areas farther east. Difference in adaptability to western alkaline soils and to greater concentrations of salts or of a particular ion may be another factor controlling distribution of the two species.

Opuntia compressa ranges southward to the Gulf and southern Atlantic coasts, where there is a "Garden of Eden" for subtropical types of prickly pears. The ecological factors favoring these cacti include year-round warmth and sandy, well-drained, somewhat disturbed or at least unstable soil in an area of considerable rainfall. In this habitat several species may grow about equally well, and so may the hybrids, which abound.

In the extreme south, *Opuntia compressa* varies more than in the north and is composed of three or more complex varieties (Fig. 3–17) which hybridize with other species. Along the coasts, as at Beaufort in North Carolina and in dunes behind the South Carolina beaches, var. *compressa* and *Opuntia Drummondii* produce extensive hybrid swarms (Fig. 3–18). In Florida all varieties of *Opuntia compressa* intergrade with the complex of *Opuntia stricta* including its variety known as *Opuntia Dillenii* (Fig. 3–19). Hybridizing, especially of *Opuntia compressa* with other species, is so common

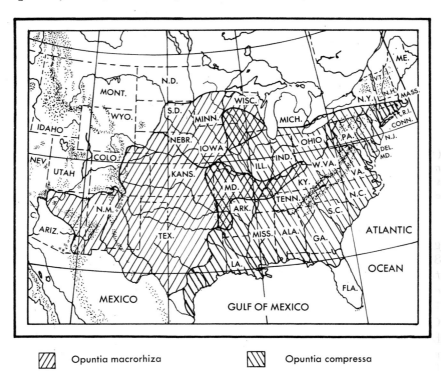

| ▨ | Opuntia macrorhiza | ⧄ | Opuntia compressa |

Fig. 3–16. Approximate distribution of two species of small, juicy-fruited prickly pears, as indicated. (Base map copyright by Denoyer-Geppert Co., Chicago. Used by permission.)

that the best-known manual of the flora of the southern states lists about thirty "species" of prickly pears, based mostly on elements in the hybrid swarms of the seven or eight actual species.

Inasmuch as only comparatively few gene combinations produce plants capable of survival farther north, the rich pool of genes in the interbreeding populations along the southern coasts affects only the

Fig. 3–17. Some of the south (Gulf and Atlantic) coastal forms or varieties of *Opuntia compressa* (names to be applied after further study), these plants from Florida: (1) plant from Astor Park; (2) from Fort. Pierce; (3) from Ormond Beach; (4–5) from near Marco.

Fig. 3–18. Prickly pears—*Opuntia Drummondii, Opuntia compressa,* and plants from a presumed hybrid swarm at Crescent Beach, South Carolina: (1) *Opuntia Drummondii,* Ponte Verde, Florida; (2) *Opuntia compressa,* Warren, Arkansas; (3–10) plants from the Crescent Beach population.

Fig. 3–19. *Opuntia stricta* (spineless), *"Opuntia Dillenii"* (spiny), and inter-mediate forms of the types abundant in Florida: (1) *Opuntia stricta,* Fernandino Beach; (2) *"Opuntia Dillenii,"* Coot Bay, Everglades; (3–4) plants with some spines; (3) from Coot Bay; (4) from Big Pine Key.

77

Fig. 3–20. The California desert scrub oak (the taxon *californica*) (status undetermined, described as *Quercus turbinella* subsp. *californica*) and its intergradation with the scrub oak (*Quercus dumosa*): (1) in the desert-edge version of the California Chaparral (Piru Creek, California); (2) twigs from 25 individuals of the desert scrub oak, selected at random (east of Cajon Pass); (3) twigs from a presumed hybrid swarm of the desert scrub oak and the scrub oak (west of Cajon).

peripheral Gulf and Atlantic population of the wide-ranging *Opuntia compressa*. Consequently, through most of its range the species is relatively stable.

The following are examples of field observation of intergradation of taxa in relationship more specifically to the isolating effects of water, temperature, soil type, and direction of slope.

Water

Closely related taxa may be restricted to adjacent areas with marked differences in the quantity of water available to plants. This occurs because in each area there is natural selection of the individuals having genes enabling them to thrive or at least to survive.

In California there are great contrasts in wetness or dryness of climate within short distances. The most important factor controlling precipitation is the presence or absence of barriers between a given locality and the prevailing westerly winds from the ocean. Since the terrain is rough and mountains may shield areas from the rain-bearing winds, each valley has its own phase of climate, and within a few miles the annual rainfall may vary by several hundred per cent. For example, at Claremont, in the chaparral on the western side of the mountains, the average annual rainfall is 17 inches, but 60 airline miles eastward at Palm Springs, in the desert "rain-shadow" of the mountains, it is about 3 inches.

The California desert scrub oak, the taxon *californica* [1] (see page 98), grows just above the deserts in a narrow dry belt along the eastern side of the mountain axis of southern California (Fig. 3–20).

No individual character completely segregates the desert-edge scrub oak populations from the coastal. At many points on either the moist or the dryer side of each mountain pass low enough to be occupied by scrub oaks, some individuals have character combinations nearly duplicating those to be found commonly on the other side of the mountain range. Analysis of the local populations occurring on the irregular hills and canyonsides about each of the lower passes (4,000–5,000 feet elevation) shows an erratic trend from the characters of one population to those of the other. Thus the climatic barriers are broken down at some points, and intergradation is made possible in local habitats of varying degrees of intermediate wetness or dryness.

---

[1] The status of this taxon is under investigation. The population system has been named *Quercus turbinella* subsp. *californica*. However, either it may be classified as a variety of *Quercus dumosa* along with *Quercus dumosa* var. *turbinella* or these taxa may be considered as two varieties constituting a separate species, *Quercus turbinella*.

Fig. 3–21. The black jack oak (Quercus marilandica) and the eastern black oak (Quercus velutina): (1) black jack oak with indented leaves, perhaps introgression of genes from the black oak (Lawrenceberg, Tennessee); (2) black jack oak with the leaves scarcely indented (River Junction, Florida); (3) black oak (Chickahominy River, Virginia).

Temperature

Temperature, especially winter cold, is the determining factor in the northward distribution of many species. Their isolation may be determined in part by difference in tolerance at some critical phase of life history to freezing or to some other critical level of low temperature.

The largely southern black jack oak (*Quercus marilandica*) occurs in the Mississippi Valley as far northward as southeastern Missouri. Certain specimens resembling it have been collected in

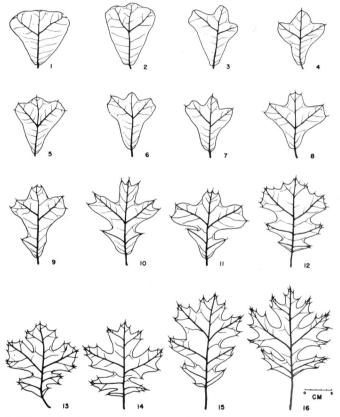

Fig. 3–22. Hybridization of the black jack oak (*Quercus marilandica*) and the eastern black oak (*Quercus velutina*), in Iowa, represented by leaf tracings: (1–2) the extreme form of the black jack oak (from the herbarium of the University of Georgia); (3–15) intermediate forms from Iowa (known locally as *Quercus marilandica* or as "*Quercus Bushii*"); (16) the black oak, from Iowa. (From Miwako Cooperrider, *American Journal of Botany* 44: 805, 1957. Used by permission.)

Fig. 3–23. Other hybrids of the black jack and species of the black oak group: (1) the eastern scrub oak (*Quercus ilicifolia*) (pine barrens, Ocean County, New Jersey); (2) hybrid between the scrub oak and the black jack oak [see Fig. 3–21 (1), (2)] (Forked River, Ocean County, New Jersey); (3) the shingle

Iowa. Usually these have been identified as *Quercus marilandica* or as *Quercus Bushii,* a proposed species sometimes accepted locally. According to an analysis by Cooperrider (1957), these plants are hybrids between the black jack oak and the more cold-tolerant eastern black oak or black bark oak (*Quercus velutina*) (Figs. 3–21, 3–22). Thus the hybrids and some individuals resulting from back-crossing are able to survive farther north than does the black jack oak. The probable limiting factor is the severity of the winter, which can be endured by some hybrid types having critical genes producing winter hardiness inherited from *Quercus velutina* but cannot be endured by either *Quercus marilandica* or some of the hybrid types with the critical genes derived from it.

Similar occurrence of a fringe of hybrids may be expected along the entire northern margin of the range of *Quercus marilandica.* This may include hybrids with other species than *Quercus velutina* (Fig. 3–23). Other southern oaks may be bounded by similar zones of hybrids. Investigation along all the border zones between species is needed for *Quercus* and other genera.

oak (*Quercus imbricaria*) (Lower Wabash Valley, Richland County, Illinois);
(4) a hybrid of the shingle oak and the eastern black oak (*Quercus velutina*)
[cf. Fig. 3–21 (3)] (Marley, Illinois).

Soil Type

Soil factors alone or in combination with other features of the
environment may contribute to the segregation and limit the intergradation of species. Muller (1952) found that *Quercus Margaretta*
(or *Quercus stellata* var. *Margaretta*) (Fig. 3–28) of the southern
states is restricted to deep sand. *Quercus stellata* (the post oak),
which ranges from Kansas and Texas to southern New England and
the Carolinas, occurs on various clay and gravel or sandy clay substrata. The hybrids of the two occur on intermediate (mixed) soil
types, and they do not penetrate significantly the areas to which
the parental plants are restricted.

Quercus dumosa (Fig. 3–1) of California is restricted to the
shallow soils of hills and of mountainsides, prevailingly to those of
south-facing slopes; *Quercus Engelmannii* (Fig. 3–3) occurs in pure
form on only the deep soils of valleys (see pp. 57, 92). Thus, the
Engelmann oak forms "islands" composing an archipelago extending along the inner portion of the Pacific Slope from Pasadena in

Fig. 3–24. The effects of altitude and of direction of slope upon vegetation: (1) Meeting zone of the California Oak Woodland (which occurs in areas of greater rainfall and lower temperatures) and the Pacific Grassland. On the higher hills the oak woodland occupies both the north-facing slopes (to the right) and the more favorable portions of the south-facing slopes; on the lower hills it is restricted to the most favorable locations on the north-facing slopes, while the grassland occupies the south-facing slopes and a large portion of each

southern California to northern Baja California, and each island is surrounded or at least partly bordered by a zone of hybrids. One of the most extensive of these zones is in the upper portions of the city of Monrovia, where no two oaks are alike and where character combinations range from approximately the equivalent of those in one species to those in the other (Fig. 3–4). At these levels the gentle slopes of the bases of hills and the small ravines between them provide a wide range of habitats intermediate between those of the south-facing mountainsides and the valley. In these exceedingly localized habitats or pockets the selection of characters shifts toward those of one species or the other, but nowhere is the population uniform. Evidently the two species are separated not by genetic characteristics restricting interbreeding but by soil factors, and, where these break down, so do the species boundaries.

Direction of Slope

South-facing slopes in the Northern Hemisphere are exposed to the sun, and temperatures are higher than on north-facing slopes. Consequently, water evaporates more rapidly on south-facing slopes and, in temperate regions, vegetation tends to be less dense and of lower stature [Fig. 3–24 (1)]. The lesser amount of vegetation produces less leaf mold and therefore a thinner, poorer soil. Commonly, in the middle portions of their distributional ranges, according to latitude or compensating altitude, many species may grow on both north- and south-facing slopes. In southern areas (or at lower elevations) they are restricted to north-facing slopes or to deep soils or subirrigated valleys; at the north limit of latitude (or at the limit of altitude) the same species may be restricted to south-facing slopes.

Quercus Morehus (Fig. 3–25), the "oracle oak" of California, is the classic hybrid oak of the West. It occurs only in the upper portions of the California Oak Woodland, in areas where both the interior live oak (*Quercus Wislizenii*), characteristic of the woodland,

north-facing slope (innermost North Coast Ranges on the western border of the Sacramento Valley near Williams, California). Commonly temperature decreases and rainfall increases with altitude. (2) The interior live oak of California (*Quercus Wislizenii*), common in both the California Oak Woodland and the California Chaparral, in the upper parts of its range limited to south-facing slopes; branches and acorns (Santa Ana Mountains). (3) The California black oak (*Quercus Kelloggii*), a tree similar to the large oaks of eastern North America, growing primarily in the Sierran Montane Forest but also in the upper levels of the California Oak Woodland, where it is restricted to north-facing slopes: twig and acorns (Mount St. Helena, Napa County).

Fig. 3–25. (1) The "oracle oak" (called *Quercus Morehus*)—the F_1 generation (or its approximate equivalent in selection of characters) from natural crossing of the California interior live oak (*Quercus Wislizenii*) and the black oak (*Quercus Kelloggii*).

and the California black oak (*Quercus Kelloggii*), more characteristic of the Sierran Montane Forest just above the oak woodland,
occur together or near each other [Fig. 3–24 (2, 3)]. The individuals of *Quercus Morehus* are commonly solitary, as would be
expected of F_1 hybrids resulting from sporadic hybridization of the
two species. It was named as a species by Kellogg in 1863 and was
later nicknamed "oracle oak" by Jepson because of the oracular certainty of the many individuals who, before experimental studies
proved its nature, had pronounced the plant either a species or a
hybrid.

Hybrid swarms produced by interbreeding of the interior live oak
and the black oak have been observed in the upper chaparral areas
in Cold Creek Canyon, east of Ukiah, Mendocino County; along
both the north and the west sides of Mount Konocti. Lake County;
at Buckeye and Hospital Rock camps, Sequoia National Park, Tulare
County; and on the grade between Banning and Idyllwild, River-
side County. In all these particular hybrid populations just within
the upper edge of the California Oak Woodland there are some plants
intermediate between the commonly recognized species *Wislizenii*
and *Kelloggii* and innumerable plants intermediate between the
probable F_1 hybrids and *Wislizenii*.

Plants collected in 1959 at Hospital Rock Camp (Fig. 3–26) included individuals ranging in character combinations and quantitative characters from those of one species to those of the other. These
were growing on an east-facing slope at 2,700 feet elevation, near
the lowest point in the local range of altitude (2,500–6,500 feet) of
Quercus Kelloggii. Here *Quercus Kelloggii* is restricted to north-
facing slopes, or at least to those not in the direct rays of the afternoon sun. This is the mid-level in the range (1,000–4,500 feet) of
Quercus Wislizenii, which occurs here in the oak woodland on all
slopes but the extreme north-facing ones. The east-facing slope at
Hospital Rock affords an intermediate environment which is within
the tolerance of both species and of their hybrids.

At Buckeye Camp, one-half mile east of Hospital Rock and at
the same elevation, the steep south-facing canyon wall of Kaweah
River supports no black oaks other than *Quercus Wislizenii*, and no
hybrids were found there. Where the soil is deeper, at the base of
the slope at the upper edge of the camp ground, *Quercus Wislizenii*,
"oracle oaks," and a complete series of intergrades were found in
1956, but there were no plants approaching the characters of
Quercus Kelloggii more closely than the F_1. This is in harmony
with the ecological conditions of the south-facing slope, and their
modification at the edge of the flat near the stream.

Fig. 3–26. A presumed hybrid swarm of the Californian interior live oak and the black oak [cf. Fig. 3–24 (2), (3)]: a leaf or a twig from each of a group of individuals occurring in an intermediate habitat between those occupied by the two species at Hospital Rock, Sequoia National Park, the characters ranging from approximately those of the live oak (left) to those of the black oak (right).

HISTORICAL FACTORS. Climates change during thousands of years or even during shorter periods. In the area about Naco and Hereford in Cochise County, southeastern Arizona, there are skulls of mammoths which, according to radioactive-carbon dating of the sites, lived there only 12,000 years ago. The remains of other organisms accompanying the mammoth skulls indicate a much cooler and more moist climate than that of Cochise County today. The area is now one of relatively dry desert grassland. In Alaska, even more recent climatic fluctuation is indicated by the retreat of many

Fig. 3–27. Relatively rapid changes in recent geological time: the Mendenhall Glacier, near Juneau, Alaska, a glacier which has receded 5 miles in less than a century; a melt-water river emerges from the hole in the foreground.

glaciers, as, for example, the Mendenhall Glacier (Fig. 3–27) (near Juneau), which has melted back about 5 miles in less than a century. Changes in the forests of eastern North America are recorded by layers of different kinds of pollen in the adjacent peat bogs.

Climatic change leaves its mark upon the intergrading populations of living species. For example, according to Muller (1952), the distribution of hybrid zones of *Quercus Havardii* (the Havard oak) and *Quercus stellata* (the post oak) (Fig. 3–28) has been determined partly by soils but also by fluctuation of climatic factors. The Havard oak is confined to deep sand of dry areas from southeastern New Mexico to Oklahoma; the post oak grows on various clay and gravel or sandy clay substrata in moister regions from the

Fig. 3–28. Intergrading members of the white oak group (subgenus *Lepido-balanus*): (1) the post oak (*Quercus stellata* var. *stellata*) (Falmouth, Virginia); (2) *Quercus stellata* var. *Margaretta* (McNab, Arkansas); (3) the Havard oak (*Quercus Havardii*) (McKay, Texas).

eastern edge of the Great Plains to the Middle West, East, and South (Fig. 3–29). Contrary to the direction of the prevailing westerly winds which might carry pollen, hybrids occur on intermediate soils in the dry areas 150 miles farther west than does *Quercus stellata*. Therefore, perhaps the hybrids are remnants from a pluvial period, most likely in Pleistocene time.

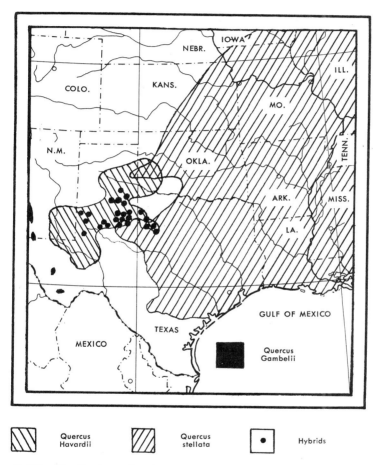

Quercus Havardii   Quercus stellata   • Hybrids

Fig. 3–29. Distribution of oaks in a pattern probably resulting from hybridizing in Pleistocene times, hybrids of the Havard oak (*Quercus Havardii*) and the post oak (*Quercus stellata*) occurring in an area farther west than the latter species. The prevailing wind is from the west, and carrying of pollen westward is unlikely. The closely-related Gambel oak (*Quercus Gambelii*) occurs on the high mountains to the west. (Base map, Goode Map Series, copyright by the University of Chicago. Distribution based in part upon Cornelius H. Muller, Evolution 6: 155, 1952. Used by permission.)

In southern California the trend toward a drier climate has favored the chaparral species, and some areas of oak woodland have disappeared (see pp. 57, 83). Although *Quercus Engelmannii* is no longer present, its genes linger on in the remnants of hybrid swarms now being absorbed into *Quercus dumosa*. In areas of taller-than-average chaparral, scrub and semiscrub oaks exhibiting one or several features of the Engelmann oak appear to indicate patches of oak woodland "swamped out" both ecologically and genetically in the past.

Evolution of Hybrids in Response to Local Climate. Hybrids are able to survive only in favorable habitats, and commonly the suitable habitat niches where they grow are also occupied by the parental species and by the associated members of a well-balanced and established plant community. Thus most hybrids must compete with other plants selected by the environment and probably better adapted than they. Usually hybrid swarms occur either in permanent intermediate habitats somewhat removed from the parents, as do the plants intermediate between the Engelmann oak and the scrub oak, or in disturbed habitats where the advantages to the selected normal inhabitants have been removed. For example, Silliman and Leisner (1958) studied a population of hybrid oaks derived from crossing the white oak [Fig. 3–6 (2)] (*Quercus alba*) and the chestnut oak, *Quercus Prinus* (Fig. 7–6) in the Piedmont of North Carolina, near Chapel Hill. The hybrids were restricted to areas disturbed by fire or lumbering. Where the white oak and the chestnut oak grew together in an undisturbed environment, there was no intergradation.

A hybrid population, if it survives, may not retain all its members, and a selection from among them may exploit a special niche or area not suited to either parental species. The following is an example of this type of population and of the classification problem it raises:

In northern Arizona, sorting of the characters occurring in hybrid swarms has produced a significant local population of prickly pears. The original hybrids appear to have been derived from two only remotely related species, *Opuntia phaeacantha* of the juicy-fruited group and *Opuntia erinacea* of the dry-fruited group (Figs. 3–30, 3–31). Local hybrid swarms from these species occur in southern Utah, for example, at Springdale and in the Buckskin Mountains, and in northern Arizona, especially on the Navajo Reservation. Near the Colorado River, south and east of the Navajo Bridge, there is an extensive population of prickly pears which combine charac-

Fig. 3–30. The supposed parental species which gave rise to *Opuntia Nicholii* [(F. Fig. 1–8 (2)]: (1) *Opuntia phaeacantha,* Hueco Mountains, Texas; (2) *Opuntia erinacea,* Navajo Reservation, Arizona.

teristics of the two species. Probably this population is of hybrid origin, but the characteristics included in it have been sorted according to local climatic and other conditions so that they approach uniformity, varying within a relatively narrow range.

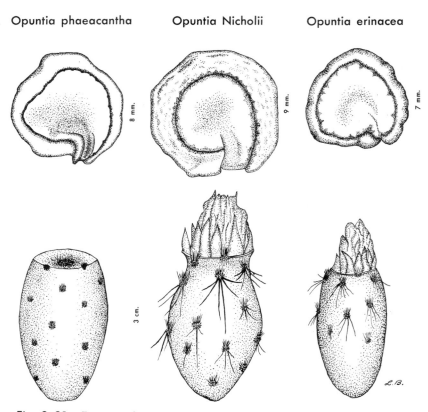

Opuntia phaeacantha   Opuntia Nicholii   Opuntia erinacea

Fig. 3–31. Fruits and seeds of three prickly pears, as indicated. *Opuntia erinacea* and *Opuntia Nicholii* have fruits which dry up as the seeds become mature; *Opuntia phaecantha* has juicy fruits.

In 1950, these plants were named *Opuntia Nicholii* [Figs. 1–8 (2), 3–31], and an ancient hybrid origin was postulated. At that time only one parent, *Opuntia erinacea*, was known to occur within about 60 miles of the Navajo Bridge. However, in 1957, *Opuntia erinacea* and *Opuntia phaeacantha* (var. *major*) were found growing together about 10 miles south of the bridge (Figs. 3–32, 3–33, 3–34). Accompanying them was a hybrid swarm including plants with many character recombinations and including a few individuals which

Fig. 3–32. Presumed hybrids of *Opuntia phaecantha* and *Opuntia erinacea*, growing at higher levels than, and about 10 miles south of, the population system of *Opuntia Nicholii* [cf. Figs. 1–8 (2), 3–30, and 3–31] which probably was derived originally from interbreeding of these two species and which is still only questionably distinct from them.

duplicated *Opuntia Nicholii.* The two parental species of the hybrid swarm occurred in a somewhat different ecological belt at an elevation about 1,000 feet higher than the population of *Opuntia Nicholii.*

Fig. 3–33. Clones of individuals of hybrid prickly pears propagated by rooting of the stem joints and death of some of the connecting joints, the plants being members of a presumed hybrid swarm resulting from interbreeding of *Opuntia phaeacantha* and *Opuntia erinacea.* Four clones are shown in the foreground and middle of the picture; other phenotypes are to be found in clones just beyond the limits of the photograph.

This difference in altitude may account for the local sorting of the character combinations found in the special, much less variable population of *Opuntia Nicholii* on the lower plains in the vicinity of the Navajo Bridge.

This new information raises the question of the status of *Opuntia Nicholii* as a species. Certainly it constitutes a significant local population relatively well differentiated from all but a few of the many types of plants occurring in the hybrid swarms. Within it certain characteristics are well stabilized. Nevertheless, its specific rank is open to question. If, on the other hand, varietal rank is to be assigned, then the variety must be classified under one species or the

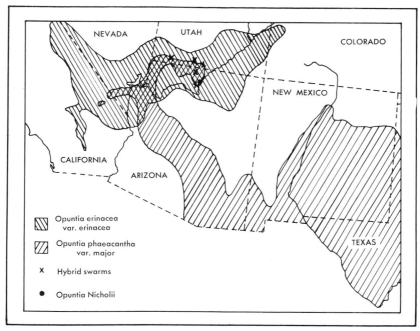

Fig. 3–34. Distributional map showing the occurrence of *Opuntia Nicholii* and its near relatives, as indicated [see Figs. 1–8 (2), 3–30, 3–31, 3–32, and 3–33].

other. Although *Opuntia Nicholii* includes some characters of one parental species and some of the other, the characters are drawn nearly equally from the two. A clear-cut and definite answer to the question is not available. If *Opuntia Nicholii* were known from only a few herbarium specimens or from plants propagated vegetatively in flowerpots, its striking and distinctive combination of characters would leave little doubt of its status as a species.

Hybrid swarms between species may be sorted into various genetic combinations, different ones being prevalent in unlike areas or in special ecological niches.

The desert scrub oak, the taxon *californica* (Fig. 3–20), occurs in southern California from the inland parts of Ventura County to the southern edges of Antelope Valley and the Mojave Desert and the western edge of the Colorado Desert. The blue oak (*Quercus Douglasii*) [Fig. 3–6 (3)] occurs through most of the Coast Range and Sierra Nevada foothill regions of northern California [Fig. 5–15 (1)]. Intergradation of these species occurs in a vast hybrid swarm 300 miles long, ranging through the South Coast Ranges from

Fig. 3–35. A population sample composed of specimens from 22 individuals chosen at random from a natural population of oaks occurring on the very dry inner margin of the South Coast Ranges west of Coalinga, California (see text). Each packet contains several twigs. The plants, marked by metal tags, may be revisited for collection of acorns and flowers. The population tends to feature, more than any other type, very small trees similar to the blue oak (*Quercus Douglasii*) but with small, narrow leaves.

the vicinities of King City and Coalinga southward to Tejon Pass and thence to Cajon Pass, north of San Bernardino (see Fig. 3–42). At the northern extremity of hybridization the oaks approach irregularly the character combinations of average *Quercus Douglasii;* nearer the southern extremity, beyond the southern edge of Antelope Valley, the characters of the blue oak dwindle away, being replaced by those of the desert scrub oak. Characters of the blue oak appear in only a few individuals along the southern edge of the Mojave Desert (see also Tucker, 1952a, 1952b).

Some local populations in the area of the great hybrid swarm include only fairly stable selections from a relatively narrow range of gene combinations. For example, in the dry Temblor Range on the western side of the San Joaquin Valley above McKittrick a local population is made up wholly of small trees resembling *Quercus Douglasii* but having largely the leaf and acorn characters of the taxon *californica*. On the still drier slopes just west of Coalinga a local population of small trees and large shrubs (Fig. 3–35) resembles both the blue oak and the taxon *californica,* but relatively many individuals follow one pattern—small trees with very small elongate leaves of the blue oak type. This may represent an incomplete sorting out of certain gene combinations and an incipient variety derived by natural selection in a hybrid swarm.

Just north of Tejon Pass, at Lebec, in the area where on the average the characters of the taxon *californica* are about as abundant as those of *Quercus Douglasii,* there is a series of more-or-less east-west ridges. On the south-facing slopes of these ridges the characters of the taxon *californica* predominate (Figs. 3–36, 3–37 and 3–38), but on some slopes no single individual has only the characters of this taxon. On the north-facing slopes of the same ridges, the characters of *Quercus Douglasii* predominate, but on some slopes individuals to be classified strictly as this species are, at most, rare (see Figs. 3–51 to 3–53). The sorting of various phenotypes, according to ecological pockets formed by even relatively slight variations in direction of slope, shows the remarkable sensitivity to the environment of plants with differing gene combinations. Even a few degrees difference in direction, according to the compass, produce a marked effect on the population.

The taxon *californica* is typical of the dry borders of the desert; *Quercus Douglasii* inhabits the foothill areas of northern California, which, though relatively dry, are moister than the desert edge. Some of the characters correlated with this incomplete ecological segregation are structural. For example, the leaves of the taxon *californica* are smaller than those of *Quercus Douglasii,* and their lower ratio of surface to volume should be favorable to survival on the hot, dry south-facing slopes with their characteristic thinner soil. Probably other characters are physiological. These are invisible and can be detected only by experiment, but they are almost certainly in part responsible for the sorting which results in plants with more genes of the taxon *californica* on one slope and with more of *Quercus Douglasii* on the other. Probably some of the visible characters are concentrated on one side of each hill, not necessarily because they provide an advantage to the plants, but because they happen to be associated or linked with more subtle advantageous physiological characters.

Fig. 3–36. Segregated populations of the desert scrub oak (the taxon *californica*, status to be determined), an evergreen shrub, on the south face of a high hill, and of the blue oak (*Quercus Douglasii*), a deciduous tree, on the north face of the same hill: (1) desert scrub oak; (2) blue oak. The plants on these slopes show little evidence of past hybridization, but in intermediate habitats at the base of the west-facing slope more hybrids appear. Near Tejon Pass, California.

Fig. 3–37. Partly segregated oak populations on an east-west ridge on the Tejon Ranch north of Lebec, California, the plants on the north-facing slope (left) averaging much larger and approaching the character combinations of the blue oak (*Quercus Douglasii*), the plants on the south-facing slope (right) approaching the combinations of the desert scrub oak (taxon *californica*) (cf. the same ridge in Fig. 3–38).

Chains and Networks of Intergrading Species. Two species may intergrade not only with each other but also with still others. Thus species may form chains or complex networks of partly segregated and partly interbreeding population systems. The following is an example from the North American white oaks:

In eastern North America, many species of oaks are known to hybridize. Brief references to species which form striking F_1 hybrids, mostly those which have been named as supposed species, are given in *Gray's Manual* (Fernald, 1950). The more subtle intergradation through hybrid swarms and incompletely divergent populations were, of course, well known to Fernald (e.g., Fig. 3–39), but these phenomena occur in nearly all plant genera and cannot be summarized in a manual of regional flora. Even the reported instances of striking hybridization, as summarized in Table 3–1, indicate a network of interbreeding populations among the ten species of white oaks, and especially among the northern species. The southern species have been studied less thoroughly, but complex hybridization is indicated by botanists who know them.

Fig. 3–38. Oak populations on an east-west ridge on the Tejon Ranch north of Lebec, California (the ridge in Fig. 3–37): (1) south-facing slope, the plants more nearly related to the desert scrub oak (taxon *californica*); (2) north-facing slope, the plants more nearly related to the blue oak (*Quercus Douglasii*). Leaves had fallen from most individuals on the north-facing slope but had persisted on most individuals on the south-facing slope. Note the greater persistence of the light snow on the north-facing slope (photographed February 20, 1960).

102

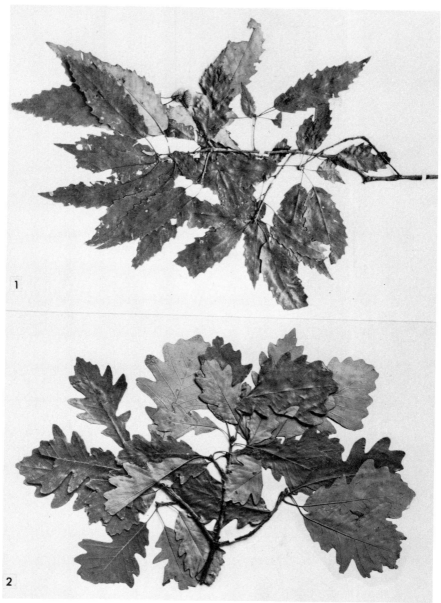

Fig. 3–39. The yellow oak (*Quercus Muehlenbergii*) and its hybrid with the white oak (*Quercus alba*): (1) the yellow oak (Cotter, Arkansas); (2) the hybrid (Bluffton, Indiana).

TABLE 3–1

Hybrids of Eastern North American White Oaks

(As reported in the eighth edition of *Gray's Manual*, by Fernald, 1950.)

No. in *Gray's Manual*	Species of *Quercus* (e.g., *Quercus alba*)	English Name (e.g., White Oak)	Hybridizing with Species Marked with "x"										Geographical Distribution, Deciduous Forests of Eastern North America
			1 *alba*	2 *stellata*	7 *Muehlenbergii*	4 *macrocarpa*	5 *bicolor*	8 *prinoides*	9 *Prinus*	3 *lyrata*	6 *Michauxii*	10 *virginiana*	
1	*alba*	white		x	x	x	x	x	x	x	x		General
2	*stellata*	post	x			x	x	x	x	x			General
7	*Muehlenbergii*	yellow	x			x	x						Northern and upland
4	*macrocarpa*	mossy-cup	x		x								Northern and upland
5	*bicolor*	swamp white	x	x		x				x			Northern and median
8	*prinoides*	chinquapin	x			x							Northern and median
9	*Prinus*	chestnut	x	x									Northern and median
3	*lyrata*	over-cup	x									x	Border and southern
6	*Michauxii*	basket	x							x			Border and southern
10	*virginiana*	live											Southern

The post oak (*Quercus stellata*) (Figs. 3–28, 3–29) intergrades with the Havard Oak (*Quercus Havardii*), which occurs as far westward as the sand hills east of the Pecos River in southeastern New Mexico. There it reaches points only a few airline miles away from, but considerably lower in altitude than, the Gambel oak (see below) in the mountains of New Mexico. Tucker (1961) shows evidence that the highly variable complex of forms commonly known as *Quercus undulata* occurring on dry hills in and about the entire southern portion of the Rocky Mountain system is the derivative of an ancient series of crosses of six species. These include *Quercus Muehlenbergii* (an eastern species), *Quercus Havardii* (Great Plains), *Quercus Mohriana* (Edwards Plateau and trans-Pecos Texas), *Quercus Gambelii* (Rocky Mountain Montane Forest and areas just lower in altitude), *Quercus arizonica* (Arizona, New Mexico, and northern Mexico), and the taxon *turbinella* (Arizona to Texas). The oaks of the post oak group are related closely to the Gambel oak (*Quercus Gambelii*), and the many intermediate forms in the *Quercus undulata* complex connect the eastern group of white oaks with that species.

In Arizona the Gambel oak intergrades (Fig. 3–40) with a far different highland and desert-edge oak, the taxon *turbinella*. For example, intergradation occurs in Zion Canyon, Utah, and on the disturbed soil of sand dunes at the base of a cut bank 9 miles west of Pipe Spring, in Arizona just south of the Utah boundary. In the latter area there is a hybrid swarm in which some plants approach the Gambel oak in their characters and others tend toward duplication of the taxon *turbinella* (see also Tucker, Cottam, and Drobnick, 1961).

In the hills and valleys just below the Mogollon Rim in central Arizona the taxon *turbinella* hybridizes with an entirely different complex of oaks, including *Quercus arizonica* (Fig. 3–41), and there is another series of intermediate plants and of recombinations of characters.

The closely related and intergrading taxa *turbinella* (Figs. 3–40, 3–41) and *californica* (Fig. 3–20) are almost certainly varieties of a single species (see p. 79), and the taxon *californica* is the pivotal member of the alliance of Californian white oaks discussed in various examples above. The chain or network of intergradation of oaks branches in two directions from the taxon *californica*, which (1) intergrades with *Quercus dumosa* (Fig. 3–1), which hybridizes in many places with *Quercus Engelmannii* (see Fig. 3–3), and (2) integrades with *Quercus Douglasii* (the blue oak) [Figs. 3–6 (3), 3–42, 3–43, 3–44].

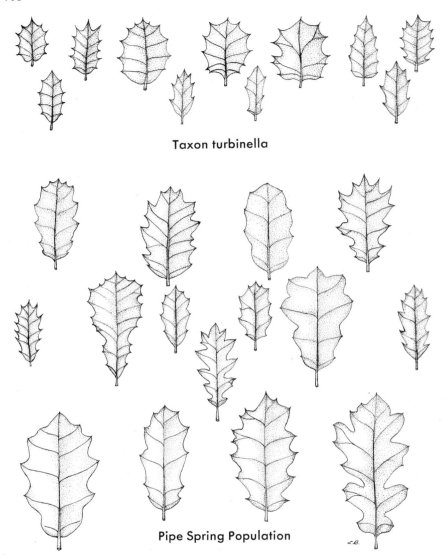

Fig. 3–40. Hybridization of the Gambel oak (*Quercus Gambelii*) and the strongly dissimilar southwestern desert scrub oak (the taxon *turbinella*, status to

Quercus Gambelii

be determined), as indicated. The Pipe Spring, northern Arizona, population is
presumably of hybrid origin.

Fig. 3–41. Intergradation of the Arizona oak (*Quercus arizonica*) and the southwestern desert scrub oak (the taxon *turbinella*, status to be determined),

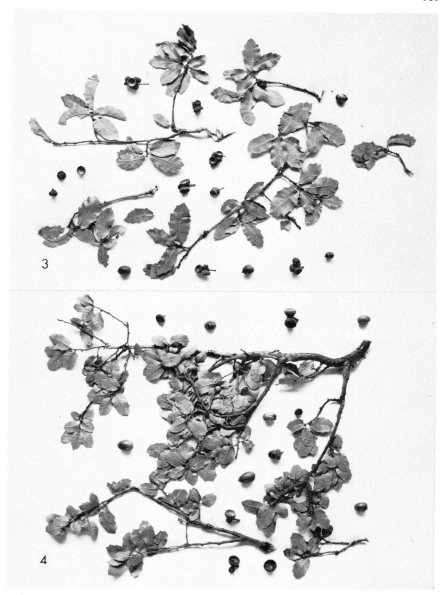

in the Mingus Mountains, northern Arizona: (1) Arizona oak; (2–3) intermediate types; (4) the scrub oak.

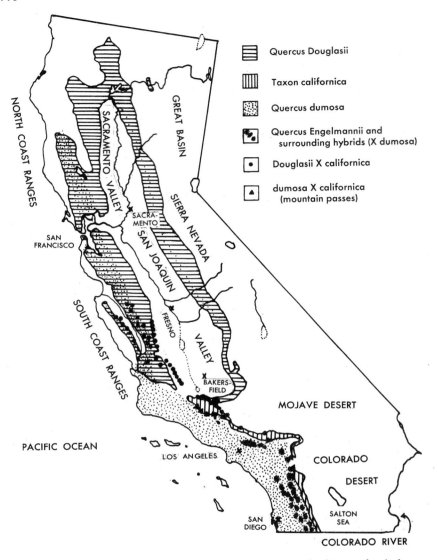

Fig. 3–42. Approximate distribution of a group of white oaks (subgenus *Lepidobalanus*) in California.

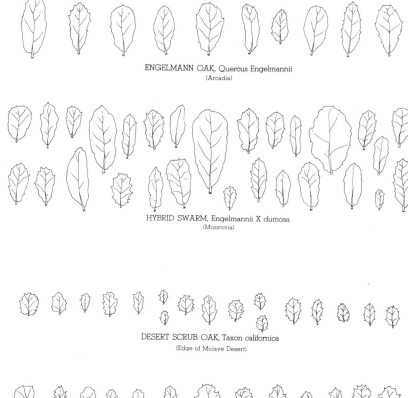

ENGELMANN OAK, Quercus Engelmannii
(Arcadia)

HYBRID SWARM, Engelmannii X dumosa
(Monrovia)

DESERT SCRUB OAK, Taxon californica
(Edge of Mojave Desert)

HYBRID SWARM, Taxon californica X Douglasii
(Lebec)

Fig. 3–43. Leaf drawings showing variation within the species represented in Fig. 3–44 and the intergradation from one to another. (From Lyman Benson, *Plant Classification*, D. C. Heath & Co., 1957, pp. 444–445. Used by permission. By J. D. Laudermilk.) (Fig. 3–43 continued on next page.)

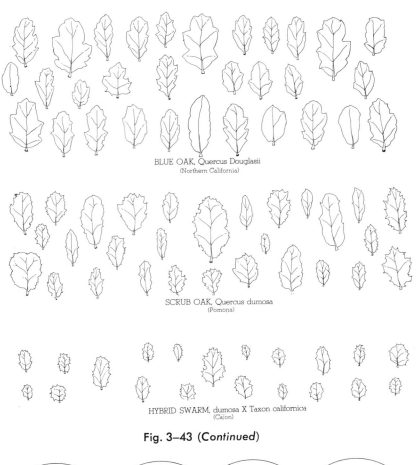

BLUE OAK, Quercus Douglasii
(Northern California)

SCRUB OAK, Quercus dumosa
(Pomona)

HYBRID SWARM, dumosa X Taxon californica
(Cajon)

Fig. 3–43 (Continued)

| Quercus Engelmannii | Quercus dumosa | Taxon californica | Quercus Douglasii |

Fig. 3–44. Figure representing the degrees of intergradation of four taxa of Californian oaks (Fig. 3–43), as indicated. (From Lyman Benson, *Plant Classification*, D. C. Heath & Co., 1957, p. 450. Used by permission.)

112

Fig. 3–45. The valley oak of California (*Quercus lobata*), a species characteristic of the deep soils of valleys in the California Oak Woodland in areas where the blue oak (*Quercus Douglasii*) [see Figs. 3–6 (3) and 5–15 (1)] dominates the poor, shallow soils of the hillsides. These species hybridize at least sometimes. (Kelseyville, Lake County.)

At opposite extremes of the Californian portion of the chain, as developed so far, are the scrub oaks and the blue oak, which bears some resemblance to the eastern white oaks. But *Quercus Douglasii* hybridizes occasionally with such other northern-California oaks as the gigantic valley oak (*Quercus lobata*) (Fig. 3–45), similar to the eastern white oak (*Quercus alba*). The valley oak attains a height of more than 100 feet, a trunk diameter of up to 10 or 12 feet, and a spread of at least 150 feet; the deeply lobed leaves are strictly deciduous early in the fall; and the acorns are up to 2 inches long, several times the size of scrub oak acorns. Altogether, the resemblance between the evergreen shrubby scrub oak and the valley oak is no greater than between an alley cat and a tiger.

In the chaparral of the Coast Ranges of northern California, *Quercus dumosa* intergrades with the leather oak (*Quercus durata*); in the North Coast Ranges, according to Stebbins (1950, p. 25), *Quercus Douglasii* hybridizes with the Garry oak (*Quercus Garryana*). Furthermore, according to Tucker (1953), both *Quercus dumosa* and *Quercus durata* hybridize with *Quercus Garryana* near the coast in, and just south of, the San Francisco Bay region. Since the Garry oak occurs northward to Puget Sound and Vancouver Island, this extends the population network geographically from southern California to British Columbia.

Thus the branched chain or network of hybridizing white oaks embraces the entire oak belt of Canada and the United States.

NUMERICAL OR GRAPHIC ANALYSIS OF ASSOCIATION OF CHARACTERS

Anderson has devised and published methods for analysis of association of characters in taxa and their hybrids. These are described in detail in *Introgressive Hybridization* (1949) and in earlier publications. A few simple applications are outlined below.

Correlation of Two Pairs of Characters by Scatter Diagrams. Two pairs of characters or their measurements may be plotted on coordinate paper for an analysis of their mode of association. For example, Fig. 3–46 is a correlation of the leaf length and the depth of leaf lobing in a population of oaks occurring 9 miles west of Pipe Spring, northern Arizona, August 9, 1953 (see also Fig. 3–40). These collections are thought to represent a hybrid swarm (x) of *Quercus Gambelii* (G) and the taxon *turbinella* (status undetermined, see pp. 105–107) (t). The former species has leaves usually

5–13 cm. long and deeply lobed; the latter taxon has leaves usually 1.5–3.5 cm. long and only shallowly spinosely toothed. The length and the depth of primary lobing of a representative well-developed large leaf of each individual from which a specimen was collected are plotted against each other. Similar measurements of leaves from representative herbarium specimens of the two species are shown in the same diagram.

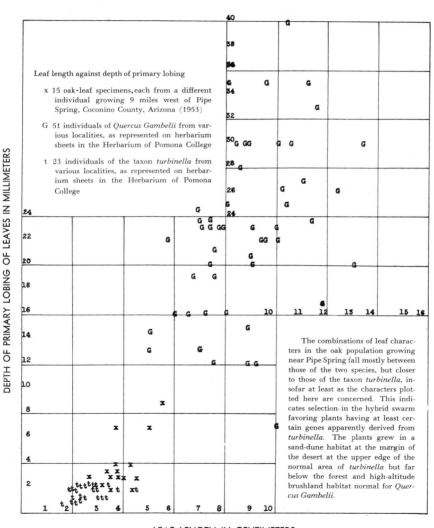

Leaf length against depth of primary lobing

x 15 oak-leaf specimens, each from a different individual growing 9 miles west of Pipe Spring, Coconino County, Arizona (1953)

G 51 individuals of *Quercus Gambelii* from various localities, as represented on herbarium sheets in the Herbarium of Pomona College

t 23 individuals of the taxon *turbinella* from various localities, as represented on herbarium sheets in the Herbarium of Pomona College

The combinations of leaf characters in the oak population growing near Pipe Spring fall mostly between those of the two species, but closer to those of the taxon *turbinella*, insofar at least as the characters plotted here are concerned. This indicates selection in the hybrid swarm favoring plants having at least certain genes apparently derived from *turbinella*. The plants grew in a sand-dune habitat at the margin of the desert at the upper edge of the normal area of *turbinella* but far below the forest and high-altitude brushland habitat normal for *Quercus Gambelii*.

DEPTH OF PRIMARY LOBING OF LEAVES IN MILLIMETERS

LEAF LENGTH IN CENTIMETERS

Fig. 3–46.

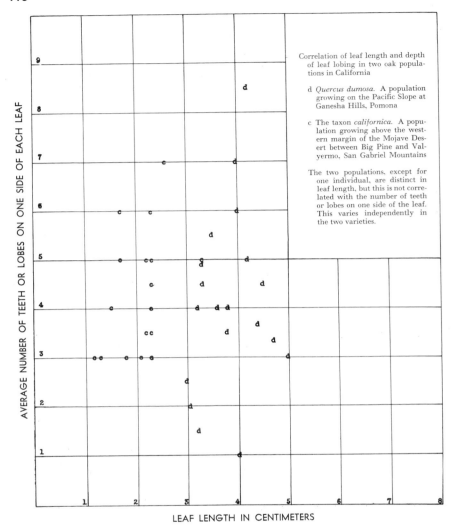

Fig. 3–47.

Another example, Fig. 3–47, is a check upon the correlation of leaf length and number of marginal teeth in two populations of oaks. This has a bearing upon the validity of distinction of *Quercus dumosa* (d) and the taxon *californica* (c) and their status as species or varieties. In these particular populations, one character (leaf length) showed little overlapping but the other (number of teeth) varied independently of leaf length in both populations. The average number of teeth per side of the leaf was more variable in the var. *dumosa* population than in the taxon *californica*, but it included the entire range found in the latter. In short, these characters are not correlated.

Proportion of Length and Width of an Organ. Observation of the sizes and shapes of the leaves of the scrub oak, *Quercus dumosa*, and the Engelmann oak, *Quercus Engelmannii*, indicates that on the average the leaf of the Engelmann oak is longer (Fig. 3–48). Yet the leaves of some scrub oaks are as long as those of many Engelmann oaks. Measurement of a typical large leaf from each of 30 scrub oaks gave a range in length from 2.3 to 5.9 cm. For 30 Engelmann oaks the length ranged from 4 to 8 cm. Plotting length against breadth showed that the shorter leaves of the scrub oaks varied in relative length and breadth but that the longer leaves were proportionately much broader than Engelmann oak leaves of the same length. Segregation was not complete, but the tendency was marked. This was suspected from observation and confirmed by plotting the measurements. Plants from a probable hybrid swarm had leaves ranging from one extreme of length to the other. They were of all types, but tended to be narrow as in the Engelmann oak even when they were as short as those of the scrub oak.

Correlation of Association of More than Two Pairs of Characters. A weakness of scatter diagrams is their restriction to correlation of the occurrence of only two character pairs in combination. The following are methods of including additional pairs of characters.

PICTORIALIZED SCATTER DIAGRAMS. Anderson has added other factors by recording marks or pictures on scatter diagrams.

In Fig. 3–49, leaf length and width are plotted against each other, and in addition a bar on the left side of each letter indicates that the leaf is lobed or toothed and another one on the right indicates that the tooth ends in a small spine. The data are from a population of the taxon *californica* (c) located between Big Pine and Valyermo and from herbarium specimens of *Quercus Douglasii* (D) of northern California.

In Fig. 3–50, similar data from the peculiar plants occurring in the southwestern corner of an island of *Quercus Douglasii* (x) at the Oak Flats Fire Guard Station (10 miles north of Castaic on U.S. 99) are added to the main outline of the data in Fig. 3–49. The leaves of the oaks in this portion of the island are smaller than

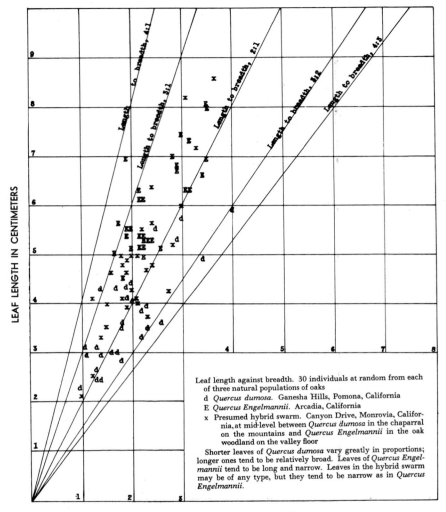

Leaf length against breadth. 30 individuals at random from each of three natural populations of oaks

  d *Quercus dumosa.* Ganesha Hills, Pomona, California
  E *Quercus Engelmannii.* Arcadia, California
  x Presumed hybrid swarm. Canyon Drive, Monrovia, California, at mid-level between *Quercus dumosa* in the chaparral on the mountains and *Quercus Engelmannii* in the oak woodland on the valley floor

Shorter leaves of *Quercus dumosa* vary greatly in proportions; longer ones tend to be relatively broad. Leaves of *Quercus Engelmannii* tend to be long and narrow. Leaves in the hybrid swarm may be of any type, but they tend to be narrow as in *Quercus Engelmannii.*

LEAF WIDTH IN CENTIMETERS

Fig. 3–48.

those of the blue oak through the bulk of its range in northern California, and on many trees they are less blue. Some mature trees are of small stature. The visible characters indicate probable past hybridization with the desert scrub oak. This is confirmed by the scatter diagram.

Additional characters may be included by adding more marks

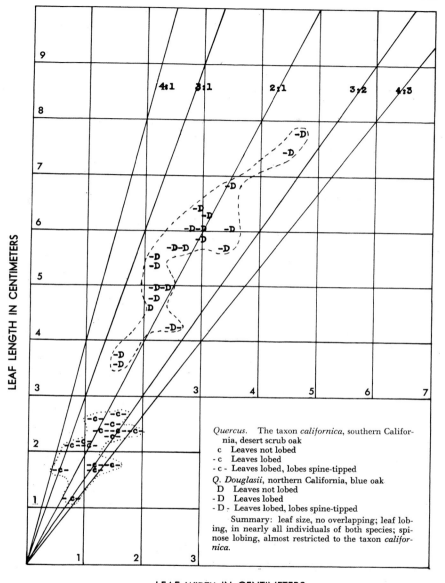

LEAF WIDTH IN CENTIMETERS

Fig. 3–49.

Quercus.   The taxon *californica*, southern California, desert scrub oak
  c   Leaves not lobed
  - c   Leaves lobed
  - c -   Leaves lobed, lobes spine-tipped
Q. Douglasii, northern California, blue oak
  D   Leaves not lobed
  - D   Leaves lobed
  - D -   Leaves lobed, lobes spine-tipped
   Summary: leaf size, no overlapping; leaf lobing, in nearly all individuals of both species; spi-
nose lobing, almost restricted to the taxon *californica.*

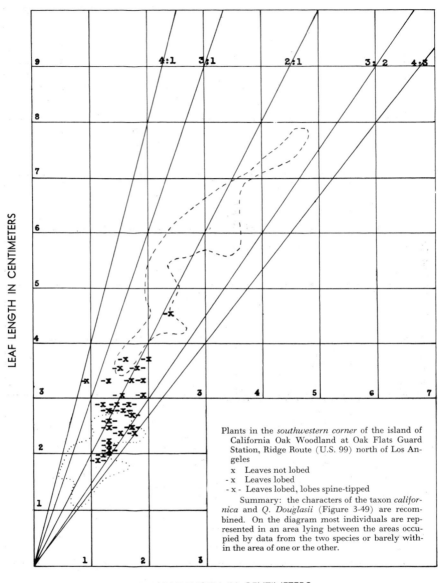

Plants in the *southwestern corner* of the island of
California Oak Woodland at Oak Flats Guard
Station, Ridge Route (U.S. 99) north of Los An-
geles

x   Leaves not lobed
- x   Leaves lobed
- x - Leaves lobed, lobes spine-tipped

   Summary: the characters of the taxon *californica* and *Q. Douglasii* (Figure 3-49) are recombined. On the diagram most individuals are represented in an area lying between the areas occupied by data from the two species or barely within the area of one or the other.

LEAF WIDTH IN CENTIMETERS

Fig. 3–50.

or by the use of simple pictures instead of letters. More complex additions form a *pictorialized scatter diagram.*

THE HYBRID INDEX AND BAR DIAGRAMS. Anderson's methods include evaluation of the association of any number of quantitative characters by assigning arbitrary point values to the expression of each feature. The characters of two populations of oaks were scored arbitrarily for some of the characters ordinarily differing in the taxon *californica* and *Quercus Douglasii*, the variants in each pair of characters being assigned arbitrary point values from 0 to 5 according to relative size or degree. Five character pairs varying in accordance with quantitative factors were studied, and the scores of individual plants composing a population of each species were used as the basis for a bar diagram, Fig. 3–51. A composite score of 0 represented the extreme of the taxon *californica,* a score of 25 the extreme of *Quercus Douglasii*. Intermediate scores indicated intermediate plants, presumably resulting from hybridization, each such score being known as a *hybrid index*. Although individuals of the two populations approached each other in total scores, overlapping of scores in this example was slight.

Subsequent research has shown that other characters might well have been included, and these appear in the results of later investigation. Also, in this instance leaf length and width have been found to vary in almost direct proportion to each other. Consequently, ultimate use of both of these characters employed in the preliminary study is open to question. The effect is doubling of the value given to leaf size. A better procedure may have been multiplication of length by width to obtain a factor representing size instead of using either measurement alone. This illustrates the necessity for many preliminary studies such as this and of the type employing scatter diagrams before determination of the characters which should be included and of the point values they should receive. Unless much time can be devoted to painstaking quantitative analysis of large numbers of individuals in each of numerous populations, the value of the study for classification purposes lies primarily in the impetus to observation and to analysis of the combination of characters rather than in production of "statistics."

Figures 3–52 and 3–53 are an analysis of the relationship of character combinations to ecological factors which may keep two taxa separate from each other or at least provide a tendency toward isolation (see pp. 98–102).

POLYGONAL GRAPHS. Davidson (1947) devised an application of polygonal graphs to comparison of patterns involving several char-

NUMBER OF INDIVIDUALS HAVING EACH SCORE

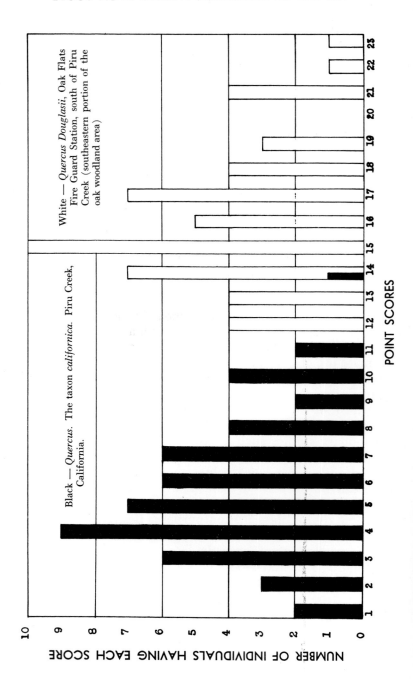

White — *Quercus Douglasii*, Oak Flats Fire Guard Station, south of Piru Creek (southeastern portion of the oak woodland area)

Black — *Quercus*. The taxon *californica*. Piru Creek, California.

POINT SCORES

NUMBER OF INDIVIDUALS HAVING EACH SCORE

Characters of natural population of the oak taxon *californica*, desert scrub oak, and of *Quercus Douglasii*, blue oak
Arbitrary point scores based upon the following:

Height of mature plant. 0-5 points. 5-10 feet, 0; additional point for each 10 feet

Number of stems ascending from ground level. 0-5 points. 6 or more stems, 0; 5 stems, 1; 4 stems, 2; 3 stems, 3; 2 stems, 4; 1 stem, 5

Leaf color. 0-5 points. Pure green, 0; up to 5 points for degree of glaucousness in accordance with the standards adopted

Leaf length. 0-5 points. Less than 1 cm., 0; 1-2 cm., 1; additional point for each cm. up to 5 points

Leaf width. 0-5 points. Less than 5 mm., 0; 5-10 mm., 1; additional point for each 5 mm. up to 5 points

Fig. 3–51.

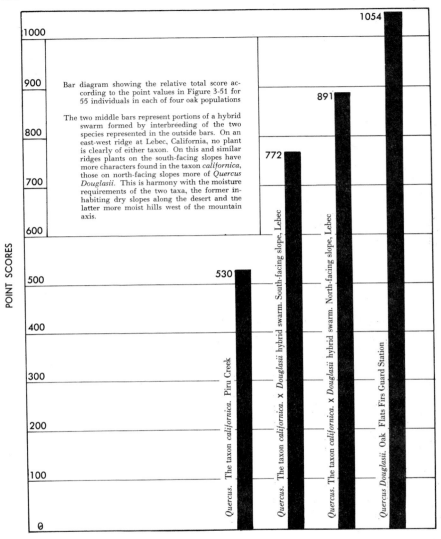

Bar diagram showing the relative total score according to the point values in Figure 3-51 for 55 individuals in each of four oak populations

The two middle bars represent portions of a hybrid swarm formed by interbreeding of the two species represented in the outside bars. On an east-west ridge at Lebec, California, no plant is clearly of either taxon. On this and similar ridges plants on the south-facing slopes have more characters found in the taxon *californica*, those on north-facing slopes more of *Quercus Douglasii*. This is harmony with the moisture requirements of the two taxa, the former inhabiting dry slopes along the desert and the latter more moist hills west of the mountain axis.

Fig. 3–52.

acters as they are manifested in two or more related taxa. This method is explained in Fig. 3–54.

The results of quantitative research, like those of other methods of study, must be interpreted with caution. An obvious weakness occurring in all types of research, but particularly dangerous in interpretation of measurements, is the notorious gullibility of the human mind for statistics and other numerical data. Reduction of data to numbers may result in too literal an interpretation through overlooking the fact that the figures are based upon human judgments. Accuracy demands quantitative determination according to arbitrary numerical values of, for example, the color of the leaves. The human eye may be an accurate quantitative instrument, but its record is not

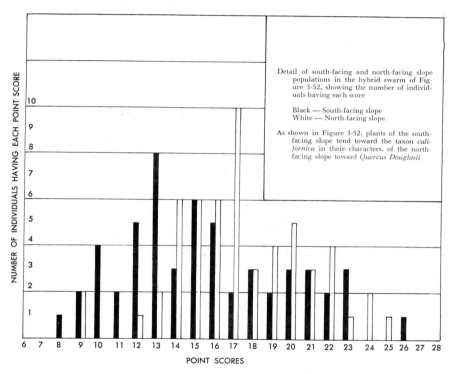

Detail of south-facing and north-facing slope populations in the hybrid swarm of Figure 3-52, showing the number of individuals having each score

Black — South-facing slope
White — North-facing slope

As shown in Figure 3-52, plants of the south-facing slope tend toward the taxon *californica* in their characters, of the north-facing slope toward *Quercus Douglasii*

Fig. 3–53.

necessarily so. Checking against color standards is, at best, inaccurate. Measurement of leaf length may be accurate, but the selection of leaves to be measured and the assignment of point-value ranges is arbitrary. Consequently, this type of study may yield only an indication of the combination of characters. Nevertheless, if the limitations are kept in mind, the preparation of charts may be a useful stimulus to accuracy, to discovery of facts otherwise overlooked, to observation of many individuals, and to focussing attention upon the combination of characters rather than upon single characters.

Polygonal graphs for comparison of patterns of several characters as they are manifested in two or more related taxa

Under this method a measurement or score for each quantitative character is
placed at the proper distance from the center on a different radius of a circle. Connection of the points on the radii forms a polygon characteristic of the taxon, as illustrated below for eight characters such as those in the following list:

A, leaf length	E, density of stem trichomes
B, ratio of leaf length to width	F, Depth of corolla lobing
C, Stem diameter	G, Fruit length
D, Internode length	H, Number of seeds per fruit

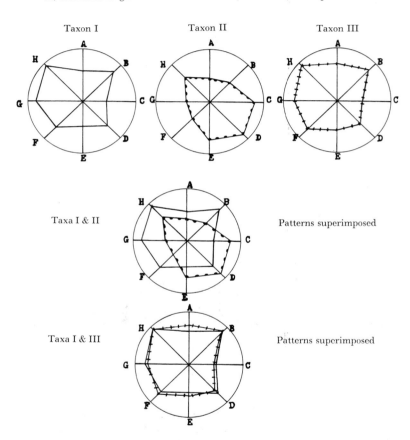

On the basis of coincidence of polygons, these character patterns indicate taxa
I and III to be related closely and probably indistinguishable, but II tends to be
strongly differentiated.

Fig. 3–54.

INTROGRESSIVE HYBRIDIZATION

Often a flow of genes from one species to another may be detected in the field. This process greatly increases the complexity of classification. *Introgression* (Fig. 3–55; see also Anderson, 1949, 1953) of genes from one species into another occurs through back-crossing of the F_1 hybrid to one of the parental species. The individuals resulting from this cross, and their descendants, then may continue to breed with the same parental species until later genera-

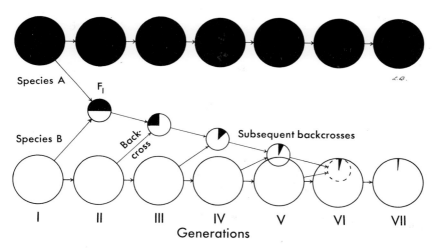

Fig. 3–55. Diagram illustrating introgressive hybridization—the interbreeding of species, followed by backcrosses to one parent and ultimate absorption of some genes from one species into at least some members of the population of the other.

tions resemble it so closely as to be absorbed into its general population. Ultimately the descendants of this series may be noticed only after keen observation. They preserve in some individuals of one parental species genes from the other. These factors add to the adaptability of the species, and, in a special environment or in later geologic time, under changing conditions, they may be the genes enabling the species to survive with modification.

Heiser (1947; see also Anderson, 1952) studied the hybridizing of two now widely distributed species of North American sunflowers, *Helianthus annuus* and *Helianthus petiolaris*, probably native on the Great Plains (possibly in different areas) but now both widespread as weedy introductions (Fig. 3–56). Abnormalities in meiosis of the F_1 generation are correlated with a fairly high degree of sterility, but

Fig. 3-56. Hybridization of sunflowers, *Helianthus annuus* and *Helianthus petiolaris*: (1) *Helianthus annuus* (Ontario, California); (2) *Helianthus* of a type common in the populations of *annuus* but perhaps derived from interbreeding with *petiolaris* (Pomona, California); (3) *Helianthus petiolaris* (Camino del Diablo, Arizona). Both species may have been originally native on the Great Plains, but both have spread widely with the disturbance following the advent of Caucasian man. The new habitats have been favorable often to hybrids with one gene combination or another, and the present populations are complex.

hybrid swarms were found in Arizona, Missouri, and Illinois, the field plants corresponding well with hybrids produced artificially.

Natural introgression of genes appears to have occurred through backcrossing of occasional hybrids to one or the other or both parental species, but there has been no strong tendency toward amalgamation of *Helianthus annuus* and *Helianthus petiolaris* into a single taxonomic unit. Heiser suggests that characters acquired by each from the other may have been important in enabling both to produce races capable of exploiting the new environments which have developed after disturbance of the natural vegetation following the coming of white men.

THE INTERPRETATION OF FIELD STUDIES

Classification of species, varieties, and other taxa is the organization of natural populations of related plants (or animals) into units. This requires two steps (see pp. 281–285):

1. Determination of the degree of differentiation, that is, the number of characters marking the taxa.

2. Determination of the degree of isolation of each taxon from its nearest relatives, that is, of the degree of constancy of the combinations of differentiating characters. This requires learning the makeup of each unit forming a part of each taxon, such as a variety of a species, and working out, if possible, the evolutionary factors responsible for maintaining it as a separate unit. It is of first importance to know which forms represent stable populations perpetuating themselves through reproduction, and which are transitory or unstable, as, for example, the members of hybrid swarms.

Only a few groups of cacti discussed above are considered to constitute species. Although along the easternmost edge of the Great Plains and along the Gulf and Atlantic beaches intergrading forms of *Opuntia compressa* and other species do occur, they form a relatively small percentage of the individuals in the group as a whole and for the most part are too highly heterozygous to be segregated reasonably even as varieties.

Among the oaks discussed above, the various ecologically segregated taxa are connected by intergrading populations, presumably hybrid swarms, but in most cases these unstable groups are relatively minor in extent of distribution or in frequency of occurrence and in number of individuals as compared to vast populations clearly of one taxon or the other.

Classification of the cherries is deferred for lack of information.

"INTUITIONAL" THOUGHT PROCESSES IN
INTERPRETING DATA

Anderson (1951, 1957) has analyzed the observations and "intuitional" thought processes of the systematist in relation to genetic variations studied in the field (or in the herbarium). The taxonomist recognizes a known species at a glance by means of the entire pattern of characters, just as he may recognize a friend without conscious analysis or cataloging of all the features involved. A plant with slight variations from a familiar character pattern is noted immediately, just as is a brother of a well-known person. These phenomena, long known to systematists, are scrutinized and placed on a solid foundation by a geneticist.

The concordant and discordant variation patterns described by Anderson are exactly what the taxonomist looks for in the field and the herbarium. Plants of a usual population within a species vary within a consistent (concordant) pattern of character combinations. Plants of hybrid swarms or of populations formed locally where specific or other taxonomic "lines" break down show unexpected (discordant) diversity of character combinations.

Concordant and discordant patterns may be observed most readily in the field, but they may be detected in the herbarium. They become evident ultimately in their full form from a synthesis of data of all types.

SUMMARY

The living plant in the field is the source of data upon which herbarial, morphological, biogeographical, chemical, physiological, ecological, or cytogenetic data are based. Ideally, these studies require a complete spectrum of the characters of each individual and depend upon representation of as many individuals and populations as possible.

Whether or not herbarial material may be adequate to permit a preliminary survey of the entire range of forms within a species, far more can be seen in the field than indoors. This includes the variation within a single species and the gradual or irregular intergradation of taxa and the irregularities of character combinations occurring in various degrees over many miles.

Intergradation of natural populations usually is explained by hybridization and formation of hybrid swarms, but an equally logical explanation is incomplete divergence, that is, only partial segregation ever since the trend toward separation began. Either historical condition may exist.

Delimiting of taxa depends upon the degree of intergradation or of discontinuity between populations. Field analysis indicates but does not prove restriction of intergradation primarily in accordance with genetic, geographical, or ecological isolation. Ecological isolation involves combinations of past and present factors, one or two of which may predominate. The most readily detected include water, temperature, soil factors, and direction of slope. In special localities, hybrid swarms may diverge in composition in accordance with local conditions, producing local populations forming incipient varieties or species.

Intergradation may connect species and varieties, forming long chains or complex networks of interbreeding populations spread over thousands of miles.

Numerical or graphic methods of analysis are useful in studying the association of characters in the field and therefore in assessing the degrees of interrelationship of population systems and of taxa.

Sometimes, in a local ecological situation, certain gene combinations derived through hybridization may be preserved while others are eliminated. This may result in segregation of a local variety or, ultimately, of a local species. However, in nature the few hybrids which survive in a well-balanced community usually breed back to one parental species of the cross from which they resulted. Backcrossing soon produces generations scarcely distinguishable from members of that parental species, and ultimately the backcrosses bring into this population system a few genes from the other species. These genes may be the ones which, with later change of climatic or other ecological conditions, may result in some elements of the species being preserved while others die out.

Anderson has analyzed the intuitional thought processes necessary to classification in terms of recognition of concordant and discordant patterns in the variation of characters of individuals and of taxa as represented in the field (or the herbarium). These analyses are applicable to data of all types.

SUGGESTED READING

ADDISON, GEORGE, and ROSENDO TAVARES. 1952. Correlation of the capacity for successful grafting of branches of one species on another with the capacity of the same species for hybridizing.

ANDERSON, EDGAR. 1948. *Hybridization of the habitat.* Evolution 2: 1–9. Publication of the principle.

———. 1949. A monograph on the principle of introgression and on methods of its study. The original publication was by ANDERSON and HUBRICHT, 1938.

———. 1951.

ANDERSON, EDGAR. 1952. A readable, semipopular book summarizing many phases of the application of genetic, cytological, numerical, ecological, and other methods to problems of hybridization, history, and origin of crop, weed, and native plants.

———. 1953. See same title, 1949.

———. 1957. Analysis of the reasons why taxonomists, even specialists who have dealt with different floras, are in close agreement when they are asked to classify the same plant materials.

COOPERRIDER, MIWAKO. 1957.

DAVIDSON, JOHN F. 1947. See Fig. 3–54.

DUFFIELD, J. W. 1940. Discussion of uniformity of chromosome numbers as one of the reasons for the widespread interbreeding of species of *Quercus*.

ELLIOTT, F. C. 1949. Discussion of hybridization and distribution of hybrids of the introduced forage grass *Bromus inermis* and the native *Bromus pumpellianus* (Alaska to Manitoba and the Rocky Mountains). A more elaborate instance of hybridization after the removal of geographical barriers than the case of *Quercus Robur* (see also HEISER, 1951, below).

EPLING, CARL. 1947. Discussion of incomplete isolation of species by adaptation of flower structure to pollination by different types of bees, and of the ability of the hybrids to contribute to the variability and adaptability of both species and to provide a large number of new gene combinations potentially significant when ecological conditions may change.

FASSETT, NORMAN C., and BARBARA CALHOUN. 1952. Discussion of the factors tending to maintain the distinctness of species of cat-tails, including differences in tolerance of the salinity and of the pH of the water in which the plants grow.

———, and JONATHAN D. SAUER. 1950. Discussion of hybridization of tropical lowland and highland species in intermediate habitats disturbed by man.

FROILAND, SVEN G. 1952. Use of the hybrid-index and polygonal-graph methods of analysis of populations to determine whether the proposed species is based upon a hybrid swarm.

GRANT, VERNE. 1949. A reappraisal of the significance of floral isolating mechanisms as barriers to interspecific hybridization, including both structures of the flower which favor one kind of pollen transfer over another and the constancy of the pollinators in visiting only or largely certain types of flowers.

———. 1953. Consideration of a group of sexually reproducing, usually diploid population systems in which the morphological discontinuities are blurred by occasional natural hybridization.

HALL, MARION T. 1952. Consideration of the tendency of the characters of hybrids to be present in groups, perhaps indicating the effect of linkage in hindering recombination of genes producing multiple-factor characters.

HEDBERG, OLOV. 1958. Exposition of the difficulty of analysis of species restricted to remote regions.

HEISER, CHARLES B., JR. 1947.

———. 1951. Analysis of putative natural hybrids matching closely the artificial hybrids of an introduced and a native taxon (see also ELLIOT, above).

HESLOP-HARRISON, J. 1952. A brief survey indicating potential value of using statistical methods in solving taxonomic problems.

MULLER, CORNELIUS H. 1952. Analysis of genetically compatible sympatric species between which the amount of intergradation is governed primarily by the soil (edaphic) factors controlling the survival of hybrid offspring.

PALMER, ERNEST J. 1948. A historical account of the literature of hybrid oaks, and of field study by the author, followed by a list of named hybrids.

SILLIMAN, FRANCES E., and ROBERT S. LEISNER. 1958.

STEBBINS, G. LEDYARD, JR. 1950. Highly recommended as a thorough and excellent treatment of the field of evolution.

———, E. B. MATZKE, and C. EPLING. 1947. Analysis by the hybrid-index method.

TUCKER, JOHN M. 1952a. Study of plants intermediate between the blue oak and the desert scrub oak, paralleling some of the research presented in Chapter 3.

―――. 1952b. Discussion primarily of the problem of segregation of *Quercus dumosa* and the taxa *californica* and *turbinella*. Based upon independent parallel investigation of some of the problems discussed in Chapter 3.

―――, and CORNELIUS H. MULLER. 1956. Postulation of the subtropical origin of a taxon late relict in eastern Washington and still later relict in Arizona.

―――, and JONATHAN D. SAUER. 1958. Use of a triangular graph for analysis of populations of five species occurring in the rich soil of a delta and of hybrids surviving in extensive hybrid swarms.

TURRILL, W. B. 1950. Development of the thesis that an artificial classification may be constructed upon the basis of any of several sets of characters, but a natural classification must be based upon all character combinations. Presentation of an interpretation involving parallel evolution, hybridization, and the restrictive effects of natural selection in various environments of the past and present.

ZOBEL, BRUCE. 1951. Evidence of natural hybridization of pine species and of the evolutionary significance of introgression from the Jeffrey pine to the Coulter pine.

―――. 1953. Discussion of isolated populations showing relatively little variation, perhaps in keeping with a relatively short period of isolation possibly resulting partly from recent human activities.

chapter

4

Data from Microscopic
Morphology[1]

The plant characters observed most commonly in the herbarium and in the field relate to gross morphology or at least to features detected readily by external examination with the naked eye. Sometimes, as with color, these features are (at least in part) manifestations of the internal chemical characters of the plant (see Chapter 6) or, as with texture, of the plant's underlying microscopic structure. The dissecting microscope reveals external detail of surface characters and of structures much too small to be observed clearly with the unaided eye; the compound microscope makes available for study internal features of the tissues composing the organism; the electron microscope may reveal still smaller taxonomically significant structures of the cells and the nature of their chemical composition.

Microscopic, or at least minute, structures may be of primary significance in governing the basic features of biological processes. Consequently, they may be responsible for the course of evolution leading to the differentiation of species and other taxa and, therefore, may be one key to classification.

THE EVOLUTIONARY AND TAXONOMIC SIGNIFICANCE
OF SYSTEMS OF MINUTE STRUCTURES

As was pointed out in Chapter 1, minute characters having a vital role in such important phases of life history as sexual reproduc-

[1] In this and the three following chapters, a complete coverage of the subject is not attempted. The object of this book is to call attention to the significance of each field in classification and to give examples rather than to present a full treatise on the contributions of each type of study to the subject as a whole.

tion are responsible in part for the development and isolation of species. Consequently, they occur in one group of plants and not another and are important markers of taxa. The following is an additional example:

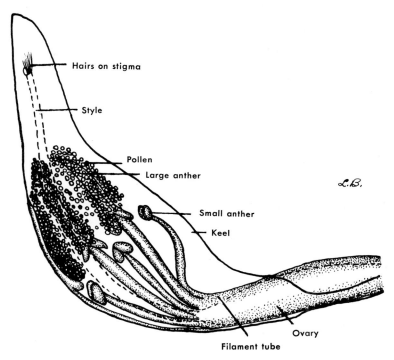

Fig. 4–1. The keel enclosing the stamens and the pistil of the typical pea-type (papilionaceous) flower of a small lupine, *Lupinus nanus* var. *Menkerae*. As in many members of the pea family, the pollen is ejected violently from the keel but, because of the shield formed by the hairs on the stigma, usually it does not reach the stigma of the same flower. (Redrawn from David B. Dunn, *American Midland Naturalist* 55: 444, 1956. Used by permission.)

In some species of lupines (Leguminosae, or pea family), such as *Lupinus nanus* (Fig. 4–1) (Dunn, 1956), the stigma of the flower is shielded from its own pollen by a ring of stiff hairs at the base of the stigma. The pollen is shed from the anthers and accumulated in the keel of the corolla until disturbance by an insect causes its violent ejection, dusting the insect with pollen. Ordinarily some of the pollen is taken to the stigmas of other flowers, though some self-pollination does occur despite the hairs on the stigma. Closely related smaller-flowered species, such as *Lupinus bicolor*, seldom are

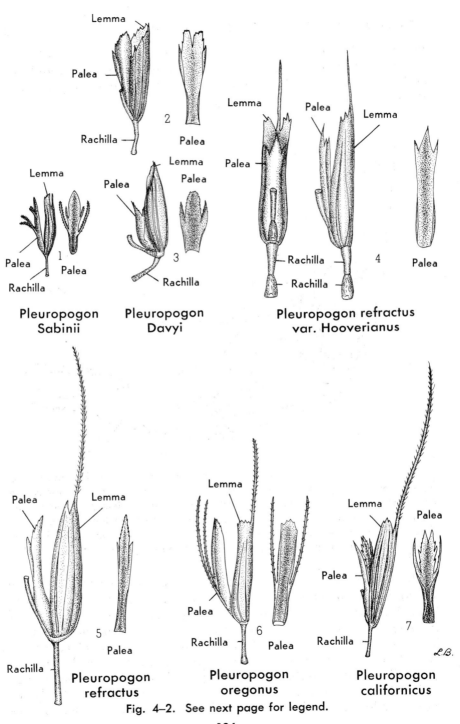

Lemma

Palea

Rachilla

2

Palea

Lemma

Palea

Palea

Lemma

Palea

Lemma

Palea

Palea

3

Rachilla

Palea

Lemma

Palea

Rachilla

Palea

Rachilla

4

Palea

Rachilla

**Pleuropogon
Sabinii**

**Pleuropogon
Davyi**

**Pleuropogon refractus
var. Hooverianus**

Palea

Lemma

Lemma

Palea

Lemma

Palea

Palea

Palea

5

Rachilla

Palea

Rachilla

6

Palea

Rachilla

7

L.B.

**Pleuropogon
refractus**

**Pleuropogon
oregonus**

**Pleuropogon
californicus**

Fig. 4–2. See next page for legend.

136

visited by insects, and in these plants the hairs of the ring at the base of the stigma are too short to prevent self-pollination. The flower may be self-pollinated either before the flower opens or soon afterward, and some flowers are pollinated without opening.

THE OCCURRENCE OF MINUTE STRUCTURAL CHARACTERS

Investigation of minute structures may provide data which reinforce, refine, or revise the taxonomic system constructed on the basis of more obvious features, thus often furnishing more conclusive evidence than could be obtained without a microscope.

Obscure characters significant in classification may occur in *minute organs*, on *surface appendages*, in *pollen grains*, in *small fruits and seeds*, in *embryos*, in the *cells of the epidermis*, in the *tissues beneath the epidermis*, or *inside the cells*.

Characters of Minute Organs. Specialized small organs may be strictly vegetative, as are bud scales, or more closely associated with the reproductive processes, as are bracts or reduced flower or cone parts.

TABLE 4–1
Variation in Characters of *Pleuropogon*

Rachilla joints: In some species these are scabrous, in others smooth; in some the lower half is swollen and bulbous, in others not.

Glumes: Variation is mostly in size (ranging from 1 to 2 mm. long in the circumpolar *Pleuropogon Sabinii* to 3.5 to 7.0 mm. in the Pacific Coast *Pleuropogon refractus* and in proportion of the first and second glumes (the second being twice as long in most species but only slightly longer in *Pleuropogon Davyi*).

Lemmas: Variation in shape and indentation is significant from species to species.

Paleas: Variation in shape, indentation, and development of the two lateral lobes (which in some species, e.g., *Pleuropogon Sabinii* and *Pleuropogon oregonus*, form scabrous elongated awns) is highly significant.

In the grass family the spikelets of the species within a genus differ in the rachilla joints, glumes, lemmas, or paleas. An example is found in the semaphore grasses (*Pleuropogon*), in which six species vary as shown in Table 4–1 and in Fig. 4–2.

Fig. 4–2. Semaphore grasses (*Pleuropogon*), diagnostic characters of small structures accessory to the flowers—lemmas, paleas, and rachillas: (1–7) as indicated. (Modified from Lyman Benson, American Journal of Botany 28: 362, 1941. Used by permission.)

Insects are attracted to flowers of buttercups (*Ranunculus*) by nectar secreted by a gland on the base of the ventral side of the blade of each petal. The gland has been known for more than two centuries to vary from species to species, but until recently, except for noting the absence of a covering scale in some aquatic species, it received almost no attention for its significance in classification. Linnaeus (1754) noted (as translated from the Latin by J. E. Smith, 1819), "The nectary in *Ranunculus* is, in some species, a naked pore; in some, it is bordered with a cylindrical margin; in others closed with a notched scale." Study shows the types of scales listed in Table 4–2 and in Fig. 4–3 to be present among the 99 species occurring in North America.

TABLE 4–2

Types of Nectary Scales in *Ranunculus*

1. A transverse ridge basal to the gland [Fig. 3–2 (C)]

2. A simple flap [Fig. 3–2 (A–B)]

3. A pocket (Fig. 3–3)

4. A forked structure produced distally and sometimes finally free from the petal at the tips of the two branches [Figs.3–2 (D–F)]

5. A circular or obovate border [Fig. 3–2 (H)]

6. A primary scale bearing the gland on its ventral surface and bearing there also a secondary scale which forms a pocket enclosing the gland [Fig. 3–2 (G)]

Scales of any of the six types may be (as shown in Fig. 4–3) proximally (basally) truncate [(1), (3), (17)], rounded (4), or angular [(5), (6), (9–11), (13), (14)] and distally (apically) truncate [(3), (7), (9), (13), (14), (15), (17)], emarginate [(1), one example in (10)], three-lobed [one example in (10)], curved outward (16), or curved inward [(12), (15)]. The scale is usually glabrous, but in a few species the distal margin is ciliate [(13), (14), (16), (17)], and similar hairs may appear on the adjacent surface of the petal (16). In nearly all species the nectary scale characters are constant, but in a few they are variable [(10), (11)].

Basic types of scales characterize the subgenera and sections of the genus, and the nectary scale characters, taken in combination with others, have made possible a consistent realignment of these major groupings. In particular, segregation of the two largest groups of species, section *Ranunculus* (synonym, *Chrysanthe*) (type 2 scale, simple flap) and section *Epirotes* (type 3, pocket), was uncertain until the nectary scale type was studied. The North American subgenera and sections and their scale types are summarized in the list in Table 4–3.

TABLE 4–3

Correlation of Nectary Scale Types with Occurrence in the Major Subdivisions of *Ranunculus*

Subgenus I. *Ranunculus*	
Section 1. *Ranunculus*	Type 2, except *Ranunculus recurvatus,* Type 3
Section 2. *Echinella*	Type 2 or 3
Section 3. *Epirotes*	Type 3, except *Ranunculus Eastwoodianus,* Type 4
Section 4. *Flammula*	Type 3
Section 5. *Hecatonia*	Type 3, 4, 5, or 6
Subgenus II. *Cyrtorhyncha*	
Section 1. *Halodes*	Type 2
Section 2. *Cyrtorhyncha*	Type 1
Section 3. *Arcteranthis*	Type 4
Section 4. *Pseudaphanostemma*	Type 4
Subgenus III. *Ceratocephalus*	Type 2
Subgenus IV. *Oxygraphis*	Apparently Type 1
Subgenus V. *Crymodes*	Type 4
Subgenus VI. *Batrachium*	Type 3, 4, or obsolete
Subgenus VII. *Pallasiantha*	Type 3
Subgenus VIII. *Coptidium*	Type 3
Subgenus IX. *Ficaria*	Type 3

Characters of Surface Appendages. TRICHOMES. The hairlike appendages of plants are trichomes; they are not comparable to the hairs of mammals. Some trichomes are formed from single cells, others from several or many. Some bear glands (swollen secretory cells) [Fig. 4–4 (4), (11)], which usually are terminal.

Rollins (1941) found the trichomes of *Arabis* (mustard family) to be unicellular and not glandular. In some species they are simple, in others branched. The branches may arise like those of a tree or a shrub [dendritic pubescence, as in Fig. 4–4 (8)], or several may radiate horizontally from a common basal center [stellate or star-like pubescence, as in Fig. 4–4 (7)], or two branches may diverge horizontally and closely against the surface (malphigiaceous pubescence). In some species of *Arabis* they are terete, in others flattened, in still others basally swollen. In a few species there is a more or less stable association of two kinds of trichomes. Variation of size of hairs within a species is common, and sometimes major differences in size are correlated with other characters marking particular species.

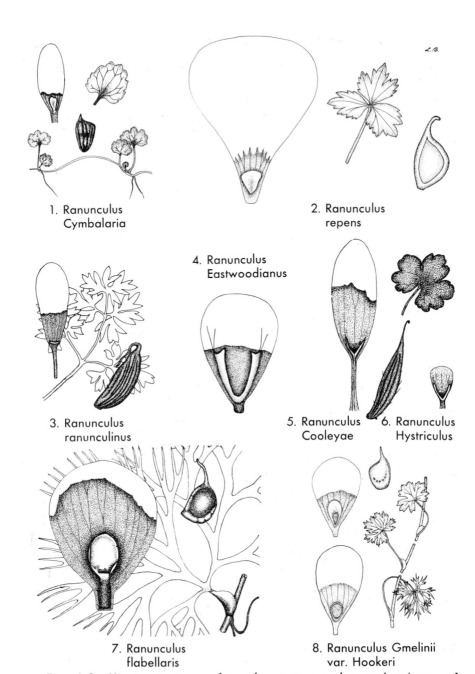

1. Ranunculus Cymbalaria

2. Ranunculus repens

4. Ranunculus Eastwoodianus

3. Ranunculus ranunculinus

5. Ranunculus Cooleyae

6. Ranunculus Hystriculus

7. Ranunculus flabellaris

8. Ranunculus Gmelinii var. Hookeri

Fig. 4–3. Minute structures of petals, nectary scales, and achenes of *Ranunculus*: (1–8) as indicated. Nectary scales: type 1—basal transverse ridge (3); type 2—simple flap (1–2); type 3—pocket (9–17); type 4—forked (4–5); type 5—circular or obovate border (8); type 6—a pocket on a primary scale

140

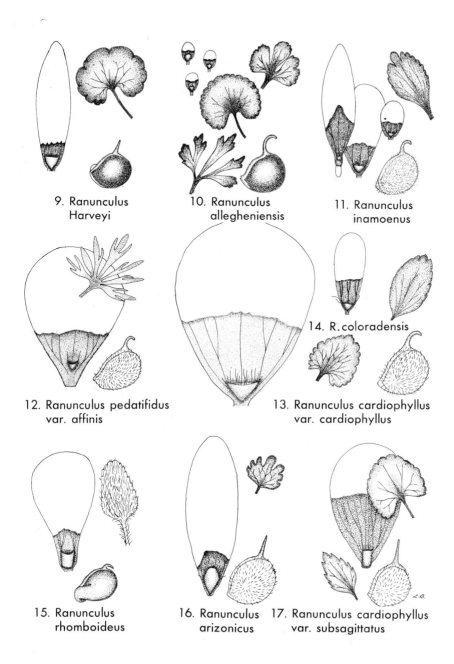

9. Ranunculus
Harveyi

10. Ranunculus
allegheniensis

11. Ranunculus
inamoenus

14. R. coloradensis

12. Ranunculus pedatifidus
var. affinis

13. Ranunculus cardiophyllus
var. cardiophyllus

15. Ranunculus
rhomboideus

16. Ranunculus
arizonicus

17. Ranunculus cardiophyllus
var. subsagittatus

bearing the gland (7). [Items (1), (3–7), and (9–17) modified from Lyman
Benson, American Journal of Botany 27: 800, 1940; and *Plant Classification*,
D. C. Heath & Co., 1957, p. 453. Used by permission.]

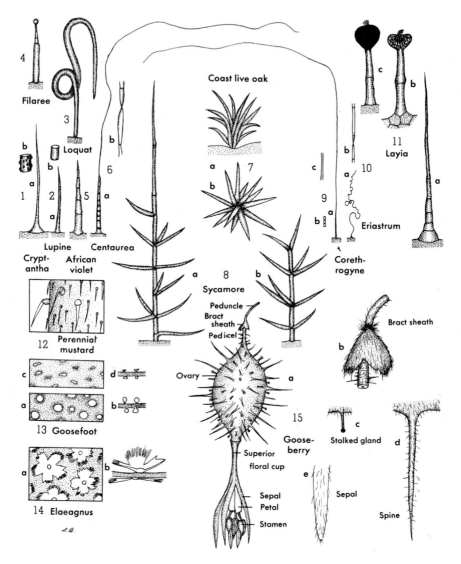

Fig. 4–4. Trichomes ("hairs"), scales, and glands: (1) simple, unicellular trichome of *Cryptantha intermedia*—(a) complete cell, (b) enlargement of a segment showing minute papillae on the surface; (2) simple, unicellular trichome of a perennial lupine, *Lupinus formosus*—(a) complete trichome, (b) enlargement of a segment showing the smooth surface; (3) unicellular trichome of a loquat (*Eriobotrya japonica*); (4) gland-tipped, multicellular trichome of a filaree, *Erodium cicutarium;* (5) multicellular trichome of an African violet, *Saintpaulia* hybrid; (6) multicellular, long-attenuate trichome of Malta (or Napa) thistle

Rollins' study (1944, 1945, 1946, 1949) of the trichomes of guayule (*Parthenium argentatum*), mariola (*Parthenium incanum*), and their hybrids is illustrated in Fig. 4–5.

Most members of the Chenopodiaceae (goosefoot family) are characterized by scales which tend to whiten at least the young stems and leaves. These are vesicle-like trichomes which dry into "scales" with the appearance of dandruff, the plants being described as scurfy [Fig. 4–4 (13)]. The abundance of scurf varies greatly within genera of the family, as between *Chenopodium album* and most forms of *Chenopodium murale* which has few. Some forms of even *Chenopodium album* may have few scales, and the stems and leaves may be clearly green. Green forms (that is, those with few vesicular hairs) are the basis for the proposed var. *viride*.

SCALES. Platelike multicellular scales are formed on the stems, leaves, flowers, or fruits of some families. In the Elaeagnaceae [Fig. 4–4 (14)] (as in the oleaster, silverberry, and buffaloberry) scales are formed on nearly all the organs of the plant.

GLANDS. Many species are distinguished by highly specialized glands occurring on the surface of an organ or elevated on trichomes or special stalks [see Fig. 4–4 (4), (11)]. Sometimes, as on the fruits of certain species of gooseberries, for example, *Ribes amarum* [Fig. 4–4 (15)], gland-tipped and glandular trichomes, bristles, or other structures, such as prickles, may be intermingled.

Hemizonia (or *Calycadenia*) *truncata* and *Hemizonia pauciflora* (tribe Madieae of the Compositae) are distinguished from *Hemizonia tenella* by the presence, on the apices of the leaves, of trichomes specialized as stalked glands, similar to those of *Layia* shown in Fig.

(*Centaurea melitensis*); (7) branched (stellate, or starlike) trichomes of the coast live oak (*Quercus agrifolia*); (8) treelike, branching, multicellular trichomes of a sycamore, *Platanus racemosa*; (9) multicellular, long-attenuate trichome of *Corethrogyne filaginifolia* var. *virgata*; (10) filiform, cobwebby trichome of *Eriastrum sapphirinum*; (11) trichomes of a tarweed, *Layia glandulosa*—(a) multicellular trichome of a type common in the Compositae (sunflower family), (b) gland-tipped trichome or "tack-shaped gland" (apical gland in longitudinal section), (c) same as (b) but at a later stage (apical gland in external view); (12) bicellular, reflexed trichomes of a perennial mustard, *Brassica geniculata*; (13) "scurf" or subglobose trichomes on the leaves of a goosefoot (or lamb's quarters), *Chenopodium album*—(a) surface view of young trichomes, (b) section, (c) surface view of old collapsed trichomes forming scurfy scales, (d) section; (14) fimbriate (fringed) scales on a leaf of an oleaster, *Elaeagnus*; (15) trichomes, spines, and stalked glands of a wild gooseberry, *Ribes amarum* —(a) young fruit, this and (b–e) as indicated.

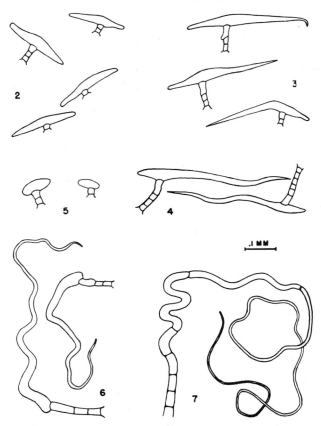

Fig. 4–5. Trichomes of two species and of a hybrid: (1) (in another figure by the original author); (2–5) trichomes of different types of guayule (*Parthenium argentatum*), a Texan and Mexican plant which produces rubber—(2) usual types of guayule; (3) "intermediate type" of guayule; (4) rough type of guayule; (5) glabrate type of guayule; (6) trichomes of an interspecific hybrid between guayule and mariola; (7) trichomes of mariola (*Parthenium incanum*), a southwestern-desert and Mexican plant. (From Reed C. Rollins, American Journal of Botany 31: 95, 1944. Used by permission.)

4–4 (11). The gland and its secretion form a mass of much greater diameter than the stalk, and the entire structure may have the appearance of a carpet tack stuck lightly into the leaf. Carlquist (1958, 1959a, 1959b) has studied the evolution of anatomical characteristics of the surface appendages of the stems, leaves, and other parts of several members of the tribe Madieae. Simple glandular biserial trichomes are found in all the Compositae. From this basic type, the capitate trichome, that is, one with an enlarged "head," has evolved. It is produced by extra divisions of the cells at the apex. Trichomes of this type have given rise in turn to the more specialized "tack-shaped glands" of *Hemizonia Fitchii*, *Blepharizonia*, and *Holozonia*. Highly developed trichomes from this line of evolution occur in species of *Hemizonia* (or *Calycadenia*), in which tack-shaped glands may even have vascular tissue in their stalks. In *Holocarpha*, specialization results in the formation of two types of glands—one formed from several initial cells, the other a hollow-stalked trichome formed from a single initial cell. Mesophyll tissue of the bract on which the hollow-stalked gland is produced is intruded into the base of the stalk.

Characters of Pollen Grains. The sculpturing of the external substance (extine, or exine) of pollen grains presents a remarkable series of microscopic characters. The evolution of pollen grains parallels to a considerable extent the evolution of other characters in the pteridophytes and spermatophytes (Wodehouse, 1935 and, especially, 1936) (Fig. 10–11). The triradiate crest formed by compression of the members of a group of four fern spores against each other (after formation by meiosis from a spore mother cell) disappears gradually in the higher plants. The characteristic feature of gymnosperm and monocotyledon pollen is a single furrow, the pollen being monocolpate. This feature occurs also in a few of the primitive families of the Ranales, but the other dicotyledons are characterized largely by tricolpate pollen, the pollen grain having three radiating furrows at the end opposite the fundamental position of the crests.

The details of surface sculpturing of pollen grains vary from family to family, and commonly the family and often the genus may be identified by the pollen grains. The markings of many types of pollen are so distinctive that, by catching and staining pollen grains on a microscope slide, it is possible to determine the relative abundance of the pollen of various plants being released into the air in a particular area at a given time. This method is used in establishing the likely causes of hay fever in the region.

Detailed study of the pollen within a family may aid in classification of genera and perhaps of species, but taxonomic use of pollen characters has been neglected (see Erdtman, 1952). An example of correlation of pollen structure with classification of species is the work of Hedberg (1946) who found ten types of pollen grains among species of *Polygonum*, each confined to a distinctive species group (Fig. 4–6).

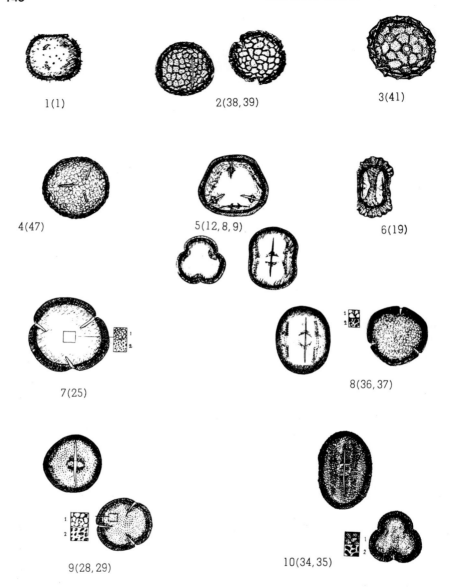

Fig. 4–6. Types of pollen characterizing species groups in *Polygonum*: types 1 to 10, as indicated by number. The numbers in parentheses are those used by the original author. (From Olav Hedberg, Svensk Botaniska Tidskrift 40: 371–404, 1946. Illustration courtesy of the author, used by permission.)

Characters of Small Fruits and Seeds. The microscopic and even the more obvious macroscopic surface as well as other features of small fruits and of seeds have been neglected in the taxonomic study of numerous plant groups. Despite the occasional appearance of a summary of seed characters, biological use of the data has been restricted largely to applied science, as in the identification of weed seeds. Taxonomic study of some seeds has appeared occasionally in the organization of a family (e.g., the Cactaceae or the Euphorbiaceae), and small fruits such as achenes have been studied in

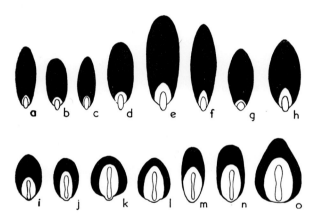

Fig. 4–7. Relative size of the grass embryo in relation to the seed as a whole in the subfamilies Festucoideae (a–h) (embryo relatively small) and Panicoideae (i–o) (embryo relatively large) of the grass family (Gramineae). (From John R. Reeder, American Journal of Botany 44: 758, 1957; illustration courtesy of the author, used by permission.)

detail for many Compositae, some Cruciferae, *Ranunculus,* some Chenopodiaceae, and other groups (see Brouwer and Stählin, 1955).

Some variation in the surface of the achene of *Ranunculus* can be seen in the illustration showing the nectary scales (Fig. 4–3). The achene may be smooth, or it may bear structures developed from the surface layers. Papillae or spines aid in segregating the section *Echinella* from all other Ranunculi; transverse corrugations mark the subgenus *Batrachium;* longitudinal nerves [see Fig. 4–3 (1), (3)] characterize the subgenera *Oxygraphis* and *Cyrtorhyncha.*

Characters of Embryos. By investigation of the embryos (Figs. 4–7 and 4–8) of about 300 species of grasses, Reeder (1957) confirmed the earlier report of Van Tieghem of two basic types of

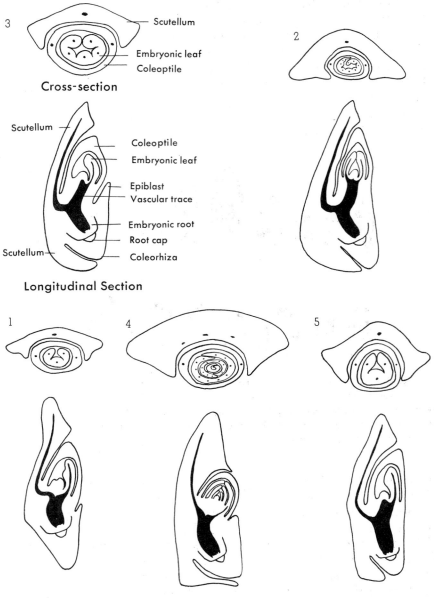

Fig. 4–8. Embryo types in the grass family (Gramineae): (1) festucoid type—scutellum free from the coleorhiza, first embryonic leaf with several bundles portion of the scutellum absent or fused with the coleorhiza, first embryonic leaf with few bundles and its margins not overlapping (see cross-section); (2) panicoid type—a distinct elongation present between the point of divergence

embryos in the grass family. In the Festucoideae, the lower portion of the scutellum is lacking or is fused with the coleorhiza and the coleoptile is inserted at about the point of divergence of the vascular trace leading to the scutellum. In the Panicoideae, the descending part of the scutellum is not attached to the coleorhiza, and the coleoptile is inserted well above the point of divergence of the vascular trace leading to the scutellum. Reeder recognized six (now revised to five) distinctive embryo types, and these suggest relationship of genera hitherto considered to be anomalous. In conjunction with other characteristics, the features of the embryo are in many cases almost the key to classification of the grasses. The Panicoideae as a group are indicated to be homogeneous. On the other hand, the Festucoideae, as traditionally circumscribed, include some groups having affinities with the Panicoideae, as is confirmed by characters of the embryo. A realignment of genera is suggested.

Characters of the Epidermis. Munz and Laudermilk (1949) investigated the microscopic surface structure of the leaves of three taxa of ash trees in search of characters of use in clearing up the confused taxonomic status of these entities. They found that *Fraxinus oregona* differed from *Fraxinus velutina* var. *coriacea* in (1) size and shape of the epidermal cells, (2) thickness of the cell walls, and (3) the microscopic ridges (sculpturing) of the cells adjacent to the guard cells of the stomata.

Occasional recombination of these microscopic and other characters suggested past hybridization of these two ashes in southern California. Although *Fraxinus oregona* does not occur there now, evidently it did in Pleistocene times, when the climate was more moist. With the postglacial prevalence of drier conditions, traces of *Fraxinus oregona* are left only in the remnants of hybrid swarms persisting in the more favorable locations.

---

of the scutellum bundle and the coleoptile, no epiblast, lower part of the scutellum free from the coleorhiza, first embryonic leaf with several bundles and with its margins overlapping (see cross-section); (3) chloridoid or eragrostoid type—vascular system similar to the panicoid type, lower part of the scutellum free from the coleorhiza as in the panicoid type, epiblast present as in the festucoid type, first embryonic leaf much as in the festucoid type; (4) bambusoid (including oryzoid-olyrioid type as now modified by the original author)—similar to the panicoid type but with an epiblast; (5) arundinoid or danthonioid type—similar to the panicoid type but with (see cross-section) the first embryonic leaf with few bundles and with the margins not overlapping. (From John R. Reeder [with slight modification by the original author], American Journal of Botany 44: 763, 766, 1957; illustration, courtesy of the author, used by permission.)

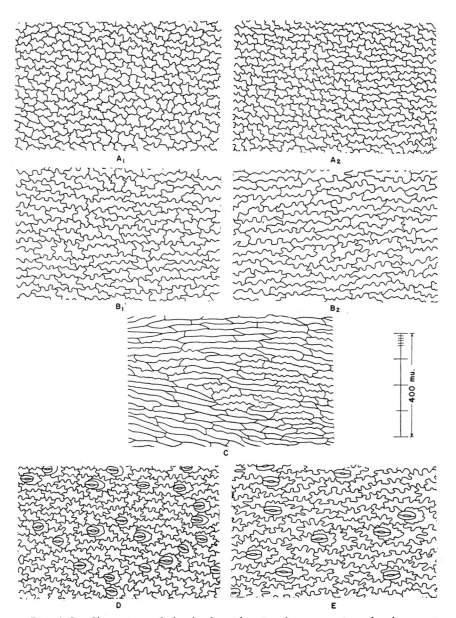

Fig. 4–9. Characters of the leaf epidermis of two species of spleenworts (ferns) and a hybrid: (A–C) upper epidermis—(A$_1$), (A$_2$) *Asplenium platyneuron*; (B$_1$), (B$_2$) *Asplenium Bradleyi,* a hybrid of (A) and (C); (C) *Asplenium montanum*; (D), (E) lower epidermis, which, although it is striking, in this case does not provide clear diagnostic characters—(D) *Asplenium platyneuron*; (E) *Asplenium Bradleyi.* (From Warren H. Wagner, Jr., Evolution 8: 109, 1954. Used by permission.)

Within *Fraxinus velutina*, var. *coriacea* (chiefly of southern California) differs from var. *velutina* (easternmost edge of California to southwestern Utah, western Texas, and northern Mexico) in the thickness and leathery texture of the leaves, in the presence of petiolules on the leaflets, and in the pattern of larger size and more diffuse content formed by the ridges radiating from the guard cells.

In order to investigate the minute leaf characters of many individuals without undue loss of time, Laudermilk devised a special method of sectioning by a simple instrument illustrated in the paper. Such techniques are of primary importance in making the investigation of microscopic characters practical.

The epidermal characters of ferns have been investigated in species and hybrids of spleenwort (*Asplenium*) by Wagner (1954), as illustrated in Fig. 4–9.

Characters of the Tissues Beneath the Epidermis. Under the surface of any part of a plant, marked variations in structure from individual to individual or from species to species may be masked. In the stem of *Ranunculus repens* (Fig. 4–10), a species common in Europe and abundantly introduced in the northern half of North America, there is relatively little strengthening (sclerified) tissue, and this is correlated with the creeping habit of the plant. In the closely related and similarly distributed *Ranunculus acris* (Fig. 4–11), the tissues between "vascular bundles" are sclerified, and therefore an erect habit is possible. The amount of sclerification may be found to vary in both species because in northern Eurasia each one includes several forms. This is particularly so in *Ranunculus repens*, which includes suberect types such as var. *glabratus*. *Ranunculus repens* and *Ranunculus acris* also differ in that the cortical parenchyma of the stems of *Ranunculus repens* is undifferentiated except for the presence of chlorophyll in the cells near the surface, where there is illumination. The corresponding cells of *Ranunculus acris* are arranged in a regular alternate pattern, with larger intercellular air spaces connecting with stomata; they compose an aerated photosynthetic tissue. Another erect species, *Ranunculus californicus* (Fig. 4–12), related to *Ranunculus repens* and *Ranunculus acris*, has similarly sclerified supporting tissues in the stem, and large, irregular intercellular cavities in the photosynthetic tissue. The epidermis of *Ranunculus acris* is more highly specialized than in the other two species, particularly more so than in *Ranunculus repens*.

Investigations of cross-sections of the leaves of a number of species of *Ranunculus* show considerable variation in the palisade layer and the spongy mesophyll tissue.

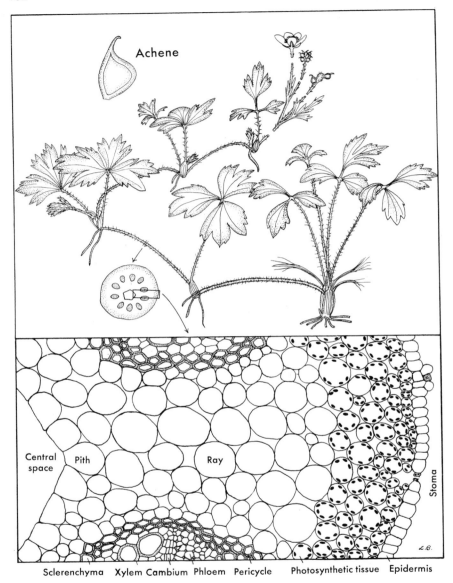

Achene

Central space Pith   Ray   Stoma

Sclerenchyma   Xylem Cambium Phloem Pericycle   Photosynthetic tissue   Epidermis

Fig. 4–10. Stem structure in *Ranunculus repens*, a European species widely naturalized in North America. Note that the medullary rays are not sclerified as in the erect species, *Ranunculus acris* (cf. Fig. 4–11) and *Ranunculus californicus* (cf. Fig. 4–12) and that the photosynthetic tissue is not as well differentiated or aerated.

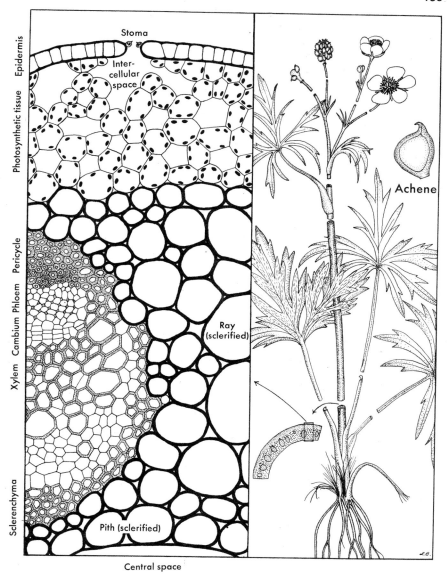

Fig. 4–11. Stem structure in *Ranunculus acris,* a European species naturalized in North America chiefly from Alaska to Greenland, Washington, Iowa,
and New Jersey. Note that the medullary rays are strongly sclerified and
therefore important in supporting the erect stems (cf., in contrast, *Ranunculus
repens,* Fig. 4–10) and that the photosynthetic tissue is well differentiated, with
aeration through larger intercellular spaces.

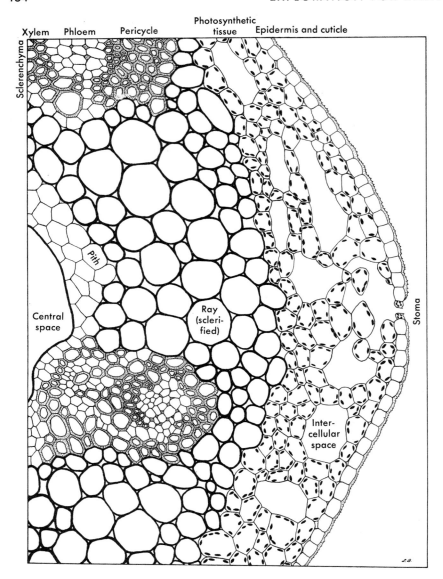

Fig. 4–12. Stem structure in *Ranunculus californicus*. Sclerification is like that in *Ranunculus acris* (Fig. 4–11), but the photosynthetic tissue is even better developed and has more aeration.

The internal structure of the leaves of native and introduced pines of the United States varies in many details characteristic of different species (Fig. 4–13). A key to the species, based upon these characters, has been published by Harlow (1947).

Another example of combining anatomy with classification is the study of *Fitchia*, a genus of Polynesian woody Compositae (see Carlquist, 1957). An important feature of this study is the application of microtechnical methods to examination of dried material from herbarium specimens, making possible a rapid survey of numerous individuals of many species, including those from remote regions.

On the generic level, Carlquist compared presence of internal characters of major related units of the Heliantheae (including *Fitchia*), occurring on islands in the Pacific Ocean, among them the characters summarized in Table 4–4. Each of the characters or its absence marks some genera but not others.

TABLE 4–4
Internal Characters of the Heliantheae

Corolla with complete or incomplete median bundles

Style with 4 veins or otherwise

Achene with numerous (8 or more) or with few wall bundles

Pappus structures vasculated or non-vasculated

Ovule with a branched trace or otherwise

Collora veins each with one or two lateral secretory canals or with only one

Stamen tips, styles, awns, achenes, receptacular bracts, or leaves with or without secretory canals

Inner surface of the style branch completely stigmatic or only partly so

On the specific level, subdivisions of *Fitchia* are characterized by presence of the internal characters listed in Table 4–5.

Characters Inside the Cells. Some internal characters of the cells have been correlated with occurrence in particular taxa. The orders of green algae are characterized by different kinds of chloroplasts. These include the "cup-shaped" chloroplasts of the Volvocales, the laminate parietal chloroplasts of the Ulotrichales and the Oedogoniales, the stellate chloroplasts of the Schizogonales, the numerous discoid chloroplasts of the Siphonales, and the spiral, straight, stellate, and other types of the Zygnematales. Specialized types mark the genera of the Zygnemataceae, for example spiral in *Spirogyra*, straight in *Mougeotia*, and stellate in *Zygnema*. Species

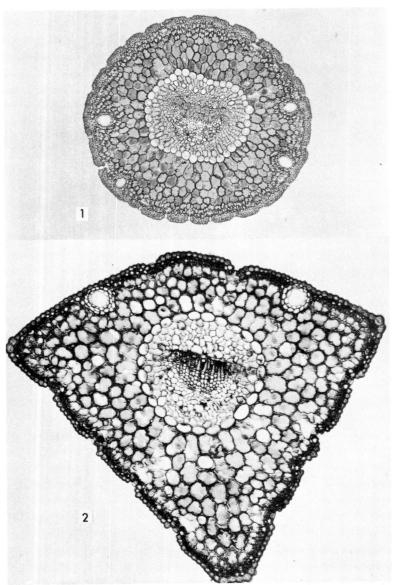

Fig. 4–13. Variation in leaf structure of pines: (1–2) white pines—(1) one-
leaf pinyon or piñon (*Pinus cembroides* var. *monophylla*), a common pine in the
mountains in and bordering the Great Basin and the Mojavean Desert; (2) limber
pine (*Pinus flexilis*), a species abundant in the Rocky Mountain system and less
common westward to a few stations in California; (3–4) pitch or yellow pines
(as opposed to white pines);—(3) long-leaf pine (*Pinus australis* [*palustris*]), a
species of the coastal plains from Texas to Virginia; (4) red pine (*Pinus resinosa*),
a species growing from Manitoba to Newfoundland, West Virginia, and New

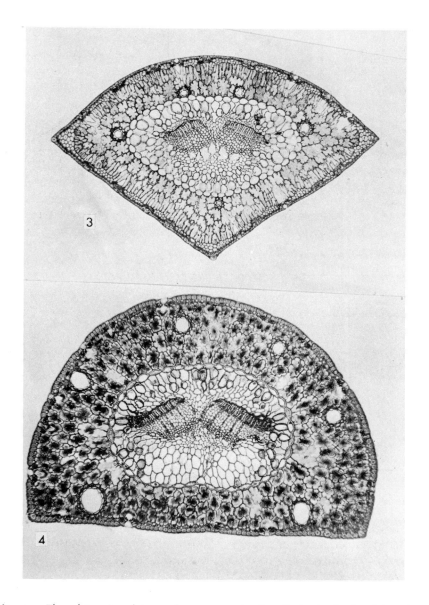

Jersey. The white pines have only one vascular bundle in the leaf. Other diagnostic characters distinguishing species or groups of species include the number of cells of thickness of the hypodermis; the number and location of resin canals; the thickness of the walls of the cells of the epidermis, endodermis, resin canal, and other cells; sclerification of cells; and the number, position, and characters of the stomata. (From William A. Harlow, New York State College of Forestry Technical Publication No. 32, 1947. Photographs courtesy of the author, used by permission.)

of *Spirogyra* differ in number of chloroplasts per cell and in width and form of the spiral ribbon.

In the vascular plants, chloroplasts do not vary markedly but some other tangible internal features of cells do. An example is the presence in some cells of crystals of various substances. Variation in wall structure usually is manifested in the tissues and is thus recorded under the preceding section. However, thick-walled cells may vary significantly in thickness.

The chromosomes have special significance because of their close relationship to inheritance. Cytological characters are discussed in Chapter 7 because of the intertwining of the subject with genetics.

TABLE 4–5

Internal Characters of *Fitchia*

Group I. *F. mangarevensis, F. rapensis.* Mangareva and Rapa islands.
  1. Leaves thick and coriaceous (leathery) because of a sclerified bundle sheath, as opposed to thin and with no sclereids except along the major veins.
  2. Pith with weakly sclerified cells in irregular patches in an unsclerified background.

Group II. *F. nutans, F. tahitensis, F. cuneata.* Tahiti and (*F. cuneata*) Raiatea Island.
  1. Pith in *F. nutans* with uniformly thickened cells, in *F. tahitensis* with canals surrounded by heavily sclerified cells, in *F. cuneata* with no canals and with various types of sclerification.
  2. Awn with one bundle and in *F. nutans* with a secretory canal.

Group III. *F. speciosa.* Rarotonga Island (remote from other species).
  1. Involucral bracts unsclerified and with large, complex bundles.
  2. Awn with no secretory canal and with a unique basal structure.
  3. Achene wall with bundles.

SUMMARY

Characters of minute structures are often particularly significant in biological processes of primary importance to the organism. They may relate to nutrition and other physiological factors, to ecological relationships with the chemical and physical features of the environment or with other organisms, or to reproduction. Consequently, investigating them may be of primary importance to an understanding of the species and of the related organisms with differing microscopic characters.

Neglect of characters of minute structures is due to the difficulty of investigation. Ordinarily, gross morphological structures are seen more easily and sometimes may be more practical for use in keys. Past neglect leaves a fertile area for investigation and for correlation of new characters with better-known ones. After extensive research and careful correlation with other characters, microscopic characters may be a key to classification of taxa of any rank, clearing up confusion resulting from study of external characters alone. Whenever possible, the significance of the characters in the evolution of the plant species should be determined, for this may be the nearest approach to a real key to classification.

SUGGESTED READING

BAILEY, IRVING W. 1953b. Discussion of the contribution of anatomy to solution of difficult problems justifying much time and effort, such as revisions of families.

CARLQUIST, SHERWIN. 1957.

———. 1958. See below.

———. 1959a. See below.

———. 1959b. This and the two papers above form the basis for the discussion of the glandular trichomes of the Madieae (or Madinae).

CAVE, MARION S. 1953. Examples of use of data from embryology and cytology.

DUNN, DAVID B. 1956.

ERDTMAN, G. 1952. Largely a family-by-family review of pollen.

FOSTER, ADRIANCE S. General reference.

HAGERUP, O. 1950.

HARLOW, WILLIAM M. 1947. Of interest because of the variety of variable characters of the tissues.

HEDBERG, OLAV. 1946.

JOHANSEN, DONALD A. 1953. Important for the consideration of microscopic characters of archegonial development which are found inconsistent in the plants which, on the basis of at least some of their macroscopic characters, seem to constitute hybrid swarms.

LEWTON, FREDERICK L. 1925. An early investigation of extrafloral nectaries, oil glands, fringe hairs, persistence and adnation of involucral bracts, and chromosome numbers in relation to classification.

METCALFE, C. R., and CHALK, L. 1950. A monumental work on anatomy of major plant taxa. The introduction covers general principles.

MUNZ, PHILIP A., and J. D. LAUDERMILK. 1949.

PARKIN, JOHN. 1928.

———. 1931, 1935.

REEDER, JOHN R. 1957. A re-evaluation of classification of the Gramineae on the basis of the addition of data from embryology.

ROLLINS, REED C. 1941.

STEBBINS, G. LEDYARD, JR. 1956. Includes an excellent summary of the significance of minute structures in classification of grasses.

WODEHOUSE, R. P. 1936. A review of the evolution of spores and pollen grains in the major taxa of vascular plants.

chapter
5

Data from Paleobotany
and Their Interrelationship
with Biogeography

CLASSIFICATION OF LIVING AND FOSSIL PLANTS

Extinct plants may indicate clearly the history and relationships of living groups, but they do not define the limits of the taxa formed by their modern descendants (see Chapter 10).

Classification of living taxa takes directly into account only the organisms of the present, not those of all geological history. Any classification system must be based upon the plants or animals of restricted segments of geologic time because the organisms composing taxa change. A well-marked species of one epoch may lose members with some character combinations and shift toward predominance of those with other combinations (Fig. 5–1). Often it divides into two or more taxa. Sometimes, through interbreeding, taxa are merged or one taxon may be modified by absorption of genes (introgressive hybridization, see pages 127–129) from another. Occasionally change may occur suddenly, but it is more likely to represent a trend imperceptible to observation throughout a human lifetime or through millenia. A system of classification covering all organisms of the past as well as those of the present would represent a continuum ranging from the beginning of living organisms to all those of the current period, and no division into taxa would be possible, because there would be no gaps between population systems except in cases of allopolyploidy (see Chapter 7).

Plants known only from fossils must be classified in their own categories, for they belonged to periods and epochs of the past. Plants of bygone epochs are known only from fragmentary remains of a few individuals, and evaluation of the interrelationships of the

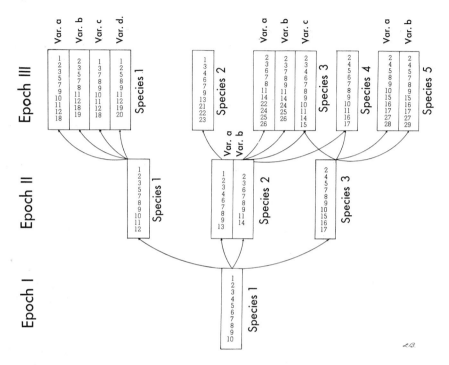

Fig. 5–1. The usual course of evolution through units of geological time (e.g., epochs): development of species and varieties of later epochs from a single species of the earliest epoch. Diagnostic characters are indicated by number for each species. In the second epoch three major population systems had evolved, each tended to retain some of the original characters, as indicated by numbers, and to have lost some. In addition each had gained new characters of its own. In the third epoch the processes had gone still further, and in some cases, as with species 4 and with species 3 variety c, hybridization of some of the units of the second epoch had produced new character combinations which had undergone further selection.

now extinct or modified natural population systems they represent or accurate classification of the plants into genera, species, or varieties may be impossible (Fig. 5–2).

The fossil record of plants, except that of some pteridophytes and gymnosperms, is too meager to permit working out detailed

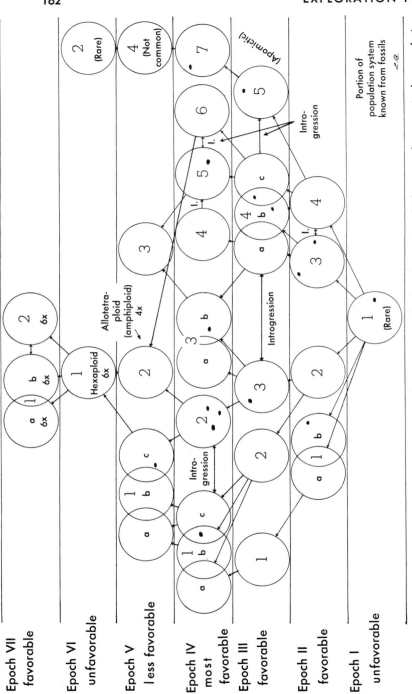

Fig. 5–2. A hypothetical example of evolution within a group of related species which arose from a single population system composing a species which existed in the first unit of geological time (e.g., epoch) under consideration. Although some degree of complexity is indicated, a two-dimensional figure does not permit a true approximation of the complexity of intergradation, hybridization (including introgressive hybridization), and ploidy which commonly exists. The dark spots indicate the portions of populations which can be represented by known fossils in even a genus the remains of which are relatively frequently preserved and discovered.

phylogenetic sequences or even to allow checking of the validity of those suggested on the basis of comparisons of living plants. Paleobotany may provide some information concerning the history and development of taxa, and it may shed light upon their relationships, which are one basis for classification. However, the record seldom contributes much.

The chief contribution of paleobotany to the classification of most taxonomic groups is evidence of the reasons for geographical and ecological isolation of living taxa and their immediate ancestors, together with information concerning the origin of their past and present distributional patterns.

THE SIGNIFICANCE OF AN ADEQUATE SERIES OF FOSSILS

When, in rare instances, there are adequate series of plant fossils, development of species may be traced with some accuracy. For example, with the aid of paleobotanical investigation, Mason (Chaney and Mason, 1930; Mason, 1932a, 1932b, 1949) worked out the relationship of the closed-cone pines of California, thus partly solving a difficult classification problem not clear from the living plants alone.

The pines studied by Mason are an endemic Californian group of four living taxa (Figs: 5–3, 5–4, and 5–5). These localized conifers are named for a character of the cones, which remain closed and persistent, in sessile whorls on the branches, for many years. Unless there is a fire, the growth of the trunk or large branches may engulf the cones, leaving them permanently embedded. Especially in the knob-cone pine (*Pinus attenuata*), (Fig. 5–5), fire unseals the exposed cones, and it not only releases the seeds and weakens the seed coat, permitting absorption of the water necessary to germination, but it also removes the litter from the ground, preparing a seed bed. The characters and distribution of the four living species are summarized in Table 5–1.

The distinctive characters and the localized occurrence of these taxa facilitate tracing evolutionary history (Fig. 5–6). *Pinus Masonii*, an extinct Pliocene species, was similar to the ancestral type of the group. *Pinus linguiformis*, another fossil species, was intermediate between *Pinus Masonii* and *Pinus attenuata*, the living knob-cone pine. The transition from the earlier types to the knob-cone pine appears to have occurred about the middle of Pleistocene times, but *Pinus attenuata* became common only relatively recently.

Pinus remorata [Fig. 5–3 (3)] became differentiated from the

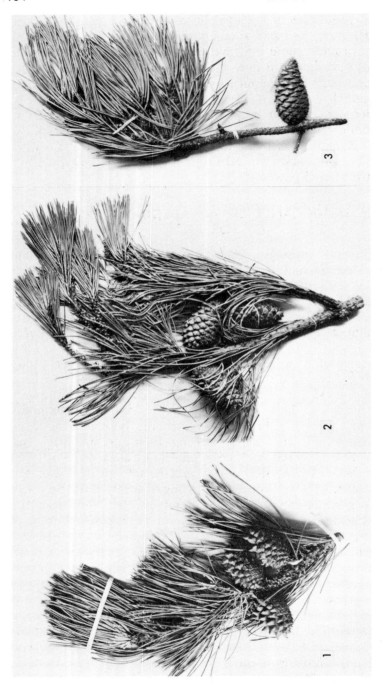

Fig. 5-3. Closed-cone pines: (1-2) forms of the Bishop pine (*Pinus muricata*) of coastal and insular California and Baja California (Pelican Bay, Santa Cruz Island, and Noyo, Mendocino County, California); (3) *Pinus remorata*, islands off the coast of southern California (Buena Vista, Santa Cruz Island).

Pinus Masonii complex in the Lower Pleistocene, giving rise to the two-needled *Pinus radiata* var. *binata* now restricted to Guadalupe Island, Baja California. The fossils of the Monterey pine, (*Pinus radiata* (Fig. 5–4), formed in Pleistocene times at the site of Carpinteria, were dominated by a two-needle phase (now largely replaced

TABLE 5–1
Characteristics of the Closed-Cone Pines

Character	P. attenuata (knob-cone)	P. remorata (Santa Cruz Island)	P. radiata (Monterey)	P. muricata (Bishop)
Leaf no.	3	2	3	2
Leaf length	7–18 cm.	7–15 cm.	7–15 cm.	10–15 cm.
Other leaf characters	Slender, rather rigid, pale yellowish green	Stouter, more rigid	Slender, bright glossy green	Stouter subrigid, dark yellow green
Cone				
Length	7–15 cm.	Under 8 cm.	8–20 cm.	5–7 cm.
Symmetry	Strongly asymmetrical	Nearly symmetrical	Asymmetrical	Asymmetrical
Position	Strongly deflexed	Spreading at right angles	Deflexed	Deflexed
Umbos on inner side (of cone)	Conical-pyramidal	Flat or slightly curving	Strongly swollen	Conical-pyramidal
Umbos on outer side (of cone)	Flattened knobs; prickle thick, incurved	Flat or slightly curving	Knobby; prickle slender	Knobby; prickle present
Geographical distribution (discontinuous in all species)	Inland; central Oregon to Ensenada, Baja California	Islands off the coast of southern California	Coastal in central California	Coastal and insular; California and Baja California

by the three-needle phase) characteristic of the living relics of this essentially Pleistocene species.

Pinus Masonii seems to have given rise directly to the Bishop pine (*Pinus muricata*) [Fig. 5–3 (1), (2)], the two being connected gradually by a series of fossils collected at Carpinteria and Millerton, California. Sterility barriers between the living species are lacking or ineffective. They hybridize where they grow naturally together, and they can be cross-fertilized under experimental conditions.

Fig. 5–4. The closed-cone pines: the Monterey pine (*Pinus radiata*), a native of coastal central California, in cultivation.

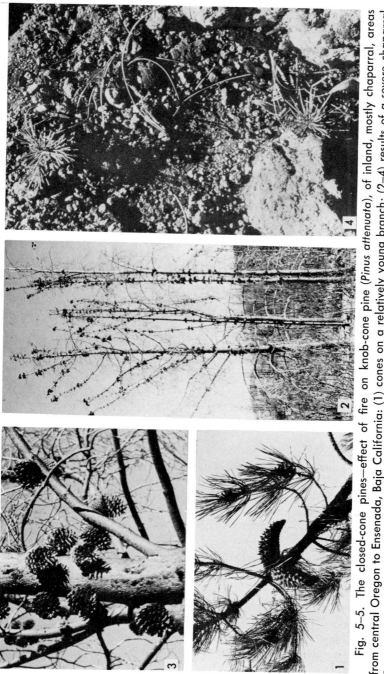

Fig. 5–5. The closed-cone pines—effect of fire on knob-cone pine (*Pinus attenuata*), of inland, mostly chaparral, areas from central Oregon to Ensenada, Baja California: (1) cones on a relatively young branch; (2–4) results of a severe chaparral fire near Mount Konocti, Lake County, California—(2) pine trees killed outright, the shrubs of the chaparral sprouting from below ground; (3) trunks and branches bearing cones unsealed and opened by fire; (4) seedlings growing beneath the dead trees in the gravelly soil cleared by fire.

As is indicated above, *Pinus remorata* is an endemic species of the islands off the coast of southern California. In the main it is a clear-cut taxon, but on Santa Cruz Island it hybridizes with *Pinus muricata*. *Pinus muricata* was absent from the islands in Pleistocene times, when *Pinus remorata* was abundant. These two species, developed in isolation, are now brought together and are merging into

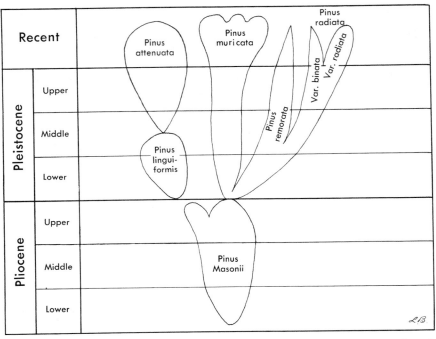

Fig. 5–6. Rough reconstruction of the approximate evolution of the closed-cone pines, based upon the publications of Mason and of Chaney and Mason. The chart is intended to convey only the main outlines of the subject and not the details, for in even this instance an attempt at graphic representation seemingly indicates more knowledge than can be obtained.

a hybrid population emphasizing some characters of one and some of the other. In time the hybrids may replace both *Pinus remorata* and *Pinus muricata* on the islands.

At La Purissima Ridge on the mainland, 30 or 40 miles from Santa Cruz Island, the population of *Pinus muricata* includes many individuals displaying characters of *Pinus remorata*. This may be due to past hybridization, but there is no proof that *Pinus remorata* ever occurred on the mainland. Mason cites evidence that it was not represented in the Pleistocene (Carpinteria) flora on the adjacent coast, although both *Pinus muricata* and *Pinus radiata* were abundant. A possible explanation is the occasional carrying of pollen by wind (not the prevailing wind) to the colony on the mainland, thus bringing pollen of *Pinus remorata* and with it genes of that species.

Although the genetic and evolutionary status of these taxa may be interpreted in the light of geological history, their taxonomic status is debatable insofar as *Pinus remorata* is concerned. Mason (1949) has pointed out the inadequacy of the system of taxonomic ranks to cover all cases. According to his interpretation, in the past *Pinus remorata* evolved into a distinct species which resembled both *Pinus muricata* and *Pinus radiata* var. *binata*, as well as var. *radiata*. In time, continuation of the current merging of *Pinus remorata* with *Pinus muricata* may require reduction to varietal status, and ultimately both *Pinus remorata* and *Pinus muricata* may be replaced by an insular variety or species derived from both.

The problems of classification of the oaks discussed in Chapter 3 receive little clarification from a study of fossils formed mostly from detached leaves. In view of the variability of leaves on even a single living plant, fossilized detached leaves are exceedingly difficult to interpret. Chaney (1949) reports gradual differentiation of species of oaks in California during Tertiary times, with the suggestion of both divergence and merging of population systems and the appearance of a meshwork (reticulum) of forms. The trend was from species with large lobed leaves, as in the white oaks similar to *Quercus lobata* of California or *Quercus alba* of eastern North America, through plants similar to *Quercus Douglasii* to forms with small entire or toothed leaves like those of the taxa *californica* and *turbinella* (see p. 105). The taxon *californica* may have arisen from a meshwork of forms combining characters now retained in varying proportions within *Quercus Douglasii* and *Quercus dumosa*.

GEOLOGICAL HISTORY, BIOGEOGRAPHY, AND CLASSIFICATION

Frequently distributional patterns of living species and other taxonomic units reflect the results of events in geological history and their impact upon the isolation and development of the taxa. These historical events relate to changes in topography, alteration of climate, and past migrations of species.

Changes in Topography. NEW LAND MASSES. Formation of new land masses is followed by invasion of species from elsewhere, and sometimes by rapid evolution. Emergence of the Hawaiian chain of islands (Midway to Hawaii) (Figs. 6–5, 6–6) made new terri-

Fig. 5–7. The vegetation of the Aleutian Islands: (1) Mount Moffett on Adak, at about the middle of the Aleutian Chain, the dense fog at the left being characteristic of the islands; (2) plants growing in the shallow tundra of Adak—the lupines (*Lupinus*) and anemones (*Anemone*) are characteristic of the West American Alpine Tundra rather than the Arctic Tundra, as are most other plants on the islands. East-Asian and west-American alpine species have been able to invade this volcanic chain, to reach an equilibrium with each other, and to occupy all the suitable habitats. There has been no explosive evolution resulting from adaptive radiation of derivatives of a few species into many otherwise unexploited habitats as in Hawaii. There may have been hybridization of Asiatic and American species occurring together only in the Aleutians, and this point is worthy of investigation.

tory available to the relatively small number of families and genera having members able to migrate across vast stretches of ocean (see pp. 225–229). Advance of the chain toward the southeast in the past has provided new land on emerging islands and at the same time left a rich variety of habitats on old eroded islands. Thus, all stages from fresh lava flows to coral sand covering the eroded (sub-surface) lava bases of long-extinct volcanoes occur in a single archipelago. With only limited competition in the variety of new environmental niches, the few invading plants and animals have undergone spectacular and rapid evolutionary change, their modified descendants exploiting numerous ecological niches occupied in other lands by competitors. The explosive evolution on new islands has given way to stability in ecological pockets on the progressively older islands, and classification of species is tied in with the variety of conditions to which completely and incompletely segregated taxa are adapted.

The volcanic Aleutian chain of islands (Figs. 5–7, 5–8) approaches Asia on the west and North America on the east. Its almost strictly alpine habitats are occupied by plants and animals common in the alpine regions of both continents, those of Asia predominating at the western end of the chain, and those of America at the eastern end. On the islands in the middle of the chain some Siberian and some Alaskan species are present. Other species either have been unable to migrate that far or have been crowded out by competitors from the other continent. Large mammals are lacking, perhaps because they could not reach the area. In general, though, the Aleutians have been available to plants and animals of many ecological tolerances. These have taken over their usual niches, leaving little to be exploited by organisms with mutant genes. For this reason the Aleutian Islands, unlike the Hawaiian Islands, are not rich in endemic species. However, hybridization of the species from the two continents is in need of study.

SEPARATION AND REJOINING OF LAND MASSES. The islands off the coast of southern California are of a northern and a southern group, the two groups being portions of Tertiary peninsulas which bounded the sides of a bay (Munz, 1935). Much of the flora of the islands is endemic, but the plants of the northern islands have greater affinity with those of the coast in adjacent Santa Barbara County, and the plants of the southern islands with the flora of more distant San Diego County and Baja California.

Topographic barriers separating natural population systems may be of long duration, but no barrier is necessarily permanent. Some

of the closed-cone pines studied by Mason (pp. 163–169) are elements of an insular forest of a Tertiary archipelago. Some of these
islands were rejoined to the mainland at some time since the Pliocene
(Mason, 1934). In some instances, such as just north of San Francisco in Marin County, the relict forest and the mainland flora occur
on the two sides of a fault line such as the San Andreas Rift. During

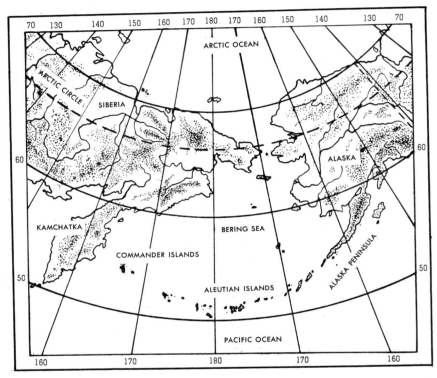

Fig. 5–8. The Aleutian chain of islands. Base map (in part) copyright by the
Denoyer-Geppert Company, Chicago. Used by permission.

the Pleistocene or more recently, the ocean bottom between these
islands and the mainland was elevated above the level of the water,
allowing the mainland species to invade the connecting area and
bringing the species of the floras into contact with each other.

MOUNTAIN BUILDING. Mountain building in volcanic areas is
spectacular, but even there it is slow. Mauna Loa in Hawaii is rising
by intermittent flows of lava, but the intervening periods range from
several to many years and flows covering the same channel may be

centuries apart. The rise of this island from the ocean floor to the surface and 13,680 above it was a time-consuming process.

Mountain building by uplift of large areas of the earth's crust is still slower. The Rocky Mountains were first formed by a rise of about 30,000 feet during the Laramide Revolution in Cretaceous times, more than 100,000,000 years ago. Since then, they have been worn down toward base level and again uplifted and partly worn down, and each change required an enormous period of time.

Uplift of mountains affects the climate of both the areas which are elevated and the regions downwind. If planetary winds, such as the prevailing westerlies or the trade winds, reach a coast line and then must cross the mountains, the rising air mass expands, cools, and drops moisture on the windward side. On the leeward side the air descends, contracts, and becomes warm, and it may even take up, rather than deposit, moisture. Thus, in the path of a prevailing wind over a warm ocean, the lowlands in the lee of a newly formed mountain range may become arid while those on the windward side are changed relatively little and the windward mountain slopes become cool and moist.

In Hawaii the northeastern side of each island is wet, and the southwestern side is dry. The trade winds deposit more than 400 inches of rain per year on the rain forest of Iao Canyon on the windward side of western Maui, but the leeward side of the same mountain, near Lahaina, is reminiscent of the Arizona Desert (Fig. 5–9).

In the path of the prevailing westerlies on the western coast of North America, the climate of the interior has been changed for an undetermined distance eastward by uplift of essentially a gigantic stone wall, the Cascade–Sierra Nevada axis.

According to Chaney, Condit, and Axelrod (1944), early in the Miocene epoch, perhaps 25,000,000 years ago, the area from the Rocky Mountains to the Pacific Ocean was a plain broken here and there by hills and low mountains (Fig. 5–10). The northern part, north of the sites of San Francisco and Salt Lake City, was covered by a forest representing a rich flora which encircled the Northern Hemisphere. Descendants of this widespread though probably variable forest type are still dominant in temperate eastern Asia, eastern middle North America, and the northern and mountainous parts of northwestern North America (Chaney, 1925, 1938, 1948).

At the same time the southern part of the present Pacific Slope, much of the Great Basin, and the Colorado Basin were covered largely by an oak woodland similar to that still existing in the mountains of central and southern Arizona and in northwestern Mexico (Axelrod, 1940, 1944, 1948, 1956, 1957, 1958). Uplift of the Cascade–Sierra Nevada axis slowly (if at all), from late Miocene to early Pliocene times, and rapidly afterward, modified the floras of the new mountain areas, the forest, and the oak woodland.

In the mountains, elements within species have been modified according to natural selection of the types best adapted to the new

Fig. 5–9. Rainshadows—two sides of the same low mountain (about 4,000 feet elevation) in western Maui, Hawaiian Islands: (1) Iao Canyon, on the northeastern side of the mountain, toward the trade winds, a rain forest with an average rainfall of more than 400 inches per year; (2) ravine on the southwestern (leeward) side of the mountain, near Lahaina, a desert appearing like the deserts of Arizona and with about the same annual rainfall (perhaps 10 inches at this point). Between these extremes other ravines have varying climates, and each forms an ecological pocket.

conditions. These new forms have survived climatic changes while the older types have died out. The present species, varieties, and minor variants occupy lowland, montane, and subalpine habitats. For example, each of three primarily coastal [Pacific Forest, Fig. 5–18 (1)] varieties of species of *Ranunculus*—*Ranunculus occidentalis* var. *occidentalis*, *Ranunculus orthorhynchus* var. *orthorhynchus*, and *Ranunculus alismaefolius* var. *alismaefolius*—(Figs. 5–11 and 5–12) is matched by one or more vicarious varieties occurring pri-

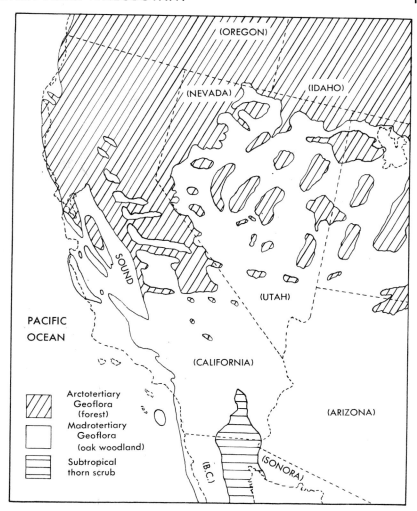

Fig. 5–10. Distribution of floras in areas west of the Rocky Mountain region in Miocene and Pliocene times. The Arctotertiary Geoflora (forest) was the forerunner of the Pacific Northwestern Flora, the Madrotertiary Geoflora (an oak woodland) the forerunner of the Sierra Madrean Flora. (Based upon Daniel I. Axelrod, Bulletin of the Geological Society of America 68: 19–45, colored map, 1957. Used by permission.)

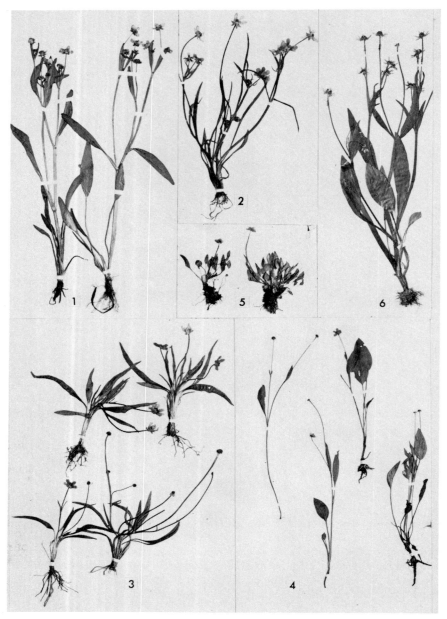

Fig. 5–11. The varieties of *Ranunculus alismaefolius*, var. *alismaefolius* surviving largely in the relatively less modified (since middle Tertiary time) Pacific Forest, the other varieties characteristic of newly formed ecological situations in the mountains or in the interior of western North America (see distributional map, Fig. 5–12).

marily in the Cascade–Sierra Nevada axis and in the mountains in and about the Columbia River Basin. Probably the three varieties occurring principally along the coast in the less-modified Pacific Forest are remnants of the once widespread prototypes of each of the three complexes of varieties, and the interior mountain types are derivatives.

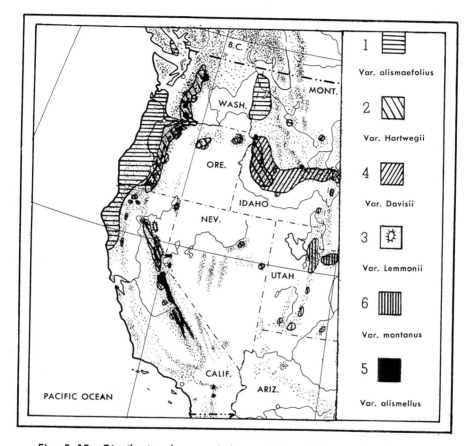

Fig. 5–12. Distributional map of the varieties of *Ranunculus alismaefolius* (numbers correspond to specimens shown in Fig. 5–11): (1) var. *alismaefolius*, Pacific Forest (Plummer, Idaho); (2) var. *Hartwegii*, Sierran Montane Forest (Child's Meadows, Tehama County, California); (3) var. *Lemmonii*, dry phase of the Sierran Montane Forest where it borders the Sagebrush Desert of the Great Basin (Prosser Creek, Nevada County, California); (4) var. *Davisii*, northwestern portion of the Rocky Mountain Montane Forest (Landmark, Idaho; type specimen); (5) var. *alismellus*, Sierran Subalpine Forest (Kaiser Pass, Sierra Nevada, California); (6) var. *montanus*, southern portion of the Rocky Mountain Subalpine Forest (Rabbit Ears Pass, Colorado). (Base map, Goode Map Series, copyright by the University of Chicago. Used by permission.)

In the lee of the Cascade–Sierra Nevada axis the climate has shifted toward decreased precipitation, summer heat, and (because of dryness) winter cold. The results are the selection, through large inland areas, of plants not requiring heavy rainfall and the differentiation from the original forest and oak woodland of various new types of vegetation in and about at least the western portions of the newly formed Columbia River Basin, Great Basin, and Colorado Basin. In the eastern parts of the Columbia River Basin the Palouse Prairie, a local grassland, has developed on the higher plains and in the lower valleys. In the lower parts of the Columbia Basin and throughout the Great Basin, Sagebrush Desert [Fig. 5–17 (1)] has become dominant in the lowlands, and in and around the Great Basin Juniper-Pinyon Woodland (Fig. 5–17) occupies the hills and low mountains. Near the boundary of the United States and Mexico the Mexican Desert Flora has migrated northward, and in the lee of the southern Californian and Baja Californian mountains it has given rise to the species characteristic of the Mojave and Colorado deserts.

Thus, topographic changes may affect the course of evolution either by producing isolation of floras and faunas and of their included species or by producing climatic changes.

EROSION. The beginning of a breakdown of barriers formed by mountains may be seen in some places. The Cascade–Sierra Nevada axis is crossed at a number of points by large rivers arising in the interior, and these carry the seeds of inland species into far different coastal vegetation types. *Ranunculus orthorhynchus* var. *platyphyllus* appears to have been introduced into the coastal Pacific Forest by the Columbia River and probably by the Klamath River, and into the Sacramento Valley by the Pit River. *Ranunculus Cymbalaria* vars. *Cymbalaria* and *saximontanus* and *Opuntia fragilis* probably reached Puget Sound via the Fraser River in southern British Columbia. *Ranunculus flabellaris* doubtless followed the Columbia River as far as western Washington and Oregon, but it has not spread to other streams. *Ranunculus aquatilis* var. *Harrisii* must have followed the Klamath River into Humboldt County, California. Several Mojavean Desert species occur in the vicinity of the Kern River above and near Bakersfield, California. This river rises in the Sierra Nevada, but its tributary, Canebrake Creek, is connected with the desert through a pass only 5,000 feet high and accessible to some desert species. Examples of (at least in this area) prevailing desert species along the drainage area of the Kern River include *Yucca brevifolia*, *Prunus Andersonii*, and *Tetradymia spinosa* var. *longispina* on Canebrake Creek, and the following farther down the watershed: *Eriogonum pusillum, Vitis Girdiana, Opuntia basilaris, Lycium Cooperi, Baccharis Emoryi, Pluchea sericea,* and *Encelia frutescens* var. *Actonii.*

The Pit River either has captured a large segment of Sagebrush Desert and Juniper-Pinyon Woodland territory east of the southern end of the Cascade Mountains in northern California or it has retained these areas as the mountains rose. This has permitted inland species to penetrate the Sacramento Valley drainage and allowed California Oak Woodland species such as the blue oak (*Quercus Douglasii*) to occupy some of the hills east of the Cascades. The Pit River gap is so low that the prevailing westerlies bear moisture directly eastward to these hills.

Three species of roses (Cole, 1956) come into contact in the area of the Pit River and its gap through the Cascades, and their intergradation is complex. These are *Rosa californica* from the foothill region [California Oak Woodland, Figs. 3–45 and 5–15 (1)] west of the Cascade–Sierra Nevada axis; *Rosa pisocarpa*, primarily of the coastal Pacific Forest [Fig. 5–18 (1)] from Washington to northwestern California and the southernmost Cascades; and *Rosa Woodsii* var. *ultramontana* from the Sagebrush Desert [Fig. 5–17 (1)] region of the Columbia Basin and the Great Basin.

Stream capture is occurring in the southern California segment of the Cascade–Sierra Nevada axis where the San Gabriel Mountains meet the San Bernardino Range along Cajon Creek northwest of San Bernardino. Here the grinding and softening of the rocks by the movements along the San Andreas Rift (fault) has permitted rapid erosion by Cajon Creek beyond the position of its normal mountain headwaters in the vicinity of Cajon into the desert and the normal watershed of the Mojave River. The scrub oak (*Quercus dumosa*) (Fig. 3–1) occurs up to the normal area for the coastal watershed at Cajon, where it hybridizes with the California desert scrub oak (the taxon *californica* [Fig. 3–20 (1), (2); see also pp. 79, 105]). In the eroded captured area to the north and northeast, the oaks are of the taxon *californica*. In this instance, stream capture has not made new territory available to the species growing on the coastal drainage. The direction has not been parallel to the prevailing westerly winds but at right angles to them. Consequently, the captured area has received little accompanying climatic change. A short distance to the south, in San Gorgonio Pass, which is only 2,700 feet high and which runs from east to west, the prevailing winds carry sufficient moisture through the gap to support coast-type vegetation for 15 miles beyond the pass into the edge of the desert area.

Alteration of Climate. Climatic changes (Fig. 5–13) may result in alteration of the seasons of precipitation, in fluctuation in quantity of precipitation, or in glaciation.

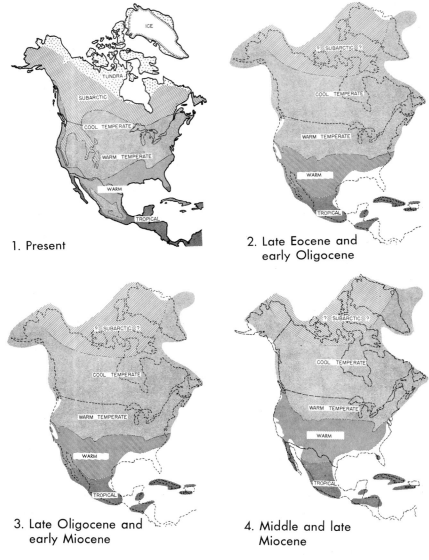

1. Present

2. Late Eocene and early Oligocene

3. Late Oligocene and early Miocene

4. Middle and late Miocene

Fig. 5–13. See next page for legend.

ALTERATION OF THE SEASONS OF PRECIPITATION. Some areas, such as much of eastern North America, have some rain or snow throughout the calendar year; others, such as southern Florida, are dry in winter and moist in summer; others, such as California, are moist in winter and dry in summer; and still others, such as Arizona, have a winter and a summer rainy season with dry periods in-between. These relationships of wet and dry periods result in selection of plants with different growing seasons—spring and summer. At each level of altitude there are two groups of plants, one adapted to seed germination, growth, and reproduction in a cool moist period, the other in a warm moist period.

The forest and the oak woodland, which in Oligocene and Miocene times, dominated the northern and southern parts of the area west of the Rocky Mountain system, grew in an area receiving year-

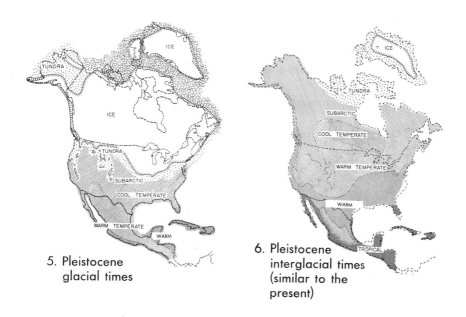

5. Pleistocene glacial times

6. Pleistocene interglacial times (similar to the present)

Fig. 5–13. Maps showing in a generalized way the changes of temperature and vegetation zones in North America during Tertiary and Quaternary geological time: (1) vegetation of the present; (2) late Eocene and early Oligocene; (3) late Oligocene and early Miocene; (4) middle and late Miocene; (5) the glacial periods of Pleistocene; (6) the interglacial periods, these having been much like the present. (From Erling Dorf, University of Michigan, Contributions from the Museum of Paleontology 13: 181–210, 1959. Used by permission. The term "subtropical" is modified to "warm"; "tropical" includes both tropical and subtropical areas of vegetation.)

Fig. 5–14. See next page for legend.

round precipitation. Cooling of the ocean since that time has reduced and nearly eliminated summer rain from the Pacific Coast and
the Columbia and Great Basin regions, but rain occurs in the summer
in the continental climate of the Rocky Mountain region, in Arizona,
and eastward near the boundary between the United States and
Mexico.

The desert vegetation now in southern California consists primarily of annual herbs with winter-germinating seeds and spring
growth and flowering. The relatively few species of trees and shrubs
are dependent for seed germination upon late summer or early fall
thundershowers, which are significant perhaps once in 5 to 20 years.
Thus, the younger woody plants are of distinct age classes. In
southern Arizona the same spring flora is present, but with it is a
rich summer flora mostly of trees, shrubs, grasses, and cacti either
not occurring or rare in California. This is developed in the presence
of rains in July and August and of seed germination and growth at
that time of year when California is dry.

The oak woodland or Madrotertiary Geoflora, which had migrated from the region of the present Sierra Madre Occidental in
northwestern Mexico, occupied in Oligocene and Miocene times the
area from about the latitude of San Francisco and Salt Lake City
southward (Fig. 5–10). This woodland is divided now into derivatives (see Axelrod, 1940, 1944, 1948, 1956, 1957, 1958), which constitute the modern Sierra Madrean Flora. The most significant
division in the original oak woodland is between the Southwestern
Oak Woodland and Chaparral (Fig. 5–14) of southeastern Arizona
and adjacent Sonora and Chihuahua, Mexico, and the California Oak
Woodland [Figs. 3–45, 5–15 (1)], the California Chaparral [Fig.
5–15 (2)], and the Pacific Grassland [also of California, Fig. 5–16
(1)]. The southwestern plants have both winter and summer precipitation, but winter and spring growth are of minor importance
because at 5,000–6,000 feet elevation the water from the light winter
precipitation evaporates while the weather is still too cold for growth.
Only the summer rainfall is effective. In the California lowlands

Fig. 5–14. Southwestern Oak Woodland and Chaparral and Desert Grassland: (1) oak woodland (5,000 to 6,000 feet elevation) at the zone of contact
with Desert Grassland (3,000 to 5,000 feet elevation) (Coronado National Forest,
southeastern Arizona); (2) chaparral (mountains west of Globe, Arizona). The
chaparral is sorted out locally, and it consists of only a few species growing also
in the oak woodland. Photograph (1) courtesy of U.S. Forest Service. From
Lyman Benson, *Plant Classification*, D. C. Heath & Co., 1957, pp. 604, 607.
Used by permission.)

Fig. 5–15. California Oak Woodland, dominant in northern California, and California Chaparral, dominant in southern California: (1) blue oaks in the hillside phase of the oak woodland (near Upper Lake) (see Fig. 3–45 for the valley phase and the valley oak); (2) chaparral, in the middle foreground the leather oak (*Quercus durata*), and at the right and left chamise brush (*Adenostoma fasciculatum*) (Mayacamas Range, Lake County).

Fig. 5–16. Pacific Grassland (growing season after winter rain) and Desert Grassland (growing season after summer rain): (1) Pacific Grassland (near Gorman, Ridge Route, U.S. 99, California), plants flowering in early April; (2) Desert Grassland (south-central New Mexico northwest of Carrizozo), cloudy time in July just before first summer rain, the grass stems of the previous summer still persisting.

summer rain is rare. Consequently, the season of effective rainfall is the primary basis for segregation of vegetation types derived from the same source (see pp. 217–220).

TABLE 5–2

Species Duplicated in the Oak Woodlands and Chaparrals
of California and Arizona

The following woody species or varieties occur in both the Southwestern Oak Woodland and Chaparral and the California Oak Woodland or the California Chaparral.

Thalamiflorae
  Rhus ovata, sugarbush
  Ceanothus integerrimus, deer brush (see also
    Table 5–4)

Corolliflorae
  Arctostaphylos pungens, manzanita

Calyciflorae
  Cercis occidentalis, western redbud
  Ribes quercetorum, oak gooseberry

Ovariflorae
  Lonicera interrupta, chaparral honeysuckle

The Southwestern Oak Woodland and Chaparral (Fig. 5–14) is relatively little modified from the Oligocene prototype, which also had summer rain. The Californian derivatives are much changed in species composition, but some species now native in the California Oak Woodland or the California Chaparral are identical with others native in the Southwestern Oak Woodland and Chaparral in Arizona (Table 5–2). More numerous species and varieties are similar but not identical (Tables 5–3, 5–4). Since the two geographical oak-woodland and chaparral floras include many related but somewhat different elements, probably the rarity of exact duplication is the result of divergent evolution. This has occurred in different climates of geographical regions isolated at least since Pliocene times by intervening arid lands.

The Sierra Madrean Flora also includes the Juniper-Pinyon Woodland (Fig. 5–17) and the Sagebrush Desert [Fig. 5–17 (1)] primarily of the Great Basin, an area of winter rain, though each of these includes some elements drawn from northern sources.

The forest which in Oligocene and Miocene times occurred north of the latitude of San Francisco and Salt Lake City has been affected also by withdrawal of summer rain. The selected species from the rich populations of the original forest now constitute three elements surviving the changes from Tertiary times to the present.

Fig. 5–17. Juniper-Pinyon Woodland and Sagebrush Desert: (1) Juniper-Pinyon Woodland on the mountains at higher levels and on rocky soil, Sagebrush Desert at lower levels and in deeper soils on the valley floor (north of St. George, Utah); (2) Juniper-Pinon Woodland, with Plains Grassland at lower elevations and on the valley soils (east of Gallup, New Mexico).

TABLE 5–3

Vicarious Species and Varieties in the Oak Woodlands and Chaparrals of California and Arizona

The following pairs of closely related vicarious woody species or varieties occur in areas indicated by the columns below.

Southwestern Oak Woodland and Chaparral	California Oak Woodland or California Chaparral
Thalamiflorae	
Berberis Nevinii var. *haematocarpa,* red barberry	*Berberis Nevinii* var. *Nevinii,* Nevin barberry
Rhamnus californica var. *ursina*	*Rhamnus californica* (several vars.)
Vitis arizonica, Arizona grape	*Vitis californica,* California grape, and *Vitis Girdiana*
Corolliflorae	
Arctostaphylos Pringlei, Pringle manzanita	*Arctostaphylos drupacea*
Arbutus arizonica, Arizona madrone	*Arbutus Menziesii,* madrone (mostly in the Pacific Forest)
Calyciflorae	
Platanus racemosa var. *Wrightii,* Wright sycamore	*Platanus racemosa* var. *racemosa,* California sycamore
Aralia humilis	*Aralia californica,* California *Aralia* (partly in the Pacific Forest)
Ovariflorae	
Echinocystis gilensis, wild cucumber	*Echinocystis fabacea* (and other species)
(These plants are not woody, but they are permanent in the vegetation because of their large underground storage organs.)	
Lonicera arizonica, Arizona honeysuckle	*Lonicera ciliosa*
Amentiferae	
Alnus oblongifolia, alder	*Alnus rhombifolia,* white alder
Quercus oblongifolia	*Quercus Engelmannii,* Engelmann oak, and *Quercus Douglasii,* blue oak

Two are the deciduous forests of eastern Asia and of eastern North America, both of which grow in climates with summer rain; the other is the Pacific Northwestern Flora of North America, which includes (Fig. 5–18) the largely coastal Pacific Forest, two mountain forests: the Sierran Montane and Subalpine forests, and the inland Palouse Prairie (Fig. 5–19). These western vegetation types have little summer rainfall, and the forests are dominated by conifers, which are more resistant to summer drought than are the deciduous trees plentiful as late as Miocene times but gradually eliminated with the cessation of summer precipitation in Pliocene times.

TABLE 5–4

Vicarious Varieties in the Oak Woodlands and Chaparrals of California and Arizona

The following species include one or rarely two varieties of woody plants occurring in both the Southwestern Oak Woodland and Chaparral and the California Oak Woodland or the California Chaparral, as well as additional varieties in California. These may be original types occurring in both areas together with additional varieties differentiated in the changing conditions of California.

Southwestern Types	Californian Types
Thalamiflorae	
Fremontodendron californicum, fremontia	
Var. *californicum* (rare)	Var. *californicum* and *F. mexicanum* (status as a species or variety undetermined)
Rhamnus crocea, redberry	
Var. *ilicifolia*	Vars. *ilicifolia* and *crocea*
Ceanothus integerrimus, deer bush	
(Partly at higher altitudes than oak woodland or chaparral.)	
A single form	Numerous complex intergrading forms
Ceanothus Greggii	
Var. *Greggii*	Vars. *Greggii* and *perplexans*
Calyciflorae	
Amorpha californica, mock-locust	
Var. *californica*	Vars. *californica* and *napensis*
Cercocarpus montanus, mountain-mahogany	
Vars. *glaber* (localized), *montanus* (rare), and *paucidentatus* (common)	Vars. *glaber* and *minutiflorus*
Amentiferae	
Quercus dumosa complex, scrub oak	
Taxon *turbinella* (Also in desert mountains within the eastern edge of California)	Var. *dumosa* and the taxon *californica*
Quercus chrysolepis, canyon live oak	
Var. *Palmeri*	Vars. *Palmeri* (rare) and *chrysolepis*

Some species in the Pacific Northwestern Flora must be considered in the light of their possible position as modified relics of the once wide-ranging Tertiary forest, the Arctotertiary Geoflora, now preserved by evolutionary adaptation to special conditions and not requiring summer rainfall. These species may include such deciduous trees as the big leaf maple (*Acer macrophyllum*), the dogwood (*Cornus Nuttallii*), the valley oak (*Quercus lobata*) (adapted to the adjacent oak woodland), the Garry oak (*Quercus*

Fig. 5–18. Pacific Northwestern Flora, forest types: (1) Pacific Forest (Kosciusko Island, southeastern Alaskan archipelago); (2) Sierran Subalpine Forest (northeast side of Mount Rainier, Washington); (3) Sierran Montane Forest (Hat Creek, Shasta County, California).

Garryana), and the California black oak (*Quercus Kelloggii*), all of which have eastern North American near relatives. Other species must be evaluated in the light of rapid evolution into varieties and vicarious species following the creation of new habitat niches due to the change of climate.

Fig. 5–19. Palouse Prairie (south-facing slopes) and Rocky Mountain Montane Forest (north-facing slope) (Grizzly Ridge, Wallowa National Forest, northeastern Oregon). (Photograph courtesy of U.S. Forest Service.)

The geographical distribution of the cactus family is related to seasonal rainfall, for all the genera except *Opuntia* are restricted to reproduction by seeds, and these germinate in moist warm weather. Although in North America the stronghold of the Cactaceae is in southern areas, cacti are native from the Yukon to Ontario and in all the states but Hawaii, Vermont, New Hampshire, Maine, and perhaps Alaska. The northern representatives of the family include only a few wide-ranging species and disjunct relict colonies of others (Fig. 5–20). Even in southern areas, except for the spreading of prickly pears and chollas into areas disturbed by man or by overgrazing, the cactus family is not on the march but is being con-

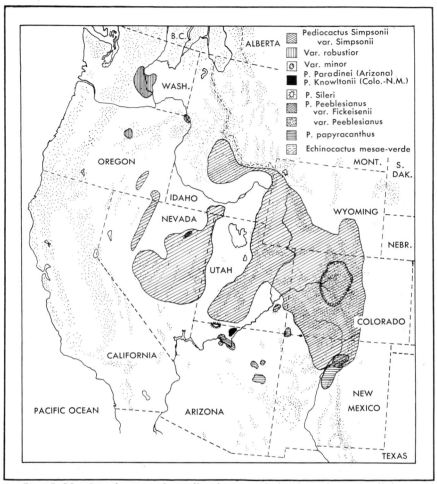

Fig. 5–20. Distribution of small relatives of the barrel cacti, all but one being species of *Pediocactus*, (classification of the group under study, the plants having been described under *Echinocactus, Pediocactus, Navajoa, Toumeya,* and other generic names). Probably these species are relics of a time more favorable to their development. Each, except *Pediocactus Simpsonii,* occurs locally on a highly specialized soil type. Some are so rare as to occur on only a few small outcrops of rock. See Cactus & Succulent Journal, 1961–62.

tained where it is established. Probably this accounts for the distinctness of certain local forms such as the varieties of *Mammillaria* (or *Coryphantha*) *vivipara,* which occur from eastern Oregon to the Rocky Mountain region and from southeastern California to Arizona and New Mexico. At some time more favorable to cacti, possibly during part of the Miocene epoch or of one of the inter-glacial periods, the forerunners of varieties of *Mammillaria vivipara* may have formed a single widespread variable population. Probably this was during a slightly more moist period than the present, be-cause cacti are sensitive to prolonged desert drought and tend to be eliminated by rodents seeking water. Probably, also, it was a period of summer rainfall.

FLUCTUATION IN QUANTITY OF PRECIPITATION. The origin and distribution of living members of the Rocky Mountain branch of the *Ranunculus occidentalis* complex can be explained in terms of wet and dry times in geological history. This group of taxa consists of the three varieties of *Ranunculus acriformis* (Fig 5–21). The variety *acriformis* occurs chiefly on the plains of Wyoming; var. *montanensis* is restricted to the mountain valleys of Idaho and west-ern Montana; var. *aestivalis* is known from a single locality in south-central Utah (see Fig. 9–4). In Pleistocene times Utah was much better watered than it is today, and numerous lakes were formed. These included the gigantic Lake Bonneville, which was practically an inland sea of which the Great Salt Lake in a small remnant. In that moist epoch the forerunners of *Ranunculus acriformis* may have been much more widespread and variable. The surviving varieties may include only a few of the genetic character combinations of a once more complex population system which included plants similar to each of the present taxa. The variety *aestivalis* is restricted now to one area 325 miles across deserts from its northern relatives. At the time of the melting of the northern ice sheets a drier climate developed on the high plains of Utah, and conditions became un-favorable for persistence of the populations of *Ranunculus acri-formis*. The southernmost representatives of the species survive, so far as is known, in only one moist spot by a spring surrounded by sagebrush desert, and the population consisted in 1948 of perhaps no more than 100 individuals. In 1960 only about 25 could be found.

GLACIATION. Long after the retreat of the great Pleistocene ice sheets, the species of plants and animals of northern North America still show the effects of disturbance and of migration away from and back into the glaciated areas, and many areas are still in successional stages following glaciation (Fig. 5–22, 5–23).

In northeastern North America the Pleistocene ice sheets ad-vanced on four occasions from the north into the middlewestern and eastern states, having extended as far south as Kansas, southern Ohio, and Long Island. Fernald (1925) and various others have found areas, including portions of the Gaspé Peninsula in Quebec, which

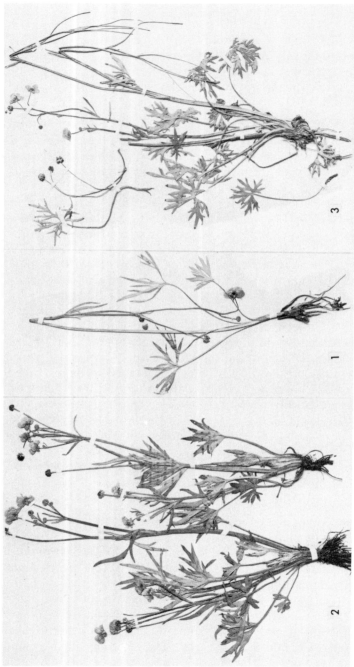

Fig. 5-21. The varieties of *Ranunculus acriformis*, probably the surviving relics of a species or species complex which in Pleistocene pluvial periods occupied at least the territory intervening between the present distributional ranges of the species, including a large area east and north of the freshwater Lake Bonneville: (1). var. *acriformis* (Little Laramie River, Wyoming); (2) var. *montanensis* (Gray's Lake, Caribou County, Idaho); (3) var. *aestivalis* (near Panguitch, Utah; type specimen). Variety *aestivalis* was observed in 1960 to include probably no more than 25 individuals about a single spring in southern Utah.

Fig. 5–22. Succession on glaciated areas—I: (1) the Canadian Shield, ancient granitic rocks laid bare by the Pleistocene ice sheets, the rocks now covered by lichens or thin tundra in far-northern Quebec between Hudson and Ungava bays; (2) granitic rocks exposed by the Pleistocene ice sheets at Frobisher Bay, Baffin Island, these partly covered by lichens and by tundra (cf. Fig. 5–23), the loose boulders in the positions in which they were freed from the glacier as the ice melted.

Fig. 5–23. Succession on glaciated areas—II: (1) lichens as pioneers invading the surfaces of granitic rocks, tundra forming between rocks, at Frobisher Bay, Baffin Island; (2) exposed granitic rocks of the Canadian Shield, covered partly by lichens and partly by tundra, at Great Whale River, east shore of Hudson Bay, Quebec.

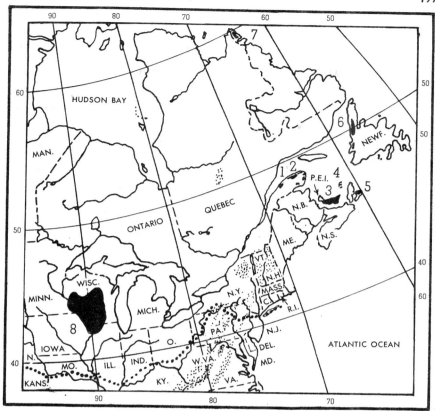

Fig. 5–24. Some areas surrounded by the Pleistocene ice sheets but not glaciated: (1) Bic, Quebec; (2) Gaspé Peninsula, Quebec; (3) Prince Edward Island; (4) Magdalen Islands, Quebec; (5) Cape Breton Island; (6) Long Mountains, Newfoundland; (7) Torngat Mountains, Labrador; (8) driftless area, Wisconsin and adjacent Minnesota, Iowa, and Illinois. (Base map copyright by Denoyer-Geppert Co., Chicago. Used by permission.)

they interpreted as not having been covered by ice (Fig. 5–24). In and near these apparently unglaciated areas there are species of plants not to be found anywhere else in the immediate vicinity and, in some cases, elsewhere in the world. In some cases (Figs. 5–25, 5–26) they are found otherwise only south of the glaciated region. Some of the plants of the Gaspé Peninsula, Anticosti Island, the Mingan Islands, and restricted localities near the upper Great Lakes (as, for example, on the Bruce and Keweenaw peninsulas and Whitefish Point) are typical of western North America and are absent or rare in the intervening areas.

Fig. 5–25. *Sullivantia renifolia* (Saxifragaceae), a relict species surviving only in unglaciated areas (see Fig. 5–26) (Apple River, Illinois).

Fernald interpreted these species as relics of preglacial times. Characteristically, as they occur in small isolated and perhaps non-glaciated areas, they are relatively or even completely non-variable and therefore specific in their habitat requirements. According to Fernald, the ice sheets exterminated all but one or a few local groups of individuals having a single genotype or few genotypes, and these survivors are exacting in their ecological requirements. Consequently, they have not been able to spread from their unglaciated strongholds into the surrounding country in competition with the more aggressive, genetically variable, and adaptable species which filled in the glaciated areas in the wake of the receding ice sheets. Although some of the refugees may have been genetically variable and capable of adaptation to new conditions and of surviving under competition, such plants, if any, have not remained restricted to former nunataks (unglaciated hills standing as "islands" in an ice sheet).

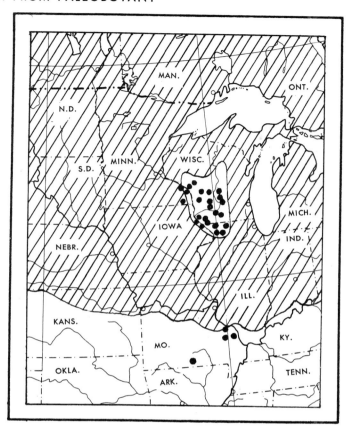

Fig. 5–26. Distribution of *Sullivantia renifolia*, almost restricted to the drift-less area in southwestern Wisconsin and adjacent Minnesota, Iowa, and Illinois (see Fig. 5–24), and the area of northeastern Missouri just south of the region covered by the Pleistocene ice sheets. (Based upon a map in a publication entitled *A Field Trip to S. W. Wisconsin*, University of Wisconsin Extension Division, 1957. Used by permission. Base map, Goode Map Series, copyright by the University of Chicago. Used by permission.)

Recent authors (e.g., Wynne-Edwards, 1937, 1939; Scoggan, 1950; and Rousseau, 1953) have questioned at least the complete applicability of Fernald's nunatak hypothesis. The species of the areas studied by Fernald are not the Arctic or alpine ones or those of acid soils which might be expected to survive thousands of years on a cold nunatak. They are mostly species of subarctic or temperate areas and calcareous (basic) soils. The later authors explain the limited distribution of the species occurring on the sites of the supposed ancient nunataks as first invaders after disappearance of the ice sheets. These plants were capable of surviving in the temporary conditions prevailing when the ice first melted, but later they were crowded out, except in particularly favorable situations, by the great wave of invaders which followed when temperate climate and ordinary forest soil conditions were restored. The first invasion of an area just freed from ice and perhaps still surrounded by glaciers is likely to be accomplished by individuals developed by the introduction of a small number of seeds and therefore including few genetic combinations. Further rigid selection may have occurred either during the invasion of the patches of soil first becoming ice-free or later on, as the pioneer species became restricted to a few favorable localities when competition from southern species became keen.

Major refugia of plants during the Pleistocene glaciations (Fig. 2–21) have been postulated by Adams (1902), Hultén (1937), Raup (1941), and others. Obviously, most species survived farther south as all zones of vegetation migrated toward areas with more favorable climates. Others remained in large areas where ice sheets did not form because precipitation was insufficient. The largest of these was in Alaska. It included the coast of the Bering Sea, as well as the Alaskan Arctic Coastal Plain and parts of the Yukon Valley. Many species and varieties native in this area are circumpolar. Some of these, as well as strictly North American plants, occur also in the glaciated areas to the south and east. Other species are native primarily in eastern Asia, occurring in North America only in the unglaciated regions east of the Bering Strait and in or near the Brooks Range. These include *Ranunculus kamchaticus* and *Ranunculus glacialis* var. *Chamissonis*. *Ranunculus gelidus* (Figs. 2–19, 2–20) follows this pattern, but it also occurs disjunctly as far south along the Rocky Mountain system as Colorado. Most of the species occurring in the larger unglaciated areas today may have been there also through Pleistocene times.

Correlation of distribution of the species of *Abies* is shown in Fig. 5–27 (for Canada, see Halliday and Brown, 1943). In Pleistocene times, the species of *Abies* occupied areas south of the ice sheets —some in the mountains of the Far West, others in eastern North America. Their ranges have been changed with the reoccupation of the glaciated areas by the American Northern Forest, of which they are a part.

Some of the most careful studies of examples of species displaced or restricted by the Pleistocene ice sheets have been based upon investigation of species of animals. Rand (1949) has studied puzzling

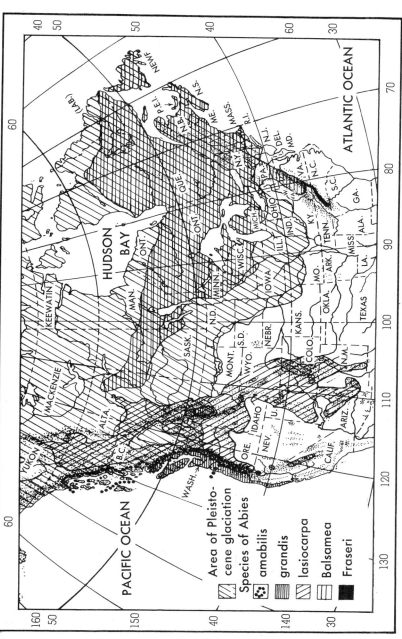

Fig. 5–27. Distribution of North American species of firs (Abies) in relation to the position of the Pleistocene ice sheets, species as indicated. The western and eastern species of the genus occupied different refugia during the glacial periods, and they have reinvaded the glaciated areas since the retreat of the ice. (Based partly upon W. E. D. Halliday and A. W. A. Brown, Ecology 24: 365, Fig. 6, 1943. Used by permission. Base map copyright by Denoyer-Geppert Co., Chicago. Used by permission.)

differentiations among closely related birds occurring in northwestern, northern, and northeastern North America. In these regions present-day barriers to interbreeding of incompletely distinguished populations of birds are inadequate to account for the divergent evolution in pairs of related taxa. Rand has correlated the geographical segregation of vicarious populations of living birds with the position of the Pleistocene ice sheet. His studies, like those of botanists, indicate the existence of Pleistocene "refugia," or unglaciated areas where birds were able to survive during the glaciations.

Franklin's grouse lives in western North American mountains, where it ranges as far north as central British Columbia and central and western Alberta; the spruce grouse occurs from Alaska and northern British Columbia to Nova Scotia. The two populations differ relatively little in morphological characters, and, where their present ranges adjoin in glaciated parts of British Columbia and Alberta, there are intermediate types with various combinations of characters. Apparently Franklin's grouse was restricted during the glacial periods to the Far West while the spruce grouse occupied northern or eastern refugia. Divergent evolution occurred in the two groups without the production of sterility barriers.

Similar patterns of distribution are shown by the Audubon warbler and the myrtle warbler and by the slate-colored junco and the Oregon junco, and by races of the white-crowned sparrows. The present distributional patterns of these birds and of many other animals, including moose, are consistent with the existence of a former barrier between the segregated populations. The Pleistocene ice sheets were a temporary barrier to interbreeding of both plant and animal populations. Removal of the barrier has resulted in some well-differentiated and some partly differentiated taxa derived from the once segregated populations.

Past Migration of Species. The distributional patterns of many plant and animal species can be explained only in terms of migrations during their geological history.

Many taxa have been limited in their migration by barriers, the most effective and enduring of which are oceans. Examples of restriction of species by water are numerous, and genera, families, and even orders may be circumscribed geographically. The cactus family (Cactaceae) occurs from the Yukon, Ontario, and Massachusetts to all of South America, but only one of the hundreds of species of cacti, a species of the highly specialized epiphytic genus *Rhipsalis*, is native on other continents. Cacti have been introduced by man in many lands, and in some, notably Australia, they have become a pest. This indicates the capacity to grow elsewhere but the inability at any time in the history of the family to cross the water barrier to other continents. This may indicate also a short history in terms of geologic time, for, according to Stebbins (1941b), mountain ranges with favorable climates for migration of a wide variety of plants probably connected Eurasia and North America at the close of the Cretaceous period. Thirty-two other families of flowering plants are restricted to the warm regions of the Western Hemisphere, and this is true of families of animals as well, for example, the family of monkeys with prehensile tails and the hummingbird family (composed of at least 300 species). Sixty-five families of flowering plants are confined to the Eastern Hemisphere, and individually some are restricted to warm regions or to particular land masses such as Madagascar, the islands of the Pacific Ocean, Australia, or New Zealand. Others are limited by ecological factors to such areas as southern Africa, which is separated from the dry regions of northern Africa by the tropics.

Some families or even species occur in the tropics of both hemispheres, these organisms having managed at some time to cross the oceans. In the temperate regions of the Northern Hemisphere many genera and some species occur in both the New and Old worlds, and in the subboreal forests some species and varieties occur on both sides of the earth. In the Arctic a high percentage of species occurs in both North America and Eurasia (Hultén, 1958). Migration between continents may have been possible for northern species much more recently than for southern; consequently, evolution along separate pathways may have proceeded farther in the south. On the other hand, the connections between continents across the north Pacific or the north Atlantic may have provided many favorable habitats for northern species and few niches suitable for southern ones.

Study of species occurring in the northern portions of either North America or Eurasia requires investigation of all the possible related species on both continents to determine whether some may be identical or may be varieties composing wide-ranging species. The flora of even a continent cannot be studied by itself.

Fossils reveal the past distributional patterns of some taxa, but for others fossil remains are lacking and reconstruction of past distribution is based upon inference. The solitary living species of related conifers (Fig. 1-9), *Sequoia sempervirens* (the coast redwood) and *Metasequoia glyptostroboides*, are shown by fossils to have occupied large portions of the Northern Hemisphere (Chaney, 1951). The living *Sequoia* is confined to California and the edge of

Oregon, and the living *Metasequoia* to a remote portion of China. The Chinese wing-nuts (*Pterocarya* spp.), the tree-of-Heaven (*Ailanthus altissima*), and the Oriental maidenhair tree (*Ginkgo biloba*) (Fig. 5–28) were once dispersed in the same way as *Metasequoia*.

The big tree, *Sequoiadendron giganteum*, occurred in western Nevada during late Miocene times (Axelrod, 1959). As the eastern Californian Sierra Nevada arose in Pliocene times and the rainfall in Nevada decreased, the trees migrated to the western slopes of the mountains. In Pleistocene times, local glaciers along the mountain axis removed the trees from the large east-west canyons such as Yosemite Valley, and *Sequoiadendron* has not been able to reoccupy them, probably because of sensitivity to the extreme winter cold of those low-lying pockets. Consequently the species occurs largely in "groves" at elevations of 6,000–7,500 feet elevation on the ridges where cold-air drainage results in a warmer winter than in the adjacent intervening canyons.

In these instances, fossils prove the pre-existence of broad patterns of dispersal, but in other instances no paleontological record has been found, and in most cases, such as those of herbaceous plants, none is likely to be found. Nevertheless, some distributional patterns, by themselves, may be indicative of migrations of the past. The family Stemonaceae is composed of three genera, two occurring in southeastern Asia and the South Pacific and one, *Croomia*, having one species occurring in Japan and another in the southeastern United States. Similarly, *Schisandra* (Schisandraceae, Ranales) is composed of several southeastern Asiatic species and one in the southeastern United States, and *Torreya* (yew family) is composed of two or three species in China and Japan, one in California, and one in Florida. These species must be relics of ancient dispersals of widespread species complexes which migrated over large portions of the earth (see also *Ranunculus*, subgenus *Crymodes*, Figs. 9–6, 9–7, and 9–8).

The subspecies and varieties of *Lobelia Cardinalis* present an example of a common pattern of distribution (Fig. 5–29) of species occurring in South and Central America, Mexico, the southern Rocky Mountains, and the Deciduous Forests of eastern North America (see McVaugh, 1952). This pattern appears to represent the results of northward migration of a species which originated in the American tropics or tropical highlands.

Lobelia Cardinalis is composed of two subspecies, one (*Cardinalis*) restricted to eastern Canada and the eastern United States, the other (*graminea*) occurring from extreme southern California (where it is

Fig. 5–28. Relict species of East Asia: (1) the maidenhair tree (*Ginkgo biloba*), an ancient tree which has existed at least since Mesozoic times, known first from cultivation about temples in the Orient, not known outside of cultivation; (2) the Chinese tree-of-Heaven, *Ailanthus altissima*, in cultivation; (3) the Chinese wing-nut (*Pterocarya*) in cultivation. These trees were associated in North America with the Arctotertiary Geoflora (see Fig. 5–13), forerunner of the Pacific Northwestern Flora (see also Fig. 1–9).

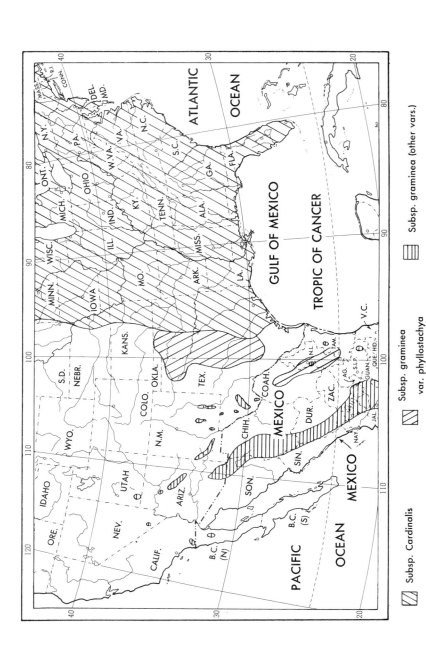

Fig. 5–29. Distribution of subspecies and varieties of *Lobelia Cardinalis*, as labeled. (Based upon Rogers McVaugh, Brittonia 2: 328, map 2, 1952. Base map, Goode Map Series, copyright by the University of Chicago. Used by permission.)

rare), Arizona, and Nebraska southward into Mexico. Subspecies *graminea* consists of several varieties restricted to north-south axes rather than east-west belts. The variety occurring from Arizona southward along the Sierra Madre Occidental into Mexico is similar to another one growing from southern Mexico to Panama and Colombia. A markedly different variety grows from Nebraska and central Texas to the Sierra Madre Oriental in eastern Mexico. In the northern area of distribution the characters of the varieties are differentiated clearly, but in southern Mexico there is a rich variety of phenotypes and some individuals combine distinctive features of these two varieties and of others, even including some characters of the eastern subspecies *Cardinalis*.

Similar species of *Lobelia* are abundant in tropical America. Some of these are related closely to *Lobelia Cardinalis,* and logically the origin of the species must have been in this region rather than in temperate North America, where species of *Lobelia* and its relatives are less common and more specialized. Thus, the migration of *Lobelia Cardinalis* probably has been from south to north along the mountain axes of Mexico.

According to McVaugh the northward spread of the species was halted or slowed, the result being an absence of these plants from the Pacific Coast (except in one or two localities in extreme southern California), from the Colorado Plateau, from all but the southern part of the Rocky Mountains, and from the isolated high mountain ranges of the Great Basin. The cessation of northern migration may have been due to depletion of genetic diversity within the populations or to changes in an unspecified environmental factor. The northern limit of *Lobelia Cardinalis,* like those of many other species, corresponds approximately to limits of the Paleozoic rocks along the line from western Texas to southern California. Since Paleozoic times, there has been much folding and faulting along this line, and it is marked now by prominent mountains and escarpments. The areas to the south generally are hotter and drier than those to the north. The most significant factor, at least insofar as absence of *Lobelia* from the Pacific Coast and the Great Basin is concerned, may be lack of summer rainfall. This is responsible for absence from California and the Great Basin of many genera and species common in Mexico, Arizona, New Mexico, and Texas.

McVaughn describes a similar distribution for the black cherries, treated as subspecies of *Prunus serotina,* and he points out the same pattern for many other species. According to McVaugh, plant groups best developed in the highlands of Mexico and Central and South America but with representatives occurring farther northward in temperate North America usually follow the distribution pattern of *Lobelia Cardinalis* and *Prunus serotina*. Usually there is a broad distribution in eastern North America and a restricted distribution in western North America.

This pattern is followed with one modification by the *Ranunculus septentrionalis* group (Figs. 2–12 through 2–18), a complex of several species developed most strongly in the Mexican Plateau region and southward along the mountain chain of South America. Its migration was probably northward, and probably it paralleled the pattern described by McVaugh. The group includes wide-ranging species in eastern North America and a single species in the western part of the continent. This disjunct species, *Ranunculus orthorhynchus*, is adapted to regions with only winter rain, where it has evolved into several varieties which occur even as far north as southern Alaska.

McVaugh considers many North American groups, including *Prunus serotina*, as having genetic lines rather sharply delineated in correlation with the pattern of geographical distribution outlined above. Such described "species" as "*Prunus virens*" and *Prunus serotina* seem separable if only the northern forms are studied. According to strong evidence, however, they are nothing more than the branches of an evolutionary tree, the main trunk of which is still in Central America. The temptation, on the basis of local studies in the United States, to consider them as separate species loses force in view of their origin and of the persistence of less well differentiated relatives occurring farther south. Thus, classification is correlated with geographical distribution and past migrations of the species or species complex.

SUMMARY

Classification must be based upon the plants or animals of a restricted segment of geological time. Taxa of one period gradually divide into others or shift in their character combinations through loss of some characters from the pool of genes and through the addition of new ones, chiefly by mutations or introgression. A system of classification involving all organisms of the past as well as those of the present thus would include a continuum ranging from the beginning of living organisms to all those of the present time, and no divisions would be possible.

The fossil record of plants, except for a few groups, is meager, and it permits working out phylogenetic sequences in only a few instances. Examples of classification of a group of species in the light of knowledge of their geological history, as with the closed-cone pines, are rare.

The chief contribution of paleobotany to classification of most plant groups is evidence of the reasons for the geographical and ecological isolation of living taxa and of their immediate ancestors. It provides some knowledge of the origin of the past and present distributional patterns. In many instances classification of living plants, including even those unknown from fossils, may be correlated with distributional patterns, which, in turn, can be explained only in the light of the geological history either of the area in which the living plants occur or of the past migrations of the species. This may provide solutions to problems of endemism and of disjunction of distribution of species and entire vegetation types.

SUGGESTED READING

ADAMS, CHARLES C. 1902. A classic paper.

AXELROD, DANIEL I. 1940. The first comprehensive paper on the origin and history of the present Sierra Madrean Flora from the Madro-Tertiary geoflora.

———. 1948. Analysis of the climate of the western United States in middle Pliocene times, when grassland and subdesert environments were of subcontinental extent, of their invasion by xerophytic species, and of rapid evolution in the new habitats.

———. 1956.

———. 1957. An interpretation of past and present floras in the light of the fossil record and of the history of mountain building in the region.

———. 1958. Summary, amplification, and revision of numerous earlier papers by the author. The Madro-Tertiary Geoflora covered much of the West. Owing to the studies of Axelrod its history is better known than those of most floras.

———. 1959. Migration of the big tree (*Sequoiadendron giganteum*) and some but not all its associates or their modified descendants from western Nevada (in late Miocene times) to the western slopes of the now much uplifted Sierra Nevada of California.

BAKER, H. G. 1959.

CHANEY, RALPH W. 1925. A classical paper on the geological history and past distribution of the redwood-forest flora.

———. 1936. A continuation and expansion of the subject of Tertiary forest floras of the Northern Hemisphere and of their modern descendants, with special reference to western North America and eastern Asia.

———. 1938. A review of general principles and of the western Tertiary floras.

———. 1940. Discussion of North America as a rising continent during Tertiary times and of the consequent trend toward a drier and colder climate with the resultant migration of forests.

———. 1947. History of floras with emphasis upon the Arcto-Tertiary and Madro-Tertiary floras.

———. 1948. Segregation of fossils of *Metasequoia* from those of *Sequoia sempervirens*, and the consequent revision of the known paleontological distribution of the latter and of the history of the Arcto-Tertiary geoflora.

———. 1949. A review of the evidence concerning major problems of phylogeny available from fossils, together with suggestions for further studies and for assembly of data which may contribute to solutions.

———. 1951. Reclassification of redwoods based on correlation of living and fossil plants.

———, CARLTON CONDIT, and DANIEL I. AXELROD. 1944. A summary of the Pliocene history of the forerunners of the Pacific Northwestern and Sierra Madrean floras; taxonomic principles involved in the study of Pliocene floras.

Dorf, Erling. 1957. Emphasis upon Tertiary and Quaternary climates.

————. 1959. An excellent summary, especially of Tertiary climates in North America.

Fernald, Merrit Lyndon. 1925. A thorough classical study, the interpretation of which became the center of the nunatak controversy.

Gentry, Howard Scott. 1950. Correlation of species distribution in the area of the Gulf of California with fluctuations in Tertiary times of the extent of land and water.

Halliday, W. E. D., and A. W. A. Brown. 1943. Maps of distribution of tree species and discussion of the relationships of present distribution to repopulation of areas denuded by Pleistocene ice.

Hultén, Eric. 1937.

Mason, Herbert L. 1932a. This and the following two papers are the basis for the discussion of the closed-cone pines in the text above.

————. 1932b. See above.

————. 1949. See above.

————. 1953. Interrelationship of taxonomy and plant geography.

Mayr, Ernst. 1951. Review of speciation along the shores of large ancient lakes at points separated by unfavorable shore segments and in separate small lakes later rejoined to the main lake.

Rand, A. L. 1948.

Raup, Hugh M. 1941. A summary of problems of plant distribution and ecology.

Rousseau, Jacques. 1953.

Scoggan, H. J. 1950. The introduction includes a discussion of glacial and post-glacial history.

Stebbins, G. Ledyard, Jr. 1942a. An example of occupation by an octoploid variety of land arisen more recently from the ocean than that occupied by the older tetraploid parental varieties.

————. 1942c. The relative adaptability of common and widespread usually genetically diverse species, and of rare and localized endemic usually more or less homogeneous species.

————. 1947. Fluctuation in rates of evolution depending on the changes in the habitats of the earth.

Tucker, John M., and Cornelius H. Muller. 1958. Evidence from living plants and from their parasites (gall insects) of the past migration of species.

Turesson, G. 1927. Discussion of repopulation of lowland and alpine areas by various ecotypes following retreat of the glaciers in the Scandinavian countries.

Wynne-Edwards, V. C. 1937.

————. 1939.

Data from Chemistry, Plant Physiology, and Ecology

Chemical and physiological-ecological characters offer an unusually promising field for investigation. Their intangibility and the difficulty of detecting and defining them have been a handicap to classification, but these difficulties present a challenge. The challenge is not to be ignored, because the physiological reactions of organisms commonly are the characters finally determining which genetic types will survive. More than any others, these characteristics are fundamental to the course of evolution of species (Gibbs, 1945, 1954).

CHEMICAL CHARACTERS

The presence of a particular compound in one taxon and its absence from a related one are likely to be connected with the evolutionary processes which brought about the original segregation of the groups of organisms. Thus, this difference may be fundamental to classification.

The significance of chemical characters has been demonstrated in relatively few cases. An example of their importance is the role of some substances in protection of the plant (Fraenkel, 1959). Living green plants are the ultimate or direct source of food for all other living organisms. Thus, green plants are vulnerable to the attacks or parasitism of many kinds of animals; they are beset by innumerable insects, mites, birds, and the herbivores of various phyla. In addition they are attacked by bacteria and fungi.

Protection may be achieved mechanically, as by growing well above the ground level, but frequently it is attained chemically. Chemical protection is not necessarily spectacular, as it is with stinging hairs of nettles or with plants to which man is allergic, such as poison ivy or poison oak; it may consist of no more than an unappealing flavor in the estimate of a particular insect or snail. One substance in or upon the leaves, stems, flowers, fruits, seeds, or bark may repel one, several, or many organisms. Another substance may be lethal to some animals or to fungi or bacteria; an antibiotic may inhibit multiplication of bacteria.

The chemical contents or secretions of the plant may eliminate many potential attackers but may be overcome by other organisms, some of which may be especially adapted to them. For example, a group of chemical substances characterizing the mustard family (*Cruciferae*) is marked by a combination of glucosides and mustard oil (Fraenkel, 1959). Some of the glucosides, for example, sinalbin and sinigrin, are distributed widely through the family. These repel many attackers but, on the other hand, have been shown experimentally to be responsible for the restriction of the larvae of cabbage butterflies to feeding upon the crucifers.

Equal evolutionary and taxonomic significance must be attached to the numerous substances which attract animals, such as the flavoring matters of fruits which attract carriers of seeds, the nectar which brings many insect and bird pollinators, and the carrion odor of the flowers of many *Araceae*, which attracts flies, the pollinating agents.

The following are examples of chemical characters relating to pigments of flowers; contents of wood, bark, and seeds; and substances within the plant which are indicated by serum diagnosis.

Pigments of Flowers. Flower color is important in evolution of species. It may be responsible for their taxonomic segregation, because it may determine whether pollination is by one type or another of insect or bird, thus bringing about reproductive isolation.

Grant (1952) found one columbine, *Aquilegia formosa*, to be pollinated in daylight by hummingbirds, which are able to see the red sepals and the red spurs of the petals. Another species, *Aquilegia pubescens*, is pollinated at night by hawkmoths, which find the pale yellow or white flowers in darkness. Evolution of other features of the flowers is in keeping with natural selection resulting from different pollinating organisms. For example, in *Aquilegia pubescens* the longer nectar-bearing spurs are suitable to the long prosboces of hawkmoths. Occasional hybridization and introgression between the species are believed to be from chance visits by pollen-collecting bumblebees (Fig. 6–1).

Plastid pigments (often yellow or red) are insoluble in water and relatively stable in plant specimens; anthocyanin pigments (lavender to purple) are water-soluble and unstable in pressed specimens. Anthocyanins are sensitive to changes in the pH of the solution, behaving much like litmus paper, that is, changing toward red in an acid medium and toward blue in a basic medium. Among the hedgehog cacti (*Echinocereus*) two major groups of species can be distinguished on the basis of pigmentation. In one group the pure red or red-and-yellow flower color is characteristic of plastid pigmentation; in the other group, colors ranging between lavender and purple are characteristic of anthocyanins. Since plastid pigments are not water-soluble or obviously sensitive to changes in pH, the flower color of one species group is retained in herbarium specimens, but, more or less regardless of the original color in the series from lavender to purple, the color of the other changes to a nondescript blue. Thus, even from study of a series of dried specimens, this chemical character may be detected, and it may be checked by simple tests of living material.

The stability of flower colors and their validity as characters marking taxonomic segregations in *Baptisia* (Leguminosae) have been tested through chromatographic analysis of the pigments (Turner and Alston, 1959). The results of chromatographic tests were compared with other characters of the species and of hybrids between them, as indicated by hybrid indexes (see pp. 121–125). Correlations of chromatographic patterns with hybrid indexes based upon pubescence of the ovary, stipule development, pedicel length, and habit of the inflorescence indicated a close relationship of occurrence of flower color and other characters distinguishing the species. The patterns of the hybrids showed remarkable recombinations of the pigmentation of the flowers of the species, as well as of the other characters.

Contents of Wood, Bark, and Seeds. Chemical characters of the wood, bark, and seeds of the pines have been summarized by Mirov (1938, 1953, 1954).

Wood. As Erdtman and his associates showed earlier, in general the heartwood phenols of the white pines [1] include dibenzyls,

---

[1] The white pines (for example, *Pinus Strobus, Pinus monticola, Pinus Lambertiana,* and the pinyon group composed of varieties of *Pinus cembroides*) have only one vascular bundle in each leaf. They have been considered to form a subgenus or a section, *Haploxylon,* as opposed to the species with two bundles, *Diploxylon.*

Fig. 6–1. Pollinating mechanisms and hybridization in columbines: (1) Aquilegia formosa, with red and partly yellow flowers and with short spurs on the petals, pollinated in daylight by hummingbirds (Manti, Utah); (2) Aquilegia chrysantha, with yellow flowers and with long spurs on the petals, these spurs equal in length to the probosces of hawk moths which pollinate the flowers at night (Huachuca Mountains, Arizona); (3) hybrid of Aquilegia formosa and Aquilegia caerulea var. pinetorum (a yellow-flowered, long-spurred type), probably resulting from the activity of an unusual pollinator such as a bumblebee—the plant growing in Zion Canyon, southern Utah, where a great variety of intermediate habitats is available and a hybrid swarm exists. Aquilegia formosa grows at lower elevations than Aquilegia caerulea var. pinetorum, which is a Rocky Mountain Montane Forest taxon.

flavones, and pinitol, which are lacking in the other pines. However, further subdivision of species groups on the basis of heartwood phenols is rarely possible.

In other instances, species or varieties are characterized by special substances. The turpentine of the western yellow pine (*Pinus ponderosa* var. *ponderosa*) contains delta-3 carene; that of the Apache pine (var. *Mayriana* or *Pinus apacheca*) does not. The oleoresin of the Jeffrey pine (*Pinus ponderosa* var. *Jeffreyi* or *Pinus Jeffreyi*) does not contain terpenes; that of the western yellow pine does.

Like other characters, chemical ones are not necessarily consistent with other features of the species. *Pinus albicaulis* (the white-bark pine), a characteristic timber-line white pine of the Cascade–Sierra Nevada axis and of the northern Rocky Mountains, has the most complex turpentine chemistry in the group. Biochemically it is connected not with the species it resembles morphologically, but with others. Different substances occurring in the turpentine suggest several possible relationships; structural characters point to others.

BARK. In the Digger pine (*Pinus Sabiniana*) and the Jeffrey pine (*Pinus ponderosa* var. *Jeffreyi* or *Pinus Jeffreyi*) 95 per cent of the turpentine consists of heptane, a saturated straight-chain hydrocarbon, C_7H_{16}. This imparts an aromatic quality to the bark of the Jeffrey pine which is lacking in its close relative the western yellow pine (*Pinus ponderosa*).

SEEDS. The seed oil of the Jeffrey pine has a higher percentage of saturated triglycerides (as indicated by iodine numbers 129–138) than does that of the western yellow pine (147–154).

Substances Within the Plant Which Are Indicated by Serum Diagnosis. Serum diagnosis has been used extensively in studying the interrelationships and classification of animals; occasionally it has been applied to plants. Diagnosis of a plant involves injection of a laboratory animal with a protein extract from the plant. After a waiting period, some of the serum (liquid derived from the blood) of the animal is placed with the protein extract of another plant. The amount of the resulting precipitate or the effect upon an indicator is an index of the degree of similarity of some features of the proteins in the extract from the two plants. It has been assumed to be an index of the degree of absolute relationship of the two taxa which the plants represent. There is no reason to believe, however, that the similarity or dissimilarity of protein extracts is any more an indicator of relationships than is any other character. Davidson and

Thompson (1956) made serological tests of six strains of Indian corn (*Zea Mays*). After the tests, the known genealogy and relationships of the strains of corn were secured from the department of agronomy which had supplied the seeds. The results indicated that among the dent corns tested serological information confirmed known relationships. However, the tests failed to distinguish dent corn from popcorn. Thus, serology taken alone is indicated to be not infallible evidence of genealogical relationships but a source of information to be considered with other data in arriving at tentative conclusions concerning classification of plants. All characters must be tested for their occurrence in some groups and not in others, and one character is, per se, no more important in classification than another. When the occurrence of all has been correlated, a tentative conclusion concerning relationships may be drawn. At first serodiagnosis was hailed, like many another discovery, as *the* solution to taxonomic problems. Ultimately, like other "solutions," it has been found to offer important data which, to be useful, must be correlated with other information. The data must be drawn from numerous individuals of each taxon and not from a single representative. Data from serodiagnoses taken alone may be no more important to classification than would be the results of a study compiling uncorrelated data on which plants contain rubber, a substance to be found in some degree through a wide range of species in numerous families.

PHYSIOLOGICAL-ECOLOGICAL CHARACTERS

Physiology and ecology provide evidence of the stability of characters under differing environmental conditions and yield data of value in tracing the reasons for past and present migrations of species and varieties and for their segregation as ecologically adapted populations. The significance of ecological factors was primary for the oaks discussed in Chapter 3. The following are more subtle examples.

The western yellow pine (*Pinus ponderosa*) is a wide-ranging species of British Columbia, the western states, the Black Hills, Texas west of the Pecos River, and northern Baja California, Mexico. The tree is prominent in both the Sierran Montane Forest [Fig. 5–18 (3), where this is the dominant tree] and the Rocky Mountain Montane Forest, and these vegetation types are referred to frequently as "yellow pine forest."

In the mountains of California, the *Pinus ponderosa* var. *ponderosa* forest is supported by no less than 25–30 inches of annual precipitation; in Arizona it requires as little as about 15 inches. This is associated with the seasonal distribution of rainfall and snowfall, as described in the following paragraphs.

In California, the one constant feature in the locally variable climate is the nearly complete restriction of precipitation (except at high altitudes) to winter and of growth to spring and early summer (see p. 181). In even the middle forest belts in the mountains, summer rain is usually inconsequential. In the forests of *Pinus ponderosa* var. *ponderosa* (2,000 to 5,000 or 6,000 feet in northern California, 5,500 to 7,500 feet in southern California), seed germination occurs in late April or early May, and growth of trees and herbs begins in May, reaches the maximum in June, and declines rapidly in July. The reproductive season for plants is principally in June, when the days are long, the nights are cold, and the air is dry.

In Arizona there are two seasons of precipitation, a lesser one in winter and a major one in summer. The winter storms are mere attenuations of the Californian winter rains. At the altitude of yellow pine forest (6,500 to 8,500 feet), the winter is cold. Toward spring much of the light blanket of snow passes directly into the atmosphere without becoming available as liquid water. For example, at Flagstaff, Arizona, in 1960 a 6-foot snow pack disappeared, leaving the forest dry and in a condition of extreme fire hazard. In May or June, when the weather becomes warm enough for plant growth, there is little moisture left. Consequently the spring season of growth and reproduction is a minor one. In July and August the summer rainy season brings ordinarily about 10 inches of warm rain, and at times there may be thundershowers nearly every day. A relatively small amount of precipitation in this short warm period promotes lush plant growth; consequently a total annual precipitation of 15 to 20 inches may be sufficient to support yellow pine forest. A high percentage of the water is available to the plants because there is no lag between a winter period of rain and snow and a time warm enough for the water to be used. In the growing and reproductive season (August) the days are becoming short, the nights are warm, and the air is moist. The three factors mentioned above affect plants—day length is associated with physiological factors which for many species are related to the time of reproduction, some flowering only when the days are long, others only when they are short; night temperature is significant to enzymatic processes; humidity is related to the water balance of the plant. Furthermore, some seeds are capable of germination only at low temperatures, others at high temperatures.

Fig. 6–2. Rocky Mountain Montane Forest dominated by the western yellow pine (*Pinus ponderosa*) (Arizona). The pines and nearly all the associated species are dependent upon rainfall in the warm summer period of July and August for both growth of adult plants and germination of seeds. Note the similarity of appearance to the Sierran Montane Forest [Fig. 5–18 (3)]. (Photograph courtesy of U.S. Forest Service.)

The temperature and day length during the moist period are responsible for much of the profound difference in species composition of the various floras occurring in California and Arizona, one primary controlling factor being the temperature at which seeds germinate (Shreve, 1917, 1925, 1942; Shreve and Wiggins, 1951; Went, 1948, 1949). In the seemingly similar yellow pine forests of California and Arizona [Figs. 5–18 (3) and 6–2] few species other than the yellow pine are the same. In California there is a spring-germinating, long-day-flowering forest flora; in Arizona there is a summer-germinating, short-day-flowering forest flora.

Sowing the seeds of the species occurring in one forest in the other would not produce any significant changes in the vegetation, because the seeds of most species adapted to one forest type ordinarily can not germinate or grow as seedlings in competition in the other. The difficulty of establishing even locally adapted seedlings is illustrated by the following example:

In 1949, following an exceedingly cold winter, seedlings of gymnosperms were remarkably abundant at Tiger Flat in the Greenhorn Mountains, a southern spur of the Sierra Nevada of California. Quadrats laid out under the direction of Dr. Edwin A. Phillips were used for recording the density of seedlings of various species, including *Pinus ponderosa*. In 1951, only an occasional 1949 seedling persisted; by 1953, there were almost none. Evidently establishment of seedlings is a difficult matter because in most years very few pine seeds germinate and few of even those germinating during a remarkably favorable year persist. Thus a pine seed from an area where germination occurs at high temperatures in the summer probably would have almost no chance of germination and survival in an area where the only available moisture was present at low temperatures in the late spring. This also is true of the opposite situation. Furthermore, if, for example, an Arizona pine seedling should become established in California, or vice versa, it would remain to be seen whether the plant would reach maturity in competition with locally adapted individuals and whether it would reproduce normally.

In normal years the seeds of *Pinus ponderosa* occurring on the plateau of northern Arizona germinate following the summer rains in July and August. Normally May and June are very dry, and, by the time soil temperatures are high enough for germination, residual moisture from the winter snows is too deep in the ground to permit any germination. However, in 1919 unusually heavy rainfall in May resulted in appreciable germination of seeds prior to July 1 (Pearson, 1923, 1942, 1950). The following quotation is from a

letter (dated February 27, 1956) from Edward M. Gaines, Research
Center Leader, Rocky Mountain Forest and Range Experiment
Station, U.S. Forest Service, Flagstaff, Arizona:

> It appears that the right combination of soil temperature and moisture is
> required for germination. In 1955, we had unusually heavy rains about the
> middle of June, but there was little or no germination until the latter part of
> July. Apparently the soil temperatures stayed too low after the June rain. . . .

Although proof depends upon experiment, it is not conceivable
that the races of western yellow pine occurring in California and
Arizona are identical. Clearly, at least there are unseen physiological differences.

The western yellow pine occurs in diverse climates and habitats,
for example, near the shores of Puget Sound, in the dry montane
forests of California, in the moist forests of eastern British Columbia,
in the generally dry but late-summer-moist mountains of southern
New Mexico and western Texas, and in the Black Hills of South
Dakota. Some local variation in visible characters can be detected,
and probably there are many locally adapted physiological or ecological forms. Segregation of local varieties or forms is difficult in
the present state of knowledge. Establishing their occurrence, if
that is possible, will require long-continued experiments and observations on many local populations because physiological features are
difficult to correlate for large numbers of individuals.

Two species of *Delphinium* grow together on a California hillside
(Epling and Lewis, 1952; Lewis and Epling, 1954). In some years
only one species is found, in other years only the other, and in still
others only hybrids between the two (Fig. 6–3). This is despite the
fact that all the delphiniums concerned are perennials, the relatively
woody root systems of which live over from year to year. Variation
in environmental factors, including particularly the amount and
seasonal distribution of rainfall from year to year, favors the growth
of one species or the other or the hybrids. Consequently, according to the year, one or another develops leaves and flowering stems.
Evidently, though, in some years both species must have developed;
otherwise there could be no hybrids. The results of Epling and
Lewis' investigation indicate that environmental conditions exert a
delicate control over the development of these species.

The hybrids of *Delphinium*, once the critical seedling stage is
past, can live in the ground for long periods. If the plants were
annuals instead of perennials, they could live over from year to year
only in seed form, and the hybrids would be less likely to persist as
long.

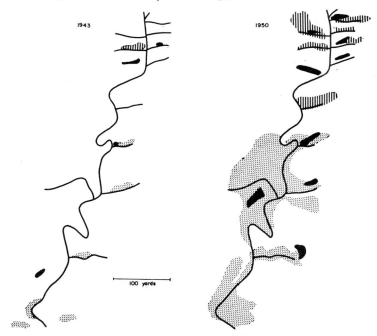

Fig. 6–3. Variation in different years of the distribution and extent of visible members of colonies of perennial species of larkspurs in one small canyon in central California: solid dark areas—*Delphinium gypsophilum* (diploid species); vertical lines—*Delphinium Hansenii* (diploid races); broken lines—*Delphinium Hansenii* (tetraploid races). (From Carl Epling and Harlan Lewis, Evolution 6: 257, 1952. Used by permission.)

HYBRIDIZATION OF THE HABITAT

As was explained in part in Chapter 3, when two species of the same genus occur together or near each other, ordinarily each has its own ecological niche among the living populations of the locality. That is, there is a certain set of physical factors, soil types, and relationships to other plants and animals to which each is restricted.

As has been shown by Anderson (1948, 1949), ordinarily hybrids between species are relatively unlikely to survive. The F_1 hybrid has intermediate characters and a selection of both structural and physiological traits of the two parents. Thus the gene complex, producing in either parent adaptation to the environment, is broken down, and usually the hybrids do not fit into the ecological niche of either parent. Those that do occur tend to be eliminated because ordinarily they must develop in the habitat favorable to the other non-hybrid seedlings. This habitat is usually that of the female parent, that is, the species which produced the seeds, because pollen usually is transported farther than seeds. Unless the hybrids happen to develop in some intermediate environment having just the right combination of environmental and biological factors, they may not survive even the seedling stage. Consequently, ordinary F_1 hybrids are not as common in nature as would be expected from the inter-fertility of species, and species which cross readily in gardens and greenhouses may grow as separate entities in the same general area in nature because there are few or no favorable habitats in which the hybrids can survive and reproduce (see pp. 63–67).

If the relatively small numbers of first generation natural hybrids do reach maturity and reproduce, usually they cross back to one parental species or the other, thus producing individuals showing chiefly the traits contributed by one grandparental type plus a smaller number from the other. Most often even these are inter-mediate characters developed in response to genetic multiple-factor systems (pp. 243–247). Relatively few factors contributed by the grandparent belonging to the species not entering into the backcross may be evident among the offspring. Probably the generation re-sulting from the backcross will be backcrossed again with the same parental species, and a series of such crosses will result in individuals practically indistinguishable from typical ones (see *introgressive hybridization*, pp. 127–129).

According to Anderson, F_2 segregations (the second generation resulting from the crossing of two homozygous lines followed by inbreeding) are rare in nature except where the environment has been disturbed in some way, usually by man, fire, or grazing animals. Hybrids survive usually in intermediate or "hybridized habitats," often those affected by human activities or other unusual factors. One of the most striking examples is illustrated by the work of Viosca (1935), of Riley (1938), and of Anderson (1949) in the southern states. *Iris fulva* and *Iris hexagona* var. *giganticaerulea*, which hybridize readily, have produced character recombinations in hybrids on agricultural land on the Mississippi Delta below New Orleans. The hybrid swarms have become established in fields, one type or group of types prevailing in one field and another to a some-what greater degree in the adjacent field. This is the result of slight differences with respect to water and agricultural methods practiced over long periods in the individual fields which result in somewhat different ecological niches, each favoring a slightly differ-ent set of combinations of the characters appearing in the hybrid *Iris* populations.

INTERGRADATION OF LOCALLY ISOLATED
POPULATION SYSTEMS

While, except in disturbed areas, establishment of F_1 hybrids in direct competition with one or both parental species may be relatively rare, a gradual shading off over some distance of one population system into another is common. Local forms representing genetic combinations within each species or other system have been selected in accordance with habitats, but some selected local representatives of one species may approach or approximate the ecological habitat requirements of certain local types occurring in the other species. Furthermore, species genetically isolated in one area may have interbreeding members elsewhere. *Thus, two population systems which maintain themselves as distinct in one place may have intergrading phases in other places.*

The ends or margins of a chain or a network of population systems may be in widely differing species, as in the case of the oaks described in Chapter 3, in two locally intersterile species connected elsewhere through populations related closely to both, or through local races all included, along with the extremes, in a single species.

As was stated in Chapter 3 (Figs. 3–12 and 3–13), the California blue oak (*Quercus Douglasii*) and the scrub oak (*Quercus dumosa*) grow side by side along the Ridge Route north of Los Angeles, but they do not interbreed. They appear to be intersterile, and each occupies a distinct ecological niche, one in oak woodland and the other in chaparral. Yet, within a few miles *Quercus dumosa* shades into the taxon *californica;* through hybrid groups, each occupying an ecological niche, the taxon *californica* merges into the blue oak.

After an intensive study of mice of the genus *Peromyscus*, Blair (1950) recognized four complexes which indicate that speciation (evolutionary segregation or differentiation of species) begins commonly in this group by simple geographical isolation of a segment of a population. He gives evidence that new species have originated on the margins of the range, on coastal islands, and probably on isolated mountain ranges. Races at opposite ends of the chains of local populations are differentiated structurally and in their preference for habitats, and the animals at the extremities of the series have genetic isolating mechanisms which either prevent or reduce interfertility. If the intermediate populations did not exist, these extremes might be considered as distinct species.

CHANGE OF ECOLOGICAL CONDITIONS AND THE
POTENTIAL SIGNIFICANCE OF HYBRIDS

The ecological niches of the present have much to do with the genetic development of the natural populations which inhabit them. Each population has been affected by past ecological relationships, and it must be prepared for further alteration in the future.

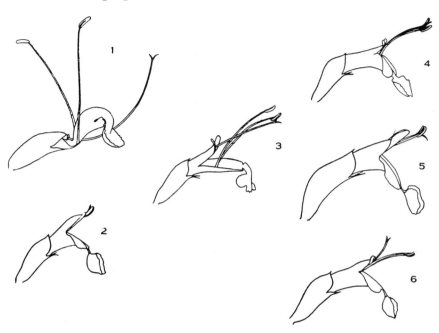

Fig. 6–4. Flower structure and hybridization of species of sage: (1) the bee sage (*Salvia apiana*); (2) the black sage (*Salvia mellifera*); (3) F_1 generation hybrid of the two species; (4–6) backcrosses to *Salvia mellifera*. (From Carl Epling, Evolution 1: 71, 1947. Used by permission.)

Epling (1947) has analyzed crosses (Fig. 6–4) between two shrubby species of sage occurring in southern California, the black sage (*Salvia mellifera*) and the bee sage (*Salvia apiana*). F_1 hybrids between these two species occur here and there in the chaparral. Backcrosses to *Salvia mellifera* occur rather commonly, but backcrosses to *Salvia apiana* are less common. This may be attributed to the flower structure of the F_1 hybrid, which much more nearly resembles that of the black sage than it does that of the bee sage.

The corollas and stamens of the two species differ radically, and pollinating insects which are effective for the black sage also may be effective for the hybrid but not for the bee sage. Although the species are more or less reproductively compatible and this permits occurrence of hybrid individuals and occasionally of localized hybrid swarms,[2] essentially the constancy of the two species is maintained, for they live in a community in which the ecological equilibrium of competition is well maintained. The small amount of gene exchange between the populations and the occasional production of local hybrid swarms may provide at the right time in the future a gene combination making up an individual or a group of individuals capable of exploiting or at least of surviving a shift in the environment.

Few habitats in Canada and the United States are not changing through agriculture, fire, lumbering, or overgrazing. Consequently, opportunities for establishment of hybrids are much greater than they were before the coming of white men (Anderson and Stebbins, 1954). This factor must be borne in mind in assessing the current distinctness of species, some of which, such as those of *Amaranthus* (Sauer, 1957), have evolved markedly within the last century through hybridizing in newly available habitats.

ADAPTIVE RADIATION

When new groups of organisms evolve or when they enter a newly accessible or newly formed environment, they tend to fill all the available ecological niches. Thus many adaptive forms radiate from a common ancestry along evolutionary lines leading to a variety of end products, each differing considerably from the ancestral stock. Examples are abundant in the flora and fauna of islands separated by significant distances from other land masses.

The Hawaiian chain of islands (as was mentioned briefly in Chapter 5), has been formed over many millions of years by the rise of volcanoes from beneath the surface of the sea, each new island forming an isolated unit rising at first steeply from the ocean to a considerable altitude. The islands (see e.g., Bryan, 1954) occur along a crack in the earth's crust running beneath the ocean for

[2] For example, Anderson and Anderson (1954) found a richly differentiated hybrid swarm growing in an abandoned and overgrown olive grove in Santa Anita Canyon in the San Gabriel Mountains in southern California near Arcadia. The plants of the adjacent areas showed little hybridization, though some introgression from *Salvia apiana* to *Salvia mellifera* could be detected.

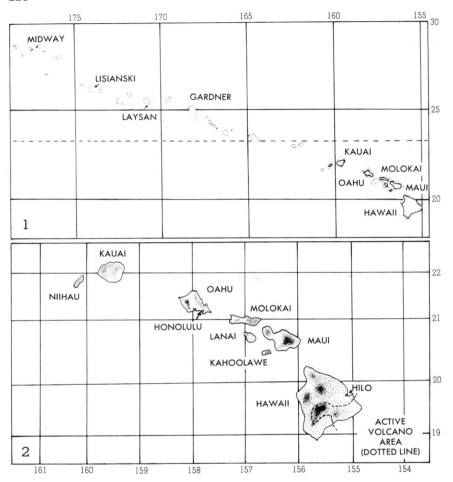

Fig. 6–5. Maps showing the Hawaiian chain of islands: (1) the entire chain, including the minor islands and remnants of islands in the western portion; (2) the Hawaiian Islands proper. The large islands are at the southeastern end of a seam in the surface of the earth beneath the Pacific Ocean. As the seam opens new islands are formed, and these are eroded gradually, ultimately becoming small islands and remnants.

about 2,000 miles from the area of Midway to the "big island" of Hawaii (Fig. 6–5). The seam has opened gradually from northwest to southeast, and active volcanoes are still present and advancing on the southeastern side of Hawaii, with primary ecological succession beginning on the lava (Fig. 6–6). At the opposite end of the chain, Midway and other ancient islands are eroded now almost to sea

Fig. 6–6. Ecological niches and forest types in Hawaii: (1) ecological niches in the steep canyons and on cliffs on Oahu, Nuuanu Pali, showing pockets in which species may be isolated, particularly in habitat niches which vary from the wet (windward) to the dry (leeward) sides of the islands (Fig. 5–9); (2) mature ohia-fern rain forest dominated by the ohia (Metrosideros) and tree ferns, on a volcanic crater, Kilauea, Hawaii; (3) koa (Acacia Koa) forest, Kokee, Kauai. The ohia-fern forest occurs at lower elevations, the koa forest at higher levels (about 4,000 feet).

level, and the remaining lava is covered by coral sand. The older larger islands such as Kauai and Oahu are partly eroded away, and their mountainsides are unbelievably steep [Figs. 5–9 (1), 6–6]. Inasmuch as all the islands are in the direct path of the trade winds, each has a phenomenally wet northeastern side with up to more than 600 inches of annual rainfall (on Kauai) and a dry southwestern side, which may resemble Arizona [Fig. 5–9 (2)]. Thus, the topography and climate of the islands provide at various altitudes (Fig. 6–6) isolated pockets and ravines which differ ecologically and many highly localized endemic species of both plants and animals are separated by only short distances.

Fosberg (in Zimmerman, 1948, 1: 107–119) estimates that the 1,729 native species and infraspecific taxa of flowering plants in the Hawaiian Islands could have originated from as few as 272 original immigrant species which arrived by one means or another during millions of years. These were a random selection of one or a few species from each of eighty-six families. Some of the original migrants have given rise to many species, each adapted to a special niche and perhaps restricted to a small area on a single island. For example, *Cyrtandra* (Gesneriaceae) consists of more than 100 endemic Hawaiian species. Other genera with large numbers of highly localized species include *Astelia, Schiedea, Pelea, Fagara, Hibiscus, Viola, Labordia, Haplostachys, Phyllostegia, Stenogyne, Coprosma, Hedyotis, Clermontia, Cyanea, Delissea, Lobelia, Bidens, Dubautia,* and *Lipochaeta* (see St. John, 1946).

The land snails of Hawaii were collected in 1851 and 1852 by John Thomas Gulick. After observing the extreme localization of species, some of which occur only a mile apart, he formulated a theory of evolution independently of his contemporaries, Darwin and Wallace (Gulick, 1905, published posthumously).

The Hawaiian birds, especially the honey creepers, have undergone rapid evolution in a pattern of adaptive radiation (Amadon, 1947). These birds, like the flowering plants and the land snails, have given rise to various evolutionary lines which have become adapted to niches occupied in other parts of the world by species of other families. In particular, evolution of the bill differs in various genera and species. In some it is short and nearly straight; in others long and curved; in others thick and well adapted to digging and prying in the bark of trees for insects, to cracking the twigs of trees for the same purpose, or breaking hard-coated seeds. Some species visit flowers for nectar but also eat insects. In *Phaeornis*, a genus of the thrush family, two species have become differentiated, one feeding on insects, the other on berries. Thus they exist side by side without competition. Among the honey creepers, three species of *Hemignathus*, one intermediate between the others and apparently ill adapted and disappearing even before disturbance by man, represent stages in rapid evolution with shift of ecological conditions.

Unfortunately, the coming of European men to Hawaii brought almost complete replacement of the lowland vegetation by plants from other parts of the tropics, together with destruction of parts of the mountain forests, large sections of forest dominated by the koa [*Acacia Koa*, Fig. 6–6 (3)] being killed even by the grazing of horses. Accompanying these changes, some of the animals, including key species of honey creepers, have become extinct and are known now only from specimens and early publications.

EXPERIMENTAL STUDIES OF ECOLOGICAL RACES

The following is an example of methods of testing the stability of characters under changing environment and, therefore, of determining their reliability for differentiation of particular taxonomic groups: A number of cuttings may be taken from the same individual plant. These genetically identical fragments are propagated in a greenhouse, and later the new plants are set out in each of several strongly dissimilar habitats, perhaps long distances apart and at various altitudes. In the meantime, cuttings from plants occurring naturally in different environments and differing somewhat from one another are brought together in the same environment. These two types of tests sometimes show particular characters to be unstable with change of environment, and sometimes the reverse.

By experiments of the type outlined in the preceding paragraph, Turesson (1922a, 1922b) obtained the following results in some of his early studies in southern Sweden:

Dactylis glomerata (orchard grass)—This species includes a broad-leaved form (called var. *lobata*) characteristic of shady situations. Transplanting this and the typical sun form into uniform environments did not affect the characters exhibited in the wild state.

Atriplex (saltbush)—The species studied included a number of coastal forms characteristic of special localities. Transplanted individuals maintained their characters in cultivation in a uniform environment.

Hieracium umbellatum (hawkweed)—Within a single species there are several types characteristic of different ecological situations such as sand dunes, sandy fields, sea cliffs of the east (Baltic)

Fig. 6–7. See next page for legend.

and west (North Sea) Swedish coasts, and interior woodlands. Study indicated that varying coastal dune forms, each adapted to a single habitat type, have arisen independently from the adjacent inland stock.

Lysimachia (loosestrife)—Characters of what appear to be local populations were found to be modified by changing the environment and therefore were considered not to be genetic.

Independently at the laboratories of the Carnegie Institution of Washington (frontispiece and Fig. 6–7) in California, H. M. Hall used the two methods outlined above and, in addition, used reciprocal transplants (exchanging the habitats by transplanting related plants) and habitat inversion (leaving the plants in place but changing the environments). In his experiments Hall (1932; Hall, Keck, and Heusi [Hiesey], 1931) studied such characters as the following: (1) in *Solidago elongata* (a goldenrod), shade forms with compact panicles and sun forms with open large panicles; (2) in *Symphoricarpus albus* (snowberry), shade forms with broad, lobed leaves and sun forms with small, entire leaves; and (3) in *Hemizonia congesta* vars. *Clevelandii* and *luzulaefolia* (tarweeds), dry-soil forms with the flowering heads in spikes, wet-soil forms with the heads in panicles, and intermediate-soil forms with an intermediate type of inflorescence. Hall's successors (Clausen, 1951; Clausen, Keck, and Hiesey, 1939, 1940, 1941, 1945a, 1945b, 1947, 1948) have conducted numerous experiments along the same line (Figs. 6–8, 6–9) and have added new methods, in particular a correlation with cytological studies (see pp. 236–243).

SUMMARY

The neglect and relatively rare use of chemical characters in classification result from their intangibility and often the relative difficulty of their determination in large numbers of individuals. These characters are important in the adaptation of populations to their environments, and the difficulty of detecting and defining them is one of the greatest handicaps to classification. They offer a fertile

Fig. 6–7. Experimental taxonomic stations of the Carnegie Institution of Washington, Division of Plant Biology: (1) Mather, in the Sierran Montane Forest, 4,600 feet, north of Yosemite Valley, California; (2) Stanford University, about 150 feet. Portions of the same individual may be planted in each of these environments. See frontispiece for timber-line station, 10,000 feet, Sierra Nevada near Mount Conness, northwest of Tioga Pass. (From Jens Clausen, David D. Keck, and William M. Hiesey, Carnegie Institution of Washington Publication (520): 8, *Fig. 3*, 1940. Used by permission.)

field for investigation. A few recent studies are shining examples of the ways in which they may be used.

The characters of natural populations reflect the genetic makeup of the population, produced by selection in accordance with the environment of the present and of all the geological periods through which the living organisms have evolved. A significant change in ecological relationships at any time in the history of the organism might have produced a different modern population as a result of past natural selection. Thus past and present ecology determine in part the nature of natural plant or animal populations, and ecological data must be taken into account in consideration of classification of species and varieties.

Fig. 6–8. Modifications in plants grown from fragments of the same individual of *Potentilla glandulosa* subspecies *Hansenii* in the three stations of the Carnegie Institution of Washington shown in the frontispiece and in Fig. 6–7: (1) at timber line; (2) at Mather; (3) at Stanford. (From Jens Clausen, David D. Keck, and William M. Hiesey, Carnegie Institution of Washington Publication (520): 76, Fig. 23, 1940. Used by permission.)

Fig. 6–9. Modifications according to ecological conditions of plants grown from fragments of the same individual of Potentilla glandulosa var. glandulosa, as indicated. Plants grown at Mather (Fig. 6–7). (From Jens Clausen, David D. Keck, and William M. Hiesey, Carnegie Institution of Washington Publication (520): 65, Fig. 20, 1940. Used by permission.)

SUGGESTED READING

AMADON, DEAN. 1947.

ANDERSON, EDGAR. 1948.

———. 1949.

———, and BURTON R. ANDERSON. 1954.

———, and G. LEDYARD STEBBINS, JR. 1954. Discussion of the rate of evolution when a new or disturbed habitat becomes available, this making possible (1) survival of many hybrids and (2) much gene interchange between taxa.

BRYAN, E. H., JR. 1954. A readable account of the major features of natural history of the Hawaiian Islands.

CLAUSEN, JENS. The papers of Clausen and his associates, DAVID D. KECK and WILLIAM M. HIESEY, are of special importance. They follow up the independent pioneer work by H. M. HALL in America and by G. TURESSON in Sweden summed up as experimental studies on the nature of species. The Carnegie Institution of Washington, Division of Plant Biology, includes a lowland laboratory and garden and subsidiary stations at 4,600 and 10,000 feet elevation. Thus the relationsh'p of the plant to differing ecological conditions may be studied experimentally and may be correlated with physiological, genetic, cytological, and other factors. The authors have published many papers and books on their investigations. Some are listed below and in the list of references at the end of this book.

CLAUSEN, JENS. 1951.

———. 1954a.

———, DAVID D. KECK, and WILLIAM M. HIESEY. 1939.

———, DAVID D. KECK, and WILLIAM M. HIESEY. 1940.

———, DAVID D. KECK, and WILLIAM M. HIESEY. 1941.

———, DAVID D. KECK, and WILLIAM M. HIESEY. 1945a.

———, DAVID D. KECK, and WILLIAM M. HIESEY. 1945b.

———, DAVID D. KECK, and WILLIAM M. HIESEY. 1947.

———, DAVID D. KECK, and WILLIAM M. HIESEY. 1948.

CONSTANCE, LINCOLN. 1953. Attention is called to (1) genecology, experimental taxonomy, and biosystematy; (2) concepts of ecological classification units; (3) natural hybridization and introgression; and (4) ecological barriers to interbreeding and their effect upon ecological studies.

CRAMPTON, BEECHER. 1954. Correlation of morphological characters of species groups with restriction to specific habitats, particularly ephemeral vernal pools.

———. 1959. See above.

DAVIDSON, JOHN F. 1952. A plea for documentation of ecological work by herbarium specimens of the plants studied.

———, and T. L. THOMPSON. 1956.

EPLING, CARL. 1947.

———, and HARLAN LEWIS. 1952. (See LEWIS and EPLING, 1954.)

FRAENKEL, G. S. 1959.

GIBBS, R. DARNLEY. 1945. Significance in classification of nitrogenous anthocyanins, anthocyanins of tulips, and fatty acids and of special substances occurring in the Cupressaceae.

———. 1954.

GULICK, JOHN THOMAS. 1905. An excellent example of independent thought.

HALL, HARVEY MONROE. 1932. Description and summary of results of transplant studies designed to learn which characters are determined by heredity and which by environment.

HIESEY, WILLIAM M. 1953. Effect of various combinations of day and night temperatures upon clones of several species and ecological races under controlled conditions.

INGLES, LLOYD G., and NORMAND J. BIGLIONE. 1952. Study of two subspecies of pocket gophers occurring in contiguous ranges with different ecological conditions.

KRUCKEBERG, ARTHUR R. 1951. Analysis of the causes of edaphic restriction, the chemical basis of edaphic endemism, and the tolerance of some species for the low nutrient availability in serpentine soils.

———. 1954. See above.

———. 1957. See above. Study of the varying degrees of intersterility of members of the *Streptanthus glandulosus* complex probably due to depletion of biotypes or genetic races once occurring in intervening areas between the endemic populations now isolated in serpentine habitats.

LEWIS, HARLAN, and CARL EPLING. 1954. (See pp. 220–221, and EPLING and LEWIS, 1952.)

McMILLAN, CALVIN. 1959. The effect of selective influences in sorting out a combination of plant species, including the pygmy cypress, with unique qualities adapted to an extremely acid local soil condition.

MASON, HERBERT L. 1954. Evaluation of the effect of evolutionary diversification upon the ability of a species to migrate.

MAYR, ERNST. 1947. Discussion of (1) geographical isolation in all degrees from slight interference to complete stoppage of gene flow between species, (2) ecological races, and (3) sympatric speciation.

MIROV, N. T. 1938.

———. 1953.

———. 1954.

PEARSON, G. A. 1942.

RILEY, H. P. 1938. Study of ecologically separated species and of the hybrids occurring in disturbed areas.

———. 1952. Ecological barriers isolating taxa and their relationship to interbreeding.

SAUER, JONATHAN D. 1957. Consideration of evolution of a group of species in North America following human disturbance of habitats.

STEBBINS, G. LEDYARD, JR. 1952. The effect of xeric environments upon isolation of population systems and the rate of evolution.

———. 1959. The thesis that, for major advances to take place, a population with a high degree of genetic variability must occur in an environment which is changing rapidly and which offers the population new ecological niches into which some of its members can be adapted rapidly.

STONE, DONALD E. 1959. An unusual arrangement in which both self- and cross-fertilization occur in the same flower and in which inbreeding is assured but outbreeding occurs, especially under the more favorable circumstances of good growing seasons.

TURESSON, G. 1922a. The original proposal of ecospecies, ecotype, etc. as ecological-genetic units as opposed to traditional taxonomic categories (see CLAUSEN, KECK, and HIESEY, 1939; CONSTANCE, 1953). This and the following papers are a classic series presenting experimental ecological and genetic data in relationship to taxonomy.

———. 1922b. See above.

———. 1925. See above.

———. 1927. See above.

TURNER, B. L., and RALPH ALSTON. 1959.

VICKERY, ROBERT K., JR., and C. DWAYNE OGZEWALLA. 1958. A comparative study of the respiratory rates of closely related species and races.

WENT, F. W. 1948, 1949. Experimental study of seed germination in desert summer annuals, winter-germinating spring annuals, unrestricted plants, and shrubs (summer-germinating).

7

Data from Cytogenetics

CHROMOSOMES

Cytology, particularly a knowledge of chromosomes, may provide an insight into the method of origin of taxa. Two outstanding classical examples of the value of cytogenetics in revealing the underlying reasons for the existence of natural populations and of the problem of classifying them are the artificial synthesis of *Galeopsis Tetrahit* (Müntzing, 1930, 1932) and the synthesis of the potential new genus *"Raphanobrassica"* (Karpechenko, 1927, 1928), as described below.

The genus *Galeopsis* (mint family) includes well-known species with reduced chromosome numbers as follows: *Galeopsis pubescens,* 8; *Galeopsis speciosa,* 8; *Galeopsis Tetrahit,* 16. A cross usually does not yield fertile offspring, but one series which started with *pubescens* and *speciosa* resulted first in a triploid resembling *Galeopsis Tetrahit* (Fig. 7–1), then in a race of tetraploids ($4\times = 32$ chromosomes, 16 from each parental species). The new race was indistinguishable from *Galeopsis Tetrahit,* a species well known and recognized by many authors since the time of Linneaus. It crossed with natural *Galeopsis Tetrahit,* and in the offspring pairing of the chromosomes in meiosis was regular. Thus, the equivalent of a natural species was synthesized from two others, and the probable mode of origin of the species was established. Study of chromosomes and breeding experiments such as this show one method by which new species arise in nature.

Raphanobrassica was synthesized from two well-known genera of the mustard family, *Raphanus* (radish) and *Brassica* (the mustards, including cabbage). Both radishes and cabbages have nine chromosome pairs, but the nine pairs in one are not wholly similar to the nine in the other. Ordinarily the plants produce sterile hybrids, but in one instance meiosis failed to occur in the nearly sterile F_1 hybrid, and a fertile tetraploid was produced. Since this plant had two full sets of radish and two full sets of cabbage chromosomes, it was completely fertile. In meiosis every chromosome paired with a homologue, and normal sexual reproduction was possible.

1. Galeopsis   2. Galeopsis   3. F_2 Plant   4. Galeopsis
   pubescens   Tetrahit   speciosa

Fig. 7–1. The synthesis of *Galeopsis Tetrahit*, a tetraploid Linnaean species of mint, by hybridization of two related diploid species, as indicated. The triploid (3) has approximately the same characters as natural *Galeopsis Tetrahit* (2) and artificially produced tetraploid *Galeopsis Tetrahit*. (From Arne Müntzing, Hereditas 13: 291, *Fig. 90a*, 1930. Used by permission.)

In most species the number of chromosomes in the adult individual is diploid, but in the plant kingdom polyploidy is common. The most common polyploids are tetraploids. These may be formed in various ways, for example, by failure of meiosis to occur and consequent fertilization of diploid eggs by male gametes from diploid pollen. This occurs naturally, and it may be induced artificially by application of colchicine to the parts in which the reduction divisions take place. In some plants, such as certain members of the nightshade family, polyploidy has been induced by pruning followed by growth from callus tissue.

Ordinary autopolyploids or autoploids, such as autotetraploids, are formed by mere doubling of the chromosome numbers of the same species. More significant from an evolutionary point of view are allopolyploids or alloploids, which have chromosomes from different sources, that is, from more than one species. An allotetraploid [1] contains a full diploid complement of chromosomes from each of two chromosomally unlike parents, as in the classical example of *Raphanobrassica* above, where this produced a new combination of genetic factors and potentially a new genus. A similar combination may produce a new allotetraploid species within a genus, provided, of course, the new species occupies the proper ecological niche and continues to reproduce and maintain itself in competition. Polyploids may have high numbers of chromosomes, as, for example, in hexaploids ($6x$), octoploids ($8x$), or still higher polyploids ($10x$, $12x$, etc.).

In some instances the number of complements of chromosomes received from the two parents may be complex and even disproportionate (for hybridization of these species, see Figs. 4–5, 7–2, 7–3). Rollins (1944, 1945, 1946, 1949) has shown that in guayule plants (native in the Chihuahuan Desert in Texas and Mexico and cultivated for rubber) there may be several chromosome complements from one parent, guayule (*Parthenium argentatum*), combined with fewer sets of chromosomes of the related mariola (*Parthenium incanum*, widely distributed in the southwestern deserts). The characters of local populations vary according to the proportion of chromosome sets of the two species. Even the type specimen (original collection upon which application of the name *Parthenium argentatum* to the species was based) of guayule was from a local race which Rollins' studies have shown to include some chromosomes derived from mariola.

In many genera, chromosome numbers are variable. For example, in one entire line of development in a particular genus the basic chromosome number may be 7, in another 8, as in *Ranunculus* (Coonen, 1939). In *Crepis* the four basic numbers are 3, 4, 5, and 6 (Babcock, 1947). Members of the Crassulaceae (Uhl, 1956) have every gametic number from 4 to 38; *Echeveria* includes species with 12, 13, 15, 16, 17, 18, 19, 21, 22, 23, 24, 25, 26, 27, 28, 30, 32, 34, and up to more than 160.

In many genera, lines of evolution from species to species have been traced by means of chromosome numbers, for example, in *Clarkia*, a genus of attractive annuals restricted to the middle por-

---

[1] **Amphiploidy**, as defined by Clausen, Keck, and Hiesey (1945a), is applied to instances in which all the chromosomes of two species are included in an individual. **Allotetraploids** are the common example.

tions of western North America. Recently, Lewis (1951, 1953a, 1953b) and Lewis and Lewis (1955) with their students (e.g., Lewis and Roberts, 1956; Lewis and Raven, 1958a, 1958b; Raven and Lewis, 1959) have made a thorough taxonomic, cytological, and genetic study of this genus, submerging within *Clarkia* the long-standing genus *Godetia*, composed of species occurring in the same region and well known as garden plants. The distinction of these two groups of species as genera has long been considered a border-line case in classification, but most conservative authors have thought

Fig. 7–2. Hybridization of guayule and mariola: (1) guayule (*Parthenium argentatum*); (2) mariola (*Parthenium incanum*); (3) hybrid. (From Reed C. Rollins, American Journal of Botany 31: 94, *Fig. 1*, 1944. Used by permission.)

them to be separate, though obviously closely related. According to the evidence of Lewis and Lewis, the generic distinction of *Godetia* is not warranted. To a considerable extent, this conclusion rests upon chromosome numbers and morphology correlated with external characters and, in some cases, with breeding experiments. Seven species groups are recognized among the diploid species, these differing by morphological characters and, in some cases, by gross differences in the chromosomes. These groups taken by themselves are well defined, but in several instances there are connecting

links, that is, groups of intermediate species. These are allopolyploids, in each case derived from the diploid groups or lower polyploid
groups. The combined evidence from gross morphology, numbers,
and morphology of chromosomes, together with the demonstrable
origin of the allopolyploid groups, shows that *Clarkia* is composed
of diverse species groups knit by alloploidy into a reticulum (net-

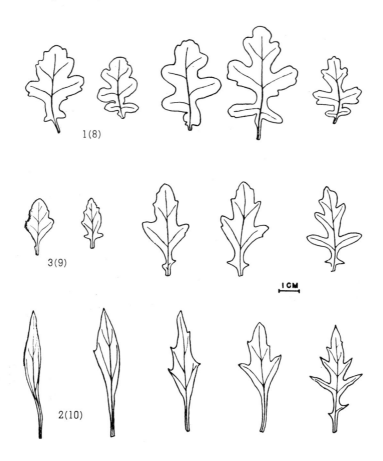

Fig. 7–3. Hybridization of guayule (*Parthenium argentatum*) and mariola
(*Parthenium incanum*): leaves indicating the range of variation among plants of
(1) mariola, (2) guayule, and (3) interspecific hybrids (numbers in parentheses
used by the original author). (From Reed C, Rollins, American Journal of Botany
31: 95, *Figs. 8–10,* 1944. Used by permission.)

work) of interrelationships and that there is no logical line of demarcation between *Clarkia* and *Godetia* as genera.

Lewis predicted, on the basis of its morphology and chromosomes, that the common *Clarkia rhomboidea* would be determined
to be an allotetraploid. Both morphological similarity and chromosome behavior indicated that *Clarkia virgata* was one of the parents.
A morphological description of the other unknown parent was drawn
up, and it was thought to have a basic haploid chromosome number
of 7. Later, specimens of a localized species, described much earlier
by Heller as *Phaestoma Mildredae* (now transferred to *Clarkia*),
were found to correspond with the description. Living material
revealed the reduced chromosome number to be 7 and subsequently
the relationship to *Clarkia rhomboidea* was demonstrated.

In *Clarkia* about two-thirds of the diploid species have 8 or 9
chromosome pairs. In the cases studied, the sets of 8 or 9 are due
to the addition of whole chromosomes to the supposed basic number,
7, as, for example, in the local species *Clarkia lingulata* (9) as opposed to the related *Clarkia biloba* (8). The basic number, 7, for
the genus is indicated by correlation with morphological and ecological characters in *Clarkia* and by the relationship to *Oenothera*
(evening primrose).

Seven species with the original reduced chromosome number of
7 occur from British Columbia to central California, chiefly in the
relatively moist areas of forests and in the ecotone between conifer-
ous forests and oak woodland. The three with 8 chromosome pairs
are restricted to drier areas in the oak woodland of the interior of
central California. The twelve with 9 chromosome pairs are restricted to still drier habitats from the margins of the San Joaquin
Valley to southern California. This suggests that the original group
of species ($x = 7$) was adapted to the more moist situations in the
forests occurring in Miocene times from the latitude of San Francisco northward and that, in general, the later-developed ones have
been adapted to the host of more xeric habitats derived from the
oak woodland (Sierra Madrean Flora) since Miocene time (see
pp. 183–186).

In *Clarkia*, differentiation of new character combinations which
may lead ultimately to speciation often occur rapidly. Adjacent
populations often may be intersterile but structurally similar while
others are morphologically different but interfertile. Probably most
of the genetically isolated populations are of short duration, but
doubtless a few are successful and persistent, becoming differentiated gradually into geographical races and ultimately into species.

The success of this genus appears to be due to the presence of innumerable locally adapted, genetically isolated, often (but not necessarily) ephemeral populations, some one or more of which may be adaptable to any change of conditions.

Chromosome numbers may vary not only among the species of a genus but also among the individuals composing a species or one of its segments. Consequently, the assumption that a count of the chromosomes of one individual represents the number for the species is not necessarily valid. The following are examples:

As was reported by Kruckeberg (1956), seven collections of *Phacelia frigida,* as was shown in initial studies by Cave and Constance, were tetraploids, but of four collections of the same species studied later by Kruckeberg only one was a tetraploid and three were hexaploids. The four cases studied by Kruckeberg were not localized; they were collected through an area several hundred miles long.

In 1952, at Blewett Pass in central Washington, Kruckeberg studied *Phacelia leucophylla* (tetraploid) and *Phacelia leptosepala* (hexaploid), which were sympatric and apparently isolated by the nature of their polyploidy. In 1953, in the same general area, further study of ten plants, all clearly of one species or the other, revealed only hexaploids.

Ward (1953, especially pp. 199–204) has summarized extensive studies on the chromosome numbers of the species of sagebrush. *Artemisia tridentata,* described earlier as having a gametic number of 18 chromosomes, was found to include diploid and tetraploid races based upon a fundamental number of 9. Analysis of morphological characters by the polygonal graph method (see pp. 121–124 and Fig. 3–54) shows the chromosomal races to have the same character pattern. Chromosome number in this species does not seem to be correlated with any possible segregation of taxonomic groups.

According to Uhl (1956), the seven species of *Sedum* native in the eastern United States include five with heteroploid races (that is, races variable in chromosome numbers), the other two species being rare and more or less uniform endemics. Two species have diploid, tetraploid, and hexaploid races; one has races with gametic numbers of 11 and 18; and another has races with gametic numbers of 14, 22, and 28. The species of *Sedum* occurring in the western United States and in Europe appear to present the same types of complications. Study by Uhl (1961) of more than 500 species of Crassulaceae shows that variation of chromosome numbers within species is rather frequent.

APPLICATION OF THE LAWS OF HEREDITY

Ideally, all cytological and genetic phases of the plants or animals to be classified should be investigated, that is, each organism should be at least as well understood as the vinegar fly (*Drosophila melanogaster*) or maize (*Zea Mays*, the Indian corn of America).

Although cytogenetic data comparable to those for the vinegar fly or maize can be brought together for relatively few species, the laws of heredity may be applied in simpler ways, and the principles resulting from experimentation with one group may be applied, with caution, to the study of another. Examples of application of the background material of genetics to classification have appeared all through this series of chapters.

Two modes of inheritance are particularly to be kept in mind in assessing the features which are seen most frequently in studying plants in the field and the herbarium. These are factor pairs with no (or incomplete) dominance and factor pairs with simple dominance.

Factor Pairs with No (or Incomplete) Dominance. A classical example of simple inheritance not involving complete dominance is determination of flower color in four-o'clock plants. The genes yielding red or white produce one or the other of these colors in the homozygous condition but pink in the heterozygous. This may be explained on the basis of neither gene being dominant or of that yielding red being *incompletely dominant* to that yielding white (lack of pigmentation). Crossing of a red-flowered plant with a white-flowered one yields the results shown in Fig. 7A for the F_1 and F_2 generations (a gene yielding red being incompletely dominant but being indicated, nevertheless, by a capital *R*, and white by a small *r*).

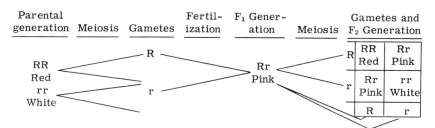

Fig. 7A. Diagram representing a cross of four o'clock plants involving one pair of genes. Neither gene is completely dominant. Gene A tends to produce red color in the flowers, a to produce white. The combination Aa is an intermediate pink.

As shown by the diagram (Fig. 7A), the F_1 generation is composed of intermediate heterozygous plants, having some red pigmentation but not as much as the homozygous red parent. The F_2 generation is composed of red, pink, and white individuals in the approximate ratio of 1:2:1.

The most frequent mode of inheritance of the characters distinguishing species is similar to that above, but with several pairs of genes affecting the same characteristic (or series of characteristics). In all pairs there is incomplete dominance. This is known as *multiple-factor inheritance.*

Classic examples of multiple-factor inheritance were reported by Nilsson-Ehle (1911), who studied crosses of various varieties of wheat. Crossing of one very dark red strain with a white strain yielded an intermediate shade of red. The F_2 generation included grains ranging from very dark red to white, with only about 1 individual in 16 of either extreme. There were three intermediate shades, dark red, intermediate red, and light red. The series of crosses was explained as is shown in Fig. 7B.

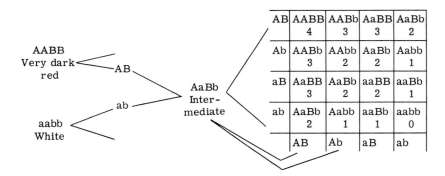

Fig. 7B. Diagram representing a cross of strains of wheat involving two pairs of genes. Dominance is incomplete in both pairs, and the contributions of genes A and B are about equal. The degree of red pigmentation of the grains ranges from O (aabb, white) to 4 (AABB, very dark red).

In the F_2 generation from the crosses in Fig. 7B, the number of factors tending to produce red ranges in various individuals from zero to four, as indicated in the squares. The concentration of pigment in the wheat grain is proportional (Table 7–1).

Crossing of another strain of very dark red wheat with the same white resulted in additional shades in the F_2 generation and only one of either extreme in about 64 individuals. This was explained as follows on the basis of three interacting pairs of genes with incomplete dominance (Fig. 7C).

TABLE 7–1

Degrees of Color Intensity in Strains of Wheat Involving Two Pairs of Genes

These genes contribute toward red pigmentation or lack of it in the grain.
Complete dominance is not involved.

No. of Genes Tending To Yield Red	Color Intensity	No. of Individuals in 16
0	None (white)	1
1	Light red	4
2	Intermediate red	6
3	Dark red	4
4	Very dark red	1

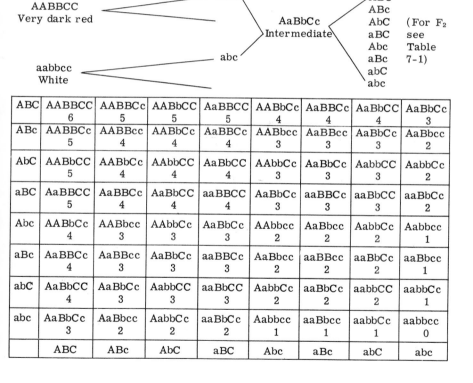

	ABC	ABc	AbC	aBC	Abc	aBc	abC	abc
ABC	AABBCC 6	AABBCc 5	AABbCC 5	AaBBCC 5	AABbCc 4	AaBBCc 4	AaBbCC 4	AaBbCc 3
ABc	AABBCc 5	AABBcc 4	AABbCc 4	AaBBCc 4	AABbcc 3	AaBBcc 3	AaBbCc 3	AaBbcc 2
AbC	AABbCC 5	AABbCc 4	AAbbCC 4	AaBbCC 4	AAbbCc 3	AaBbCc 3	AabbCC 3	AabbCc 2
aBC	AaBBCC 5	AaBBCc 4	AaBbCC 4	aaBBCC 4	AaBbCc 3	aaBBCc 3	aaBbCC 3	aaBbCc 2
Abc	AABbCc 4	AABbcc 3	AAbbCc 3	AaBbCc 3	AAbbcc 2	AaBbcc 2	AabbCc 2	Aabbcc 1
aBc	AaBBCc 4	AaBBcc 3	AaBbCc 3	aaBBCc 3	AaBbcc 2	aaBBcc 2	aaBbCc 2	aaBbcc 1
abC	AaBbCC 4	AaBbCc 3	AabbCC 3	aaBbCC 3	AabbCc 2	aaBbCc 2	aabbCC 2	aabbCc 1
abc	AaBbCc 3	AaBbcc 2	AabbCc 2	aaBbCc 2	Aabbcc 1	aaBbcc 1	aabbCc 1	aabbcc 0
	ABC	ABc	AbC	aBC	Abc	aBc	abC	abc

Fig. 7C. Diagram representing a cross of strains of wheat involving three pairs of genes. Dominance is incomplete in all pairs, and the contributions of genes A, B, and C are about equal. The degree of red pigmentation of the grains ranges from O (aabbcc, white) to 6 (AABBCC, very dark red).

In the F_2 generation from the crosses above, the number of factors tending to produce red ranges from zero to six per individual. The concentration of pigment in the wheat grain is proportional (Table 7–2).

TABLE 7–2

Degrees of Color Intensity in Strains of Wheat Involving Three Pairs of Genes

These genes contribute toward red pigmentation or lack of it in the grain.
Complete dominance is not involved.

No. of Genes Tending To Yield Red	Color Intensity	No. of Individuals in 64
0	None (white)	1
1	Very light red	6
2	Lighter red	15
3	Intermediate red	20
4	Darker red	15
5	Still darker red	6
6	Darkest red	1

As the number of pairs of interacting factors with incomplete dominance increases, the number of intermediate degrees becomes gradually greater, and the number of individuals representing either extreme approaches zero (Table 7–3).

TABLE 7–3

Interaction of Various Numbers of Factor Pairs Affecting the Same Genetic Characteristic, When Complete Dominance Is Not Involved and When the Effects of Genes in Different Pairs Are Essentially Equal

No. of Factor Pairs	No. of F_1 Gamete Types	No. of Rectangles in Chart Depicting the F_2	No. of Intermediate Degrees	Proportionate No. of Either Extreme in F_2
1	2	4	1	1:4
2	4	16	3	1:16
3	8	64	5	1:64
4	16	256	7	1:256
5	32	1024	9	1:1024
6	64	4096	11	1:4096
7	128	16384	13	1:16384
The preceding number in this series plus 1	Double the number directly above	Square of the number in the next column left	The preceding number in this series plus 2	1 over the number in the middle column

The number of pairs of factors operating may be estimated by analysis of the F_2 population to determine the proportional occurrence of the extremes (such as, with wheat, white or the darkest red). If, for example, only about 1 grain in 1,000 is white or very dark red, probably five pairs of factors are involved. Analysis of characters of this type becomes difficult as the number of factor pairs increases, because the number of degrees of intermediacy becomes greater and the distinction between degrees less. All quantitative features may be altered by the environment. Consequently, it becomes increasingly difficult to distinguish between degrees or even to be sure that the supposed extremes are not the next steps approaching them.

Such factors as color, length and breadth of organs (such as leaves or petals), height of the plant, or diameter of the stem or fruit are inherited usually in the mode described above (see *Ranunculus ambigens* and *Ranunculus Lingua*—Figs. 2–7, 2–8). The proportions of organs may be altered by different sets of genes affecting the length and the breadth (or diameter). Thus, the marked difference in the appearance of flowers of related species may be due to variation in the effects of groups of factors controlling the length and breadth of various parts, including the petals.

In general, the leaves of *Quercus Engelmannii* (Figs. 3–3, 3–48) are longer and proportionately narrower than those of *Quercus dumosa,* but these features are variable in both species. Even where there has been no interbreeding, there is some overlapping in measurement of length and of breadth. These two measurements vary within the species, and the proportion of length to breadth also varies from individual to individual. Despite strong general tendencies, this makes specific statements concerning these characters subject to many exceptions.

Factor Pairs with Simple Dominance. This is the mode of inheritance commonly discussed in detail in elementary textbooks of general biology or of botany. A single pair of factors with a dominant and a recessive yields the familiar 3:1 ratio of phenotypes in the F_2 generation. Two pairs of factors yield 9:3:3:1, and three pairs yield 27:9:9:9:3:3:3:1.

This type of inheritance is relatively much less common in the distinction of species than is multiple-factor inheritance expressed in a series of intermediate stages. The mode of inheritance of any character can be determined with certainty only by breeding experiments. A series or a blend of intermediate types, however, indicates the probability of multiple factors without complete dominance.

Lack of intermediate types between the extremes points toward factor pairs with simple dominance.

A system of populations frequently is composed of plants with one character or a group of characters occurring uniformly through a large part of its geographical range, but this character or set of characters is lacking or is replaced by another in many but not all individuals in a different area, and it may or may not be wholly replaced in still another area. If there are no plants with intermediate characters, some investigators will accord both natural groups a recognized taxonomic rank—either as species, subspecies, varieties, or forms; other investigators will consider them to be minor forms, worthy of mention but not of formal names as taxa. Classification depends in part upon the extent to which such populations or population systems are self-perpetuating entities and upon their relative distinctness (isolation) from their close relatives. The ease with which these points can be determined is related to the number of genetic factor pairs in which the plants differ (assuming dominance and no linkage).

Wherever geographical or other factors permit interbreeding, the F_1 and F_2 generations from parents differing in a single pair of factors, and the individuals resulting from backcrosses to either parent (in cases of such close relationship), probably can be distinguished only through their progeny. When the natural populations differ in a single factor pair with complete dominance, cross-breeding can not be detected with certainty by observation alone. This is because genotypes AA and Aa both yield the dominant character (only aa expressing the recessive). If in a given area factors A and a are equally abundant, the population will be composed of genotypes AA, Aa, and aa in a ratio of 1:2:1, but, except for occurrence of the two phenotypes side by side, there will be no evidence of interbreeding. Although two-thirds of the individuals with the dominant phenotype are heterozygous, they may appear to constitute a nonvariable unit.

As the number of differing pairs of factors increases, the probability of detection of heterozygous individuals by character recombinations increases. At least one character commonly marking one population system is likely to occur in combination with a character normally identifying the other. This emphasizes the importance of depending upon more than a single pair of opposed dominant and recessive genetic factors for distinguishing natural populations.

Complicating factors include (1) linkage of genes, the occurrence of more than one factor pair in the same chromosome pair; (2) multiple alleles, any two of several kinds of genes forming the members of a pair, as in the factors determining eye color of the vinegar fly, where either of the two paired genes may yield red, wine, coral, blood, cherry, apricot, eosin, ivory, buff, tinged, ecru, or white, dominance of one over another being in the order named; (3) interaction of two or more pairs of dominant and recessive factors, **AABB** yielding a result different from any other combination (as in chickens **AABB** is walnut comb, **AAbb** is rose comb, **aaBB** is pea comb, and **aabb** is plain comb) or yielding a result similar to that of one of the dominants alone but not of the other; and (4) lethal factors, which result in death of the individuals having certain gene combinations. Each of these phenomena may affect the apparent degree of genetic similarity or dissimilarity of population systems and their apparent degree of intergradation. They may underlie the occasional appearance of unusual characters.

DETECTION OF HYBRIDS

The occurrence of hybrid individuals or of hybrid swarms is significant not only in delimitation of taxa but also in interpretation of taxa described and named in the botanical literature. For example, *Opuntia compressa* (Figs. 3–14, 3–15, 3–16) has been named many times, and some of the specimens upon which names were based were derived from populations probably (but not proved to be) of hybrid origin. The list of names applied to this species or its putative hybrids includes: *Opuntia vulgaris, Opuntia Opuntia, Opuntia humifusa, Opuntia mesacantha, Opuntia cespitosa, Opuntia Rafinesquei, Opuntia intermedia, Opuntia prostrata, Opuntia fusco-atra, Opuntia macrarthra, Opuntia Allairei, Opuntia xanthoglochia, Opuntia memoralis, Opuntia sanguinocula, Opuntia Youngii,* and *Opuntia MacAteei.* The related *Opuntia macrorhiza* (or *Opuntia compressa* var. *macrorhiza*) appears in botanical literature as *Opuntia setispina, Opuntia tortispina, Opuntia cymochila, Opuntia fusiformis, Opuntia tenuispina, Opuntia filipendula, Opuntia Greenei, Opuntia oplocarpa, Opuntia plumbea, Opuntia Roseana, Opuntia Ballii, Opuntia Mackensenii, Opuntia delicata, Opuntia seguina,* and *Opuntia Loomisii.*

As the long lists of synonymous scientific names indicate, attempts in books and papers on the cacti to segregate hybrid individuals from their relatives have led to a muddle which would be hopeless if the basic nature of the problem were not understood. This multiplication of names for a single species is due primarily to the lack of a comprehensive study of the natural population systems composing the species as a whole. There has been neither a clear understanding of all the elements to be included nor much knowledge of their intergradation with other species. Even the total geographical ranges of the species have not been understood until recently.

The proposed scientific names are not to be thrown lightly aside. The plants upon which each was based must be considered carefully, and, if possible, plants similar to each should be tested to determine the question of hybrid origin and an unstable genotype. The following summary of some of the simpler practical tests includes (1) tests of chromosome synapsis and pollen and seed viability, (2) progeny tests, and (3) controlled breeding.

Tests of Chromosome Synapsis and Pollen and Seed Viability. If interbreeding is between well-segregated populations usually separated by genetic and especially cytological isolating mechanisms, a study of the chromosome synapsis and segregation at meiosis may reveal the hybrid character of some individuals, particularly of those intermediate between supposed parents or with recombinations of characters. This may be detected more simply by study of the pollen grains to determine the relative abundance of well-filled grains as opposed to abortive ("empty") ones (Fig. 7–4). If, for example, more than half the pollen grains are abortive, probably something is amiss with the meiotic process preceding pollen-grain formation. The setting of seed is a less reliable criterion because it depends upon a longer chain of events and circumstances—meiosis, development of the megagametophyte, pollination, pollen germination and growth of the tube for the required distance, compatibility of the pollen with the pistil or the megagametophyte or the endosperm, fertilization, and development of the embryo—as opposed to merely meiosis and development of the microgametophyte. Thus a greater number of factors, including physiological ones, may affect seed set than pollen development. In instances like those of the oaks used as examples in Chapter 3, these methods usually are not applicable, because most oaks within such broad groups as the white oaks or the black oaks are not segregated effectively by genetic or cytological isolating mechanisms.

Progeny Tests. The degree of genetic stability of a plant, that is, its relative approach to homozygosity and the ability to breed true, may be tested simply by growing many seeds from the same individual and comparing the characters of the seedlings.

In 1810, Michaux gave the name *Quercus heterophylla* to a plant discovered by Bartram [Fig. 7–5 (1)]. Similar individuals are not uncommon in the area in which the ranges of the following two well-known species overlap:

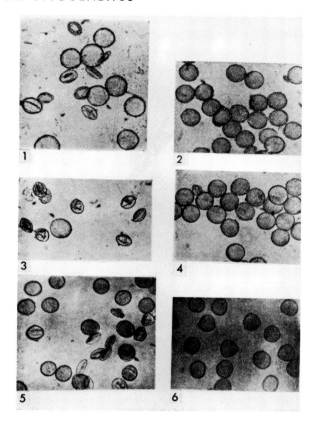

Fig. 7–4. Viable and sterile pollen grains from some species hybrids and their parents: (1) F_1 hybrid of *Galeopsis Tetrahit* × *Galeopsis bifida;* (2) *Galeopsis Tetrahit;* (3) F_1 hybrid, *Galeopsis pubescens* × *Galeopsis speciosa;* (4) *Galeopsis speciosa;* (5) hybrid, *Galeopsis ochroleuca* × *Galeopsis pyrenaica;* (6) *Galeopsis ochroleuca.* The hybrids (1), (3), (5) have some viable and some sterile pollen grains, these being readily distinguished. (From Arne Müntzing, Hereditas 13: 280, *Figs. 58–63,* 1930. Used by permission.)

Quercus Phellos (the willow oak) [Fig. 7–5 (2)], occurring from southeastern Missouri and eastern Texas to the Gulf and Atlantic coasts, as far northward as Long Island.

Quercus rubra (the red oak) [Fig. 3–6 (1)], occurring in upland or dry woods from southern Minnesota and eastern Nebraska to southern Quebec, Prince Edward Island, Oklahoma, and Georgia.

The possible hybrid nature of the Bartram oak was debated for nearly a century. Finally, MacDougal (1907) grew 55 seedlings from acorns of a Bartram oak, and these included individuals ranging

Fig. 7–5. See next page for legend.

in character combinations from those of the willow oak to those of the red oak. Similarly, Wolf (1938) grew about 900 seedlings propagated from four individuals of the "oracle oak" (see pp. 85–88 and Fig. 3–25). Some of these plants resembled the interior live oak, some of the black oak, and some the "oracle oak"; others were intermediate. Seedlings found growing under a few "oracle oak" trees displayed about the same variation as those grown in the garden.

Allard (1932) investigated hybrid individuals of the white oak group including those thought to result from interbreeding of the white oak (*Quercus alba*) [Fig. 3–6 (2)] and the chestnut oak (*Quercus Prinus* [*montana*]) (Fig. 7–6), growing in the vicinity of Washington, D.C. These had been named *Quercus Saulii*. He grew about 40 seedlings from a tree on Pershing Drive near Maryland Avenue, Ashton Heights, Clarendon (Arlington), Virginia. Among the progeny, the characters of *Quercus alba* were somewhat less abundant than those of *Quercus Prinus*, but there was considerable variation in character combinations of the white oak and the chestnut oak. In autumn, the leaves of the white oak become coppery red, those of the chestnut oak a deep red-brown. Both types appeared among the progeny of the tree on Pershing Drive. Other plants had yellow leaves not tinted by anthocyanins. One individual, obviously of the *Quercus alba* type, had deep red leaves unusual for any white oak; these were promptly deciduous, like those of the chestnut oak. Another plant having the leaf structure and the deep red-brown color of the chestnut oak held its leaves like the white oak. Although pollination of the pistils of the tree producing the 40 seeds was not controlled, certainly its offspring did not produce a nearly uniform population which could be considered to constitute a species or a variety, and there is little doubt that the tree was highly heterozygous.

Allard (1949) used the characters of even very young seedlings to determine the hybrid nature of their parents. His measurements of the mean total number of lateral lobes per leaf in seedlings dis-

Fig. 7–5. Hybridization of eastern black oaks: (1) the Bartram oak, a classical hybrid described as *Quercus heterophylla*, actually produced sporadically by interbreeding of the willow oak (*Quercus Phellos*) and the red oak (*Quercus rubra*), occurring where the ranges of these two species overlap on the inner portions of the Gulf and Atlantic coastal plains. (From André Michaux, North American Silva 1: 64, Pl. 18, following p. 64, 1810.) (2) willow oak (Jacksonville, Florida); (3) Shumard red oak (*Quercus Shumardii*) (Wayne County, West Virginia); (4) hybrid (Moulton, Alabama).

Fig. 7–6. Hybridization of eastern white oaks—the white oak (*Quercus alba*)
[Fig. 3–6 (2)] and the chestnut oak (*Quercus Prinus*): (1) chestnut oak (Ithaca,
New York); (2) hybrid (Biltmore, North Carolina).

tinguished clearly plants of the white and the chestnut oak types and intermediate forms. This character tended to be correlated with the pubescence on the undersides of the leaves.

Not understanding the nature of the hybrid swarms of *Quercus dumosa* and *Quercus Engelmannii* (see pp. 57, 83–85, 92, 117–118), botanists have named two of the hybrid types as supposedly distinct taxa, *Quercus dumosa* var. *elegantula* and *Quercus grandidentata*. The form commonly interpreted as var. *elegantula* is common in the hybrid swarms (Fig. 7–7; but note the lectotype specimen of var.

Fig. 7–7. The Hybrid oak known as *Quercus dumosa* var. *elegantula*, a form common in hybrid swarms of the scrub oak (*Quercus dumosa*) and the Engelmann oak (*Quercus Engelmannii*) (specimen from Claremont, California). Actually, the epithet *elegantula* is misapplied (cf. Fig. 12–5), and its nomenclatural combinations are synonyms of *Quercus Engelmannii*.

elegantula, Fig. 12–3). *Quercus grandidentata* is known from only three collections. With some difficulty, the type plant (originally named individual) of *Quercus grandidentata* (Fig. 7–8) was located in the hybrid swarm in Monrovia Canyon by students in classes at Pomona College. In 1949 Avery H. Gallup planted seeds from the type tree, and in 1951 Donald H. Ford planted additional seeds. In both groups of seedlings no two were alike. Individuals ranged in leaf characters from those resembling *Quercus dumosa* to those resembling *Quercus Engelmannii*, and none displayed the characters of the female parent either in the juvenile foliage after three months or in the adult foliage after nearly ten years (Fig. 7–9).

Fig. 7–8. The type individual of the plants described as *Quercus grandidentata*, at Monrovia, California: (1) arborescent plant about 15 feet tall, spreading over about 25 feet; (2) branch, with leaves peculiar to this and two other individuals once growing in Pasadena and Glendora, and with acorns.

Fig. 7–9. Progeny test of *Quercus grandidentata*: (1) the two leaves at the left from the type individual (Fig. 7–8), each of the others from a seedling grown from its acorns, the leaves taken in January, 1951, when the seedlings were three months old; (2) a twig from each of the surviving individuals represented in (1), taken in 1960 when the seedlings were nearly ten years old. The seedling plants showed at both times character combinations ranging from those of the scrub oak (*Quercus dumosa*) to those of the Engelmann oak (*Quercus Engelmannii*). Pollination was not controlled, but clearly the individual named *Quercus grandidentata* is highly heterozygous, and it cannot maintain itself through genetic isolation as a natural species.

257

This incomplete evidence suggests that *Quercus grandidentata* is a hybrid with an unusual phenotype insofar as leaf indentation is concerned and that it is not a species capable of maintaining itself through even a second generation.

Although the progeny test indicates the validity of the postulate that *Quercus grandidentata* is a hybrid derived from *Quercus dumosa* and *Quercus Engelmannii*, further proof is needed. The weakness of the progeny test is that, although the female parentage is common to all the seedlings, the male parentage of the seedlings may vary according to uncontrolled pollination.

Controlled Breeding. The solution to the problem above is controlled breeding experiments. Hand pollination and bagging of the pistillate flowers of the tree at Monrovia Canyon would yield acorns of known single parentage, provided there were no factors making the plant self-sterile.

Quercus grandidentata might be synthesized by controlled cross-breeding of other oaks in the region, starting with either *Quercus dumosa* and *Quercus Engelmannii* from areas where they do not intergrade, or with hybrids in the swarm surrounding *Quercus grandidentata*. However, this would be difficult, long-drawn-out, and uncertain of results.

Observation of the hybrid swarm indicates that only one character of *Quercus grandidentata* is missing among the surrounding plants—the peculiar lobing of the leaves. If this were due to a rare dominant gene, it should have shown up in the offspring grown so far. Controlled breeding experiments with *Quercus grandidentata* might or might not indicate this to be a recessive trait covered up in its relatively rare occurrence in even the heterozygous state and revealed only when (even more rarely) it is homozygous, as in the single tree at Monrovia and two others formerly at Pasadena and Glendora. Although none of 30 progeny of the original tree has possessed the character, some progeny should have been expected to display it unless the tree were self-sterile.

Leach (1959) studied a colony of *Rhododendron Furbishii*, an azalea growing in Vogel State Park at Neel Gap, Georgia. This colony of about 100 plants had been discovered in 1934 and named as a species. Leach suspected the plants might have arisen as early-generation hybrids between *Rhododendron arborescens* and *Rhododendron Bakeri*, and he crossed representatives of these two species under controlled conditions. According to Leach, if the six-year-old plants were added to the colony in Vogel State Park, no botanist would be able to distinguish them from the indigenous population.

Rhododendron Furbishii and the known hybrids bloom at the same time and resemble each other in nearly all characteristics.

Leach obtained in Georgia seeds from self-pollinated wild plants of *Rhododendron Furbishii*. If the plants of this group had been isolated in nature for a considerable period and inbred through a number of generations, they should have been expected to have become more and more alike. Under these circumstances each generation tends to become a near duplicate of the preceding one, and ultimately a stable species may evolve through elimination of some genetic combinations and stabilization of others. On the other hand, early-generation hybrids may be expected to be highly heterozygous, therefore not to breed true. The offspring of plants of *Rhododendron Furbishii* produced a wide range of character combinations, and some of the characteristics of *Rhododendron arborescens* and *Rhododendron Bakeri* appeared among the seedlings in the classic segregating proportions, such as the well-known 3:1 ratio. Floral color ranged from the red of *Bakeri* to the white of *arborescens*, with larger numbers of intermediate pinks.

Thus, by relatively simple breeding experiments, the status of some proposed species can be determined and the classification of plants within the limits of species or as hybrids between them may be established.

APOMIXIS

In the plant kingdom asexual reproduction occurs in many forms. The term *apomixis* indicates any kind of asexual reproduction with a tendency to be a substitute for sexual reproduction.

Types of Apomixis. Apomixis includes vegetation reproduction, provided it is accompanied by inactivity or disappearance of the normal sexual reproductive processes, or agamospermy, reproduction by formation of seeds without the usual chromosome cycle of reduction divisions and fertilization (Gustafsson, 1946, 1947).

VEGETATIVE REPRODUCTION AND APOMIXIS. Non-apomictic vegetative reproduction is represented by the following examples:

In many parts of North America, in the lower portions of Little Dalton Canyon above Glendora, California, for example, there are colonies of the bracken or brake, *Pteridium aquilinum*. This is a species of large fern common through much of the moist areas of the earth and represented in this area by var. *pubescens*. In the 16 years during which the colonies near Glendora have been visited annually, no sporangia have been found. Failure to develop spores following reduction divisions prohibits formation of gametophytes and occurrence of sexual reproduction. Nevertheless, as long as conditions are favorable, the species may not only maintain itself but also may spread slowly into new ground by growth of the rhizomes.

Another example is vegetative reproduction of prickly pears and chollas (*Opuntia*) by dropping and rooting of stem joints (Fig. 7–10). Asexual reproduction is common among prickly pears, as in probable hybrid swarms of *Opuntia Engelmannii* and *Opuntia*

Fig. 7–10. Vegetative reproduction of the teddy bear cholla (*Opuntia Bigelovii*), each of the young plants having resulted from rooting of a small branch which fell from one of the parent plants (near Aguila, Arizona).

phaeacantha var. *major* occurring from Arizona to western Texas, and any form may be perpetuated as a minor race, whether its chromosome complement and other factors would permit sexual reproduction or not. The wealth of forms occurring on a single hillside or flat is perplexing unless it is accounted for by perpetuation of the offspring of many crosses. The mechanism of apomixis produces the same fundamental results as ordinary asexual reproduction.

A form of apomictic vegetative reproduction occurring in the cactus family is exemplified by two species of chollas, *Opuntia prolifera,* a species native near the coast in southern California and Baja California, and *Opuntia fulgida* (Fig. 7–11), the jumping cholla, a

Fig. 7–11. Apomixis in the jumping cholla (*Opuntia fulgida*): (1) a jumping cholla about 10 feet high and with a spread of 15 feet; (2) chains of fruits formed by growth of flower buds from the areoles of the persistent, usually sterile fruits of preceding seasons. Some of the fruits eventually fall to the ground, root, and form new plants as do fallen vegetative branches (east of Apache Junction, Arizona).

common species of the Arizona Desert. In these plants, the inferior ovary is enveloped by and adnate to the lower portion of the floral cup, which is formed by an upgrowth of the margins of the receptacle (a hypanthium). Like the vegetative stem below it, the hypanthium has areoles, or small nodal specialized areas bearing clusters of spines, each areole having been developed from the bud in the axil of an ephemeral leaf. The fruit is sterile, and during the next season new flowers may grow from one or more of the areoles. Each of these flowers ultimately produces a sterile fruit. This may continue in *Opuntia fulgida* for an indefinite number of years until the fruits occur in long branched drooping chains. Reproduction of the plant is not only strictly vegetative by rooting and budding of the readily detached vegetative branches but also apomictic through rooting of dislodged sterile fruits.

These vegetative and apomictic forms of reproduction are responsible for maintaining, even in overlapping geographical ranges, two forms or varieties of *Opuntia fulgida,* known tentatively as var. *fulgida* and var. *mammillata.* These are clearly distinct from each other, but they may or may not be considered as taxa worthy of formal scientific names, because, although isolation is complete, the differences are few and are matters of degree and isolation may be uncertain and transitory.

The constancy of apomictic minor forms of species is illustrated by other chollas and by the prickly pears of the cactus family. For example, probable hybrids (Peebles in Kearney and Peebles, 1942, p. 616; 1951, p. 585) between the jumping cholla (*Opuntia fulgida*) and a staghorn cholla *Opuntia spinosior* (Fig. 7–12) occur for several miles along the Gila River in Arizona. There is no known reproduction by seeds, only by vegetative branches and by the somewhat proliferous sterile fruits, as in *Opuntia fulgida.*

AGAMOSPERMY. Agamospermy includes instances, like those in some species of citrus fruits, such as *Citrus Hystrix, Citrus Unshii,* and *Citrus Daidai,* in which one or more false embryos may develop directly from the non-haploid tissues of the ovule—either the nucellus (sporangium) or the integument (ultimately the seed coat). This results in a wholly diploid (or polyploid) life cycle with neither reduction divisions nor fertilization. This is usually caused by either of two phenomena which lead to omission of meiosis. One is formation without reduction divisions of a "megagametophyte," including an "egg," directly from a cell of the nucellus. The other is formation of the megagametophyte from the sporogenous tissue which normally gives rise to it, but without the reduction divisions and

Fig. 7–12. Apomixis in a hybrid cholla, resulting from interbreeding of the jumping cholla (*Opuntia fulgida*) and the staghorn cholla (*Opuntia spinosior*), the protrusion at the left side of the stem base being the remains of a fruit which rooted the preceding year (Gila River near Sacaton, Arizona).

without fertilization. In any case, the chromosomes and their included genes are exactly the set of the "female parent." The net effect is an individual bearing the same genetic relationship to the female parent as would a plant developed from a branch. Since, as in some chollas and prickly pears, there is no sexual reproduction, there is no crossing, and minor races remain constant.

The Significance of Apomixis. Apomixis of all types is fairly common and occurs in many genera. Apomictic forms are so frequent in *Ranunculus auricomus,* for example, that more than 200 constant minor races are known to occur in Europe. This has caused confusion in classification through the insistence of some authors that any two plants which cannot interbreed and produce fertile offspring are of different species. Some have contended that all 200 minor forms of *Ranunculus auricomus* are separate species. The universal application of any single criterion for separation of species is not valid.

Clausen (1952) and Clausen, Hiesey, and Nobs (1958) have studied the significance of apomixis in species of *Poa*, and particularly of *Poa pratensis* the common bluegrass. Phases of their work have included the following:

1. production of hybrids between apomictic members of different sections of the genus;
2. progeny tests of hybrids and development of new apomictic strains combining genes of strongly distinguished species;
3. study of the evolutionary mechanisms resulting in constant new apomictic forms;
4. determination, in the field, of ranges of tolerance and patterns of growth of both new apomictic lines and parental lines at contrasting altitudes, latitudes, and longitudes, and under controlled environmental conditions;
5. determination of the breeding habits of apomictic types produced experimentally, and comparison of these with the breeding habits of well-established species;
6. formulation of concepts of the evolutionary mechanisms and history of species groups, especially of groups within the complex of *Poa pratensis*.

Apomixis may be significant in rapidly establishing new gene combinations which by chance are adapted to a particular environment. If a new combination is to survive it must be reproduced, but if it is heterozygous it is not likely to be duplicated by more than a few, if any, of its sexually produced offspring. By apomixis it may form many genetic duplicates of itself. These may become abundant, but they may still retain enough power of sexual reproduction to provide the variability necessary for some descendants to survive when conditions change. Thus apomixis may be a major factor in evolution of species, and it is important for consideration in its proper perspective in their classification.

The Genetic Nature of Apomixis. In the cases investigated, apomixis has appeared as a result of genetic factors. For example, the formation of bulbils (sets) instead of flowers in certain onions (*Allium*) is due to the dominant gene of a single pair. In other instances, apomixis results from recessive genes or from interaction of several pairs of factors.

THE GENE POTENTIAL OF SPECIES

Well-established and especially widespread species not only vary from place to place in the combinations of genes which enable them to be adapted to the prevailing local environments, but they also include in their genotypes the potential for much unexpressed variability. Some of this hidden potential for adaptation becomes manifest when plants are transplanted to new environments or when they are crossed either naturally or artificially with other races, varieties, or species. Knowledge of this phase of the application of cytogenetics to taxonomy is limited by the small amount of experimental work undertaken so far, and particularly by its restriction to traditional fields of research taken singly. A combination of approaches from several fields is necessary (see Clausen, 1951, 1952, 1954a, 1954b, 1958).

SUMMARY

Chromosomes are unique structures in their connection with the fundamental processes of heredity. Consequently, they may provide an insight into the method of origin of taxa. In some instances, as with allopolyploids, natural species may be resynthesized from related species. Chromosome number sequences may parallel the subdivisions of a genus, thus explaining segregations of morphological characters and the intergradation between some species but not others. They may indicate the underlying nature of hybridization when it does occur. Chromosome numbers and morphology, however, may vary within a species or other taxon.

In nature the characteristics segregating taxa are most frequently those in which dominance is not involved and in which several pairs of genes affect the same character. This results in quantitative series ranging from large to small, long to short, light to dark, densely to moderate pubescent, or shallowly to deeply indented. Inheritance involving dominance and a single pair of genes is less common.

Hybrids in nature can be detected relatively simply and fairly clearly by study of pollen grains, less reliably by the setting of seed, fairly effectively by study of the character combinations expressed phenotypically in the field, or accurately by progeny tests (especially with controlled pollination) and breeding experiments.

Apomixis is any kind of asexual reproduction with a tendency to be a substitute for sexual reproduction. Its significance is that it maintains a gene combination well adapted to a particular habitat. This combination is held constant through many asexual generations. If the individuals retain enough power of sexual reproduction to provide variability, some of the descendants are likely to be adapted to survival when conditions change. Consequently, apomixis may be a major factor in the evolution of species. In the cases investigated, the capacity for apomictic reproduction is hereditary.

SUGGESTED READING

ALLARD, H. A. 1932.
——. 1942. Hybridizing of the willow and black jack oaks.
——. 1949.
ANDERSON, EDGAR. 1937. An early and important summary of the field of cytology in relation to taxonomy.
BABCOCK, E. G. 1947. A model of application of cytological and experimental studies to taxonomic problems—the first great monograph of this type.
——, G. L. STEBBINS, JR., and J. A. JENKINS. 1942. See BABCOCK, 1947.
BROWN, META S. 1951. The feasibility of amphidiploidy as an explanation of formation of new species.
CHAMBERS, KENTON L. 1955. Application in a monograph of cytological studies to taxonomic problems.
CLAUSEN, JENS. 1952. For other papers by CLAUSEN and his associates, KECK and HIESEY, see Suggested Reading, Chapter 6.
DEAN, DONALD S. 1959. Abundance of tetraploids and diploids in undisturbed and disturbed habitats; disjunction of diploid populations.
DOBZHANSKY, THEODOSIUS. 1937, 1941, 1951. A highly recommended classical work, brought periodically up to date.
EPLING, CARL. 1947. The effect of equilibrium of competition upon the constancy of sympatric species; the effect of limited hybridization permitting some introgression and therefore increased genetic variability.
GOODSPEED, T. H. 1954. A model of genetic and cytological studies of a taxonomic group.
GRANT, VERNE. 1956b. See below.
——. 1956c. See below.
——. 1959. See below.
——, et al. 1950–1958. This and papers above constitute an outstanding review combining breeding experiments and cytological studies with taxonomy.
LEACH, DAVID G. 1959.
LEWIS, HARLAN. The papers by LEWIS et al., below, constitute one of the most significant monographs employing cytogenetic methods.
——. 1951.
——. 1953a.
——. 1953b.
——. 1957.
——, and MARGARET ENSIGN LEWIS. 1955.
——, and PETER H. RAVEN. 1958a.
——, and PETER H. RAVEN. 1958b.
——, PETER H. RAVEN, C. S. VENKATESH, and HALE L. WEDBERG. 1958.
——, and MARGARET R. ROBERTS. 1956.
McMILLAN, CALVIN. 1953. Analysis of variability in characters of cypress seedlings and in germination rates characterizing a proposed species based upon a variable population perhaps resulting from hybridization.

MORAN, REID. 1949. A good semitechnical, semipopular account of the significance of chromosomes in classification.

RAVEN, PETER H., and HARLAN LEWIS. 1959. See LEWIS, above.

ROBERTS, MARGARET R., and HARLAN LEWIS. 1955. See LEWIS, above.

ROLLINS, REED C. 1944. Presence of polyploid series allowing for varying proportions of chromosomes derived from the two parental species.

———. 1945. See above.

———. 1946. Further studies involving artificially produced crosses. See above.

———. 1949. Introgression of genes from one species to another; local apomictic strains and their protection from swamping out by interbreeding.

———. 1953. Consideration of cytological information, combined with other data, in the delimitation of genera and of their included species.

STEBBINS, G. LEDYARD, JR. 1940. The significance of polyploidy in developing large, complex, and widespread genera, but not in production of major lines of evolution.

———. 1942a.

———. 1949. The vigor and fertility of polyploids of grasses in comparison to the parental species; prediction of these features for allopolyploids from the systematic position or the chromosome numbers of the parents.

———. 1956. A review of trends of evolution and of lines of development forming the basis for a reclassification of the Gramineae; an illustrated synopsis of diagnostic characters, including minute ones; and a discussion of the role of polyploidy in evolution of grasses.

———, and FUNG TING PUN. 1953. Correlation of cytological evidence concerning relationships of three species with morphological evidence.

———, and H. A. TOGBY. 1944. An example of a cytological investigation applied to classification.

———, H. A. TOGBY, and JACK R. HARLAN. 1944. Continuation of the subject above with discussion of application of cytological data to classification of a polyploid complex.

———, and MARTA S. WALTERS. 1949. Recommended for study of methods of analysis. The conclusions have far-reaching implications for reorganization of the genera of the Hordeae.

THOMPSON, HENRY J. 1953. A monograph of a genus, based in part upon cytogenetic studies.

VENKATESH, C. S. 1959. Morphology, geographical distribution, genetics, and cytology and their indication of the status of a proposed genus.

VICKERY, ROBERT K., JR. and RICHARD L. OLSON. 1956. Illustrates the complexity of the pattern of inheritance of a single group of characters.

WAGNER, WARREN H., JR. 1954. The origin of species through hybridization involving polyploidy.

———, and THOMAS DARLING, JR. 1957. Synthesis of an allopolyploid fern species, rare in nature, by sowing in culture spores of two other species.

WARD, GEORGE H. 1953. A combination of cytology with taxonomy in monographing a complex group of species.

WHITAKER, THOMAS W. 1959. Analysis of a wild species and a cultivated species not strongly separated by barriers to interbreeding, the cultivated type perhaps having been derived under the guidance of man from plants resembling the wild type.

WOLF, CARL B. 1938. Progeny tests of "Quercus Morehus."

SUGGESTED READING ON APOMIXIS

CLAUSEN, JENS. 1954b. Development of a combination of sufficient reproductability, through apomixis, to perpetuate a successful combination of characters, and sufficient variability, through sexual reproduction, to adapt the species to changing conditions.

CLAUSEN, JENS, WILLIAM M. HIESEY, and MALCOLM A. NOBS. 1958.

EINSET, JOHN. 1951. Discussion of apomictic strains arising from reduced or un-
reduced eggs.

GUSTAFSSON, ÅKE. 1946, 1947. A complete survey of the field (see STEBBINS, 1941;
NYGREN, 1954).

NYGREN, AXEL. 1954. Summary, revision, and supplement (see STEBBINS, 1941).

ROLLINS, REED C., and D. G. CATCHESIDE. The problem of retaining apomictic reproduction for propagation of desirable strains while producing new strains through
sexual reproduction.

STEBBINS, G. LEDYARD, JR. 1941. (See GUSTAFSSON, 1946, 1947; NYGREN, 1954.)

——. 1958. Alteration of the genetic system in adaptation to greater reproductive
efficiency through self-fertilization, apomixis, and reduction of genetic recombination, with consequent occupation of more unstable habitats and greater fluctuation
in population size.

——, and E. B. BABCOCK. 1939. Discussion of apomictic strains, which are mostly
strictly local, the widespread apomicts having been derived usually from two, three,
or more sexual types.

——, and J. A. JENKINS. 1939. Predominantly apomictic reproduction with occasional sexual reproduction in heterozygous populations.

chapter

8

Synthesis of Data

CORRELATION OF DATA FROM VARIOUS FIELDS

Any step toward classification of a plant group is, by itself, an important contribution to knowledge, but the ultimate in taxonomy, as in all other subjects, is a synthesis of all the data available from every pertinent field.

Study of taxa occurring in remote lands is still dependent almost wholly upon the herbarium, each specialist evaluating the taxonomic status of certain plants in collections brought in by explorers. This produces only a tentative treatment which lacks even the refinements yielded by field studies. It does not include data from the fields of knowledge described in the preceding chapters, but it may yield an approximation of the truth. Study of the work of Asa Gray based upon the few specimens available in the collections in the Gray Herbarium of Harvard University during the American exploratory years from 1842 to 1888 reveals his clear insight into the species of the continent, despite limitations of data.

Today, by being aware of possible underlying ecological, paleontological, genetic, and cytological complications, the taxonomist can avoid the many pitfalls of an attempt to classify natural populations according to only herbarium and field data. Although any preliminary classification is only an approximation, if it is made with proper caution and is based upon thorough observation and good judgment it may be a useful approximation.

The great contribution to taxonomic botany from other fields is an understanding of basic problems and of the principles upon which

269

the science of taxonomy and the process of classification rest. The revival of taxonomic biology in recent years is due in no small part to the impetus produced especially by application of cytological and experimental techniques. *This impetus is not only from use of these techiques to solve taxonomic problems peculiar to the groups under investigation but also from the far more important discovery of general principles.* As in all research, wholly unexpected results may appear, and these may lead to a knowledge of unsuspected underlying phenomena or even open up new areas of study.

Application of new techniques does not necessarily yield fundamentally different results from those obtained by classical taxonomic methods. Often, however, cytological, experimental, or other studies drawn from various fields may solve at least in part the problems detected by observation, and they may point the way to, or confirm the need for, fundamental reorganization of taxa, as with *Clarkia* and *Godetia* (see pp. 238–242). However, application of techniques and data from other fields usually confirms at least the main preliminary outlines of taxonomic categories and provides refinement of detail, contributing more significant data not suspected after observation alone, and sometimes reversing previous decisions or indicating a need for re-evaluation or reorganization. Even though the ultimate alignment of genera, species, and varieties often differs little from that in a standard manual of the flora developed by herbarium and field studies, the newer methods place decisions upon a firm foundation and sometimes explain the fundamental nature of the underlying taxonomic problems.

Large-scale application of experimental techniques may be limited by cost, shortage of time, and certain characteristics of the organism itself. For example, the many species of oaks have a nearly uniform complement of 12 chromosome pairs (Duffield, 1940), and consequently cytological studies have yielded no key to classification. Furthermore, each species is complex. For example, collection of a specimen from each of 30 or more individuals of *Quercus dumosa* reveals no 2 to be alike, and the same is true of *Quercus Engelmannii* (see pp. 54–57, 83–85, 92, 117–118, and 255–258). Undertaking controlled breeding experiments and growing the hybrid offspring of these two species present the following questions:

1. *With Which Individuals Does One Start?* In each species there are numerous character combinations, even among the plants within a 100-foot radius. Cross-breeding of any one of these with a single individual of the other species will yield results other than

would selection of a different individual. But breeding 30 individuals of one species with each of 30 of the other would require planting an oak forest composed of 900 groups of trees, each group comprising the number of individuals needed to produce all the genetic combinations obtainable from its parents.

2. *How Much Time Is Available?* Although, fortunately, some leaf characters of the progeny of a cross can be determined tentatively within a few months and definitely within a few years, a single reproducing generation of oaks may require at least half of the active career of a research worker.

Despite some limitations to experimentation on a grand scale or to studying certain organisms, many simple experiments are both inexpensive and applicable to most plant groups. Examples are the progeny test, including control of pollination (see pp. 250–259), breeding experiments with plants having short life cycles (such as herbs, especially annuals), and ecological experiments similar to those of Turesson and of Hall and his successors, Clausen, Keck, and Hiesey (see pp. 229–231). These may be applied to selected groups of species or varieties especially difficult to classify by other means.

It is to be hoped that use of both observational and experimental methods in the future will produce at least some studies involving correlation of data from all the fields discussed in this series of chapters. Some of the nearest current approaches to such a study are those applied to *Crepis* (hawksbeard) by Babcock (1947), to *Nicotiana* (tobacco) by Goodspeed (1954), to *Clarkia* by Lewis, *et al.* (see pp. 238–242), and to *Gilia* and other Polemoniaceae by Grant, *et al.* (see Chapter 7, Suggested Reading). These works relate to the taxonomy, phylogeny, distribution, and evolution of the genera. Such treatments of plant groups may serve as models for other treatises and monographs and as sources of general principles applicable in considering groups for which less information is available.

Experimental studies similar to those mentioned in the preceding paragraph, but with much greater emphasis upon physiological factors, are being conducted by a team of research workers at the Carnegie Institution of Washington, Division of Plant Biology (e.g., Milner, Hiesey, and Nobs, 1958; Nobs and Hiesey, 1958; Elliott and Nobs, 1959). The subjects of these studies have been *Mimulus Cardinalis, Mimulus Lewisii*, and their hybrids. These plants have been studied from the following points of view:

1. *Physiology of Climatic Races.* Genetic and transplant studies have been combined with physiological measurements in experiments designed to determine which factors enable one species to thrive in one habitat but fail in another while another species does the reverse. In 1958, the authors made a survey of rates of photosynthesis and respiration of several climatic races of the two species of *Mimulus,* using limited ranges of temperature, light intensity, and carbon dioxide concentration. The range in photosynthetic response of different races of *Mimulus* was established.

2. *Response of Species of Mimulus and Their Hybrids to Contrasting Environments.* The selective effects of different environments during critical stages of germination and early seedling establishment of the two species and their F_2 progeny were studied in 1956 and later followed up in contrasting climates occurring at various altitudes, as follows (frontispiece and Fig. 6–7):

Stanford	150 feet elevation
Mather	4,600 feet elevation
Timber-line	10,000 feet elevation

A dominant gene carried by *Mimulus Lewisii,* which grows at high altitudes, suppresses formation of yellow chromoplasts in the petals, allowing only various shades of pink to appear in the flowers. This gene is lacking in the lowland *Mimulus Cardinalis,* in which the corolla is partly red and partly yellow. In the hybrids there are various shades of pink and yellow and of colors ranging from orange to vermilion. The pair of genes determining the presence or absence of yellow pigmentation appears to be linked genetically with genes affecting various features of flower structure and also with genes determining the capacity of the individual progeny to survive in the contrasting environments at the three altitudes. In general, the plants with *Lewisii*-like pink flowers survive at the timber-line, those with *Cardinalis*-type pink and yellow flowers at Stanford, and hybrids at Mather. The time of planting the seeds is important, too. Winter-sown seeds, which germinate and become established at lower temperatures, produce plants which show a high proportion of pink-flowered types.

3. *Interaction of Temperature and Light on Seed Germination.*

RECENT STUDY OF EVOLUTION

Combined cytogenetic, taxonomic, and other studies provide information concerning the origin of taxa or evolution. It is upon this relationship to evolution that a subfield combining data from cytology, genetics, taxonomy, and related fields may claim recognition. The activities of the modern student of this phase of evolution include determination as to whether species will cross and to what degree, analysis of the genetic makeup of natural populations, determination of the relationships of genetic manifestations to the underlying cytological phenomena, analysis of the isolating mechanisms resulting in the segregation of natural populations, and analysis of past and present environmental factors which may or may not permit their survival. Much has been added to knowledge of the evolutionary process and the principles concerned with it. The subject has been summarized by Stebbins (1950).

The interrelationships of the fields of evolution and taxonomy and the fields upon which they draw for data and knowledge of underlying principles are indicated in Fig. 8–1. Although the fields interlock, there may be differences in the primary objectives. According to one point of view, evolution, for example, is concerned with the mechanism of formation of new taxa, and taxonomy is concerned with classification or construction of a taxonomic system. From this viewpoint, neither is a branch of the other but each draws upon the other for much of its basic material. According to another opinion, however, these two fields are inseparable and may be treated as a single unit emphasizing both objectives. Camp and Gilly (1943) called the unified field *biosystematy.* Regardless of interpretation, no distinction between fields is sharp.

THE SYNTHESIS AND EXPRESSION OF PHYLOGENETIC DATA

The following [1] is quoted from a class instruction sheet by Warren H. Wagner, Jr., Department of Botany, University of Michigan:

One of the ultimate aims of all Biology is to determine the phylogenetic relationships of living things. As we come nearer this goal, the organization of our knowledge will become increasingly accurate, and the phylogenetic system itself will become more and more a source of understanding of the nature of structure and function.

The systematic botanist deals with the relationships of plants. In his final synthesis he must account for all characteristics of all plants without regard for whether the plants are still living or are known only as fossils. These are the major questions he asks:

1. What has been the evolutionary development of single characters and character-complexes, structural and functional?
2. What has been the evolutionary development of the populations of whole organisms?
3. What is the best way to express these conclusions in the form of the conceptual scheme most useful to scientific research?

[1] Supplied through the courtesy of its author and used by permission.

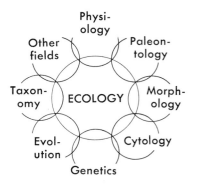

ECOLOGY — relationships of living organisms to environmental factors and to each other.

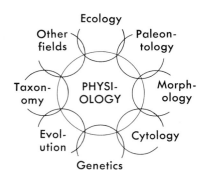

PHYSIOLOGY — study of the physical and chemical processes within the organism, i.e.: of functions.

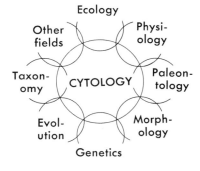

CYTOLOGY — study of the cell. In the most-frequently studied branch (karyology) the emphasis is upon the chromosomes.

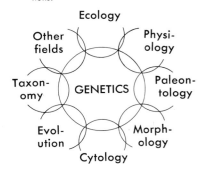

GENETICS—the study of the germ plasm or hereditary material. This includes the laws and mechanisms of inheritance.

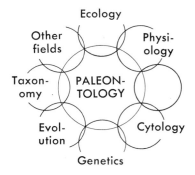

PALEONTOLOGY—history of living organisms through geologic time.

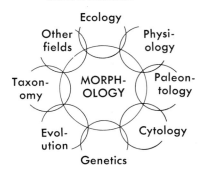

MORPHOLOGY—form and structure and their development in living organisms.

Fig. 8–1. See next page for legend.

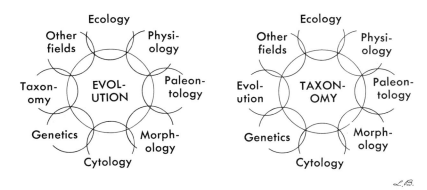

EVOLUTION — the changing of living organisms now and in geologic time; the mechanisms of forming new taxa.

TAXONOMY — classification of living organisms according to their relationships; construction of the taxonomic system.

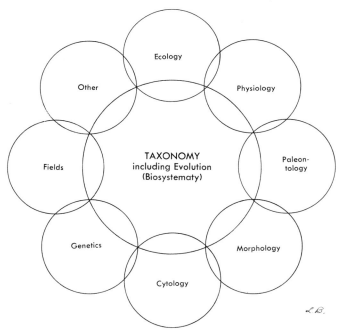

TAXONOMY—Classification of living organisms according to a taxonomic system based upon phylogenetic (evolutionary) relationships, with emphasis upon the factors responsible for segregation of the taxa

Fig. 8–1. Interrelationships of sciences. The figure series illustrates diagrammatically the relationships of interlocking fields of natural science. Each field is characterized by its special objective. With this objective in view, all other fields become contributors to the primary field. A similar figure might be constructed with additional fields as contributors or with any one of them at the center. An example of an additional significant field is philosophy.

The first question is the concern mainly of systematic morphologists and systematic physiologists, the second and third questions are more the concern of the phylogenist and taxonomist. Nevertheless, all three questions are intimately inter-related with one another. For example, our conclusions regarding evolutionary development of organisms must rest upon our knowledge of individual characters. The reverse is equally true, though often overlooked: The evolutionary development of structural and functional characters by themselves must be concluded from knowledge of whole organisms. The determination of direction of evolution in single characters must be grounded upon correlation with other characters of whole organisms.

The search for more objective and more quantitive methods of determining evolutionary pathways has engaged biologists for well over a century, and it continues today with increased momentum. Some of the methods include . . . "Advancement Indices" (Sporne, 1956) and "Correlation Coefficients" (Michener and Sokal, 1957). There has recently been an effort to find out what, if anything, is objective in the so-called taxonomic "judgement" or "intuition" (e.g., Anderson, 1951, 1957).

All of these efforts seem to be based upon a more or less common basis of viewpoint, and elements of each will probably be embodied in our future, more refined techniques. The best method will be the one which has the highest probability of being accurate or correct. One immediate concern, then, is not what *are* the pathways of phylogeny, but rather, what are the *most probable* pathways. The study of phylogeny, like much of the rest of science, therefore, becomes a problem in likelihood or probabilities.

To illustrate, we can say, "Organisms which are similar in most of their characters are probably related and share a common ancestral stock." Further, "Similar groups," and "Correlated resemblances in different lines reflect a common genetic background" (Cf. Sturtevant, 1948). If, for the sake of argument, we take the opposite view, then we are immediately faced with the problem that "The chances of a large series of correlated resemblances coming about by any other pathway than by common ancestry are exceedingly *improbable* statistically" (cf. Ownbey and Aase, 1955).

In determining phylogeny, the systematist is concerned primarily with one over-all pattern, viz., a *common ancestor* gives rise to *divergent derivatives*, some of which have changed but little (and are therefore more similar to the prototype) and some of which have changed much (and are less similar to the common ancestor). There are thus three assumptions or doctrines necessary if this pattern should be valid:

1. COMMON ANCESTRY. Plants which have in common a large number of similar characteristics have the same common ancestor.
2. EVOLUTIONARY DIVERGENCE. Evolution proceeds in various directions. Different lines will change in different characters and different character-complexes.
3. INEQUALITY OF EVOLUTIONARY RATES. Evolution takes place at different rates at various times and in different lines. Some forms will remain fairly stereotyped, resembling the common ancestor; others will change radically in the same period from the common ancestor.

At least two complications may arise to disturb the general applicability of these assumptions: In plants at least, a given line may have *two or more common ancestors* (Cf. Assumption #1 above). The phenomenon of *reticulate evolution* or origin of new lines by hybridization between already well differentiated species and genera [see pp. 55–60] must be recognized. If it is not, the conclusions will be erroneous.

Likewise, *parallel and convergent evolution* must be recognized where they occur (Cf. Assumption #2). Whole character-complexes may be involved, such as soriation in the ferns, wind-pollination in flowering plants, or gametophytic biology in vascular plants in general. Many phylogenetic errors of the past came about as a result of the researcher's failure to perceive these phenomena where they occurred. In general, a careful and comprehensive study of the plants involved should reveal where the ordinary evolutionary pattern of divergent evolution does not apply.

In order to determine the pattern of phylogeny there are, in general, three major steps involved [for application, see pp. 415–417].

1. SYSTEMATIC ANALYSIS. To find and understand all the characters of the plants in question.
2. DETERMINATION OF GROUND PLANS. To find what character states are common to all or most of the plants in order to deduce which are the probable ancestral or primitive states.
3. SYSTEMATIC SYNTHESIS. To assemble the plants according to their respective deviations from the basic ground plan and from each other.

SUGGESTED READING

CAMP, W. H. 1943. A review of the relationship of taxonomy to various fields.

CLAUSEN, JENS, and WILLIAM M. HIESEY. 1958. An important statement of the genic variability within species and of its significance.

CONSTANCE, LINCOLN. 1951. Summary and evaluation of new techniques and types of data and of their impact upon taxonomy.

——. 1956. The impact of other fields, especially experimental ones, on taxonomy.

HESLOP-HARRISON, J. 1953. An evaluation and review of the field on the basis of application of data and methods from other fields.

KECK, DAVID D. 1951. A brief summary of the status of taxonomic botany.

——. 1957. A review of problems of the systematist and of methods applied recently to their solution.

MASON, H. L. 1950. Publication of a widely adopted clarification of terms.

ROLLINS, REED C. 1952. Problems arising from application of new types of data to taxonomy, and an attempt to clarify the definition of taxa.

——. 1957. A summary of the present position of taxonomy and of the pattern for future development.

STEBBINS, G. LEDYARD, JR. 1950. A thorough and penetrating review of the field of evolution.

Part II

CLASSIFICATION

chapter 9

Principles of Classification

Species and other taxa are real entities because the natural populations of plants and animals composing them reproduce themselves for indefinite periods of time, the same or a similar association of genes being transmitted through countless generations, often with few or slight changes. Thus, either *species* or *taxon* may be defined without difficulty. The difficult problem is not what these categories are but how one taxon may be distinguished from another.

THE DISTINCTION OF SPECIES AND OTHER TAXA

Delimitation of species or of taxa of other ranks involves an assessment of the state of their evolutionary segregation by study of two interlocking usually simultaneous phases of essentially a single process—differentiation and isolation (Fig. 9–1). Except in special cases, such as sudden isolation through polyploidy, or some factor interfering with pollination or fertilization, usually one does not proceed far without the other. Nevertheless, in taxonomic research both phases must be kept in mind.

Differentiation. Unique systems of closely interrelated natural populations composing a new taxon arise usually through accumulation of characters differentiating the unit from its relatives. Constant association of characters within new groups of plants or animals commonly is aided by *natural selection* which leads to relatively rapid fixing of *adaptive characters,* features enabling an organism to survive under a special set of conditions. Accompanying these

281

are others neither adaptive nor detrimental but retained by chance, that is, through *random selection* in the genetic makeup of the organism or through genetic association with adaptive characters.

Isolation. New characters may arise without isolation of individuals from the rest of the population. However, if all members of a species are free to breed with each other and the offspring are fertile, the net result is a more variable (and perhaps gradually changing) single general population. Once elements of a taxon are at least partly isolated, evolution may proceed independently among the derivatives of the original population, there being a reduction

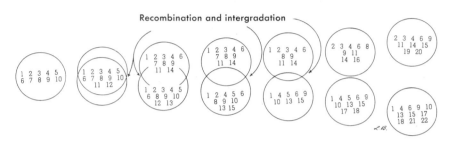

Recombination and intergradation

Fig. 9–1. Isolation and differentiation of taxa (for example, species). Divergence of the circles and their ultimate separation parallel development of isolation of population systems. Each number within a circle stands for a character, and within each of the divergent groups of plants or animals some characters are lost and replaced by others. In the course of time two or more differentiated taxa result. These share some characters retained from their common ancestry, but each has its own distinctive features.

in likelihood of gene interchange. Thus isolation of some populations from their relatives is necessary to development of new species.

Isolation of natural population systems may be due to factors which restrict or eliminate interbreeding and subsequent reproduction of hybrids. Species may be separated by genetic isolation, geographical isolation, or ecological isolation (see Chapter 2).

GENETIC ISOLATION. This category is defined broadly to include all hereditary mechanisms causing restriction or elimination of interbreeding through processes wholly internal to the organism.

Hybridizing may affect the chromosome cycle by, for example, causing failure of pairing (synapsis) of the chromosomes in the early stages of meiosis. In the usual type of *Galeopsis speciosa* and *Galeopsis pubescens* (Chapter 7) the hybrid is diploid—in this case with 16 chromosomes, 8 from each parental species. Some of these are homologous members of pairs, but others are not the members of a pair or are only partly homologous. Meiosis in these diploid hybrids does not proceed normally. Fertile pollen and ovules are infrequent or lacking, and usually the hybrids do not reproduce. Most crosses of cabbages and radishes (Chapter 7) have similar results, the 9 chromosomes from each parent lacking completely homologous mates and the hybrids being sterile. The crosses yielding artificial *Galeopsis Tetrahit* and *Raphanobrassica* were successful only because some of the gametes produced by the hybrid had two full sets of chromosomes from each parental species.

Incompatibility of the reproductive structures may restrict interbreeding. Examples include failure to interbreed because of different reproductive periods; differences in the size of pollen tubes, the growth of the larger ones through the passageway of the style of the flower being impeded; differences in the relative rates of growth of pollen; inhibition of the growth of foreign pollen by substances on the stigma; failure of attraction or union of gametes; death of hybrid embryos not adapted physiologically to development in the ovules of the female parent; and production of sterility in the hybrids.

Genetic isolation occurs commonly, though not necessarily, between closely related species, but it may exist also between individuals of the same species, as in *Mimulus* (Vickery, 1959) or the interfertile and non-interfertile, morphologically similar races of *Clarkia* described by Lewis (1953a, p. 19) (see also p. 241). It may exist between plants with little or no differentiation of other characters, but it may **not** be complete between even genera of the same family. Usually, however, species are isolated to a significant degree (more so than varieties), and commonly genera are isolated completely, though interbreeding and production of fertile offspring may occur between the more closely related species. Families and higher taxa are nearly always genetically isolated, except that certain species of closely related genera may be interfertile.

GEOGRAPHICAL ISOLATION. Geographical isolation is restriction or elimination of interbreeding through the intervention of geographical barriers. It is as effective as genetic isolation—but only for the period in which separation continues. If land masses are rejoined or if deserts, mountains, ice sheets, or other barriers disappear, the isolated units may be brought into contact once more. Unless reproductive isolating mechanisms have developed during the period of geographical isolation, interbreeding may be resumed. For example, the genus *Platanus* (sycamore, plane tree) is represented by markedly differentiated species native to the Eastern and Western hemispheres, but in cultivation they are interfertile. Removal of geographical barriers would lead to mixing of natural populations, except as ecological or other untested factors might produce at least incomplete segregation.

ECOLOGICAL ISOLATION. Ecological isolation is confinement of each of two or more related populations to restricted environmental conditions, which either separate them and prevent interbreeding or result in relatively rare development of hybrid offspring. Various ecological segregating mechanisms were discussed in Chapter 3. To these can be added mechanisms involving transportation of gameto- phytes or gametes, including, for example (in seed plants), carrying of pollen to the stigma of one species rather than of another. In the flowering plants special methods of pollination, correlated with spe- cialized flower structure, may tend to keep species largely segregated (see pp. 212–213 and, for example, Grant, 1949, 1950, 1952; Straw, 1955, 1956; Dunn, 1956).

The Effects of Differentiation and Isolation. Although taxa are tangible entities, often the distinctions between them may be in- definite and their segregation complex and difficult to interpret.

A genus with completely stable species does not come to mind. Even *Ginkgo* [Fig. 5–28 (1)], with only one species, which has existed at least since Mesozoic times, is variable. *Lathyrus* (sweet pea) is an example of a genus with relatively stable species. Senn's experiments (1938) resulted in few or no successful crosses between species, for seeds were obtained in only 4 of 458 attempts. In the three lots which germinated, the plants resembled in all observed details the female parent, indicating either pollen contamination or self-fertilization. Although Senn's work indicates complete repro- ductive isolation, Hitchcock (1952) obtained a few interspecific crosses and reported evidence of natural hybridization of a few species. Despite failure of crossing in the garden, Senn found the boundary lines between some species of *Lathyrus* to be vague.

In nearly every genus the phases of two or more closely related species genetically or otherwise isolated under the conditions prevail- ing in one locality may be replaced in other areas by differing popu- lations (see pp. 5–13, 212). Each species varies from place to place not only in visible characters but also in the often more significant but intangible physiological characters which yield adaptation to slightly differing environments. Thus, although in one locality or habitat two population systems may be clearly differentiated and even genetically isolated, usually there are gradual geographical shifts of character combinations, often including the factors respon- sible for isolation.

If advantageous new characters appear within one isolated unit of a population, the individuals possessing them may crowd out and replace the others everywhere, replace them in only the habitat(s) in which the new characters are most advantagous, or occupy a new ecological or geographical niche not available previously to any element of the larger population system.

In the earlier stages of segregation of evolving taxa, few characters differ and isolation is incomplete. Differentiation of characters tends usually to develop as isolation becomes more effective. In time the derivatives of a species may become two or more varieties. Later, as differentiation proceeds still further and isolation becomes still more effective, though not necessarily complete, some or all of the varieties may become separate species. Eventually some derivatives may give rise to other varieties or species, and ultimately any may be the starting point of a new taxon of higher rank.

The living plants and animals of the present are the results of gradual evolution through more than 500,000,000 years. Differentiation and isolation of taxa have proceeded as new inheritable characters have arisen by chance and have been successful or at least have persisted in the environment of the time and place (Fig. 9–2). Present-day taxa represent only the momentary results of evolution—changing masses of individuals in numerous stages of development in an incalculable number of directions. Inasmuch as differentiation and isolation of all taxonomic groups exist in an infinite number of degrees, definite distinctions of taxa are not necessarily to be expected. At all levels of taxonomic rank, even the plant kingdom and the animal kingdom, taxa may shade off gradually into their relatives. The groupings of organisms described in books stand for taxa only partly differentiated, some well, some poorly, and the complexity of their classification commonly is similar to that of distinction of the races of men or of the breeds of dogs. *Both differentiation and isolation of natural population systems (taxa) from each other occur in an infinite number of degrees, but the number of taxonomic ranks into which they may be classified must be few. Consequently, assignment of a natural population or population system to a taxonomic rank involves judgment.*

Setting the Limits of Taxa. If a taxon is to be accepted as of specific (species) rank, both a *significant differentiation of characters* and a *considerable degree of isolation* are expected. The degree of isolation [1] is judged by the degree of discontinuity between its genotype and those of its relatives, as expressed imperfectly in

---

[1] For methods of isolation within a species, see Vickery (1959).

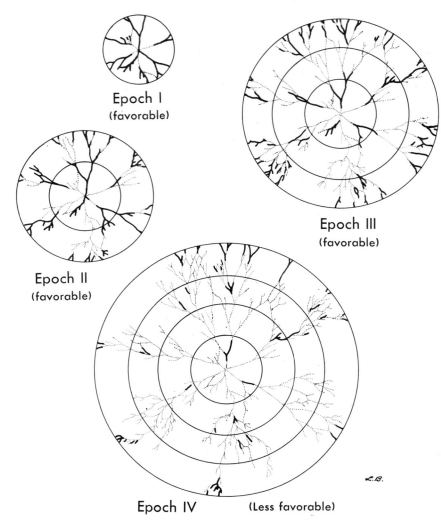

Epoch I
(favorable)

Epoch II
(favorable)

Epoch III
(favorable)

Epoch IV   (Less favorable)

Fig. 9–2. Chart showing the development of taxa through four units of geological time (epochs), the first three with favorable conditions and the fourth with less favorable ones. Solid dark lines represent plant populations living in the particular epoch; broken lines indicate populations which have died out. Three dimensions would be necessary to represent the true degree of complexity of such an example.

terms of stability of characters. If the taxon is to be assigned a lower rank, less is required; if a higher rank, more.

1. *The limits of a taxon cannot be defined quantitatively.* They depend upon the degree of differentiation and isolation from its nearest relatives, but reliance cannot be placed upon the number of distinguishing characters, because most characters occur with varying degrees of consistency, that is, they may be undermined by exceptions. Furthermore, they may be controlled by varying numbers of genes. Attempts to reduce the numbers or stability of characters to statistical terms for definition purposes are impractical.

2. *The limits of a taxon cannot be defined qualitatively, that is, in terms of kinds of characters.* A common taxonomic fallacy is that there are varietal, specific, generic, familiar, ordinal, and class characters, applying always to these ranks. No character is per se more "important" in classification than another, and no rigid caste system can be assigned to characters or types of characters. *The characters marking the limits of a taxon are the ones most nearly consistent in occurrence, or those associated in a group of diagnostic characters, regardless of their type or of the organ in which they are found.*

The characters of some organs tend to be more stable than those of others, but this does not make them necessarily "the key" to classification. Roots, for example, tend to retain ancient structures rather than to develop new ones. This is correlated with their position in the soil, where fluctuations of the physical environment are less than in air. Supporting organs such as stems tend to be more variable in external structure than roots, but less so than leaves, which vary radically, mostly in relationship to the diverse environments inhabited by plants. Reproductive structures, for the most part, are more stable in their characters than are leaves but less so than are stems. However, some reproductive parts, for example, the components of the flowering-plant pistil, may be sometimes even more variable than leaves. Constancy of structure through large groups is said to be more common in flowers than in leaves, but clear evidence for this has not been compiled.

An example of a character often assigned undue significance is apetaly, regarded by many as a character of primary "importance" in distinguishing orders of flowering plants. Apetaly was employed by Engler and Prantl as an "ordinal" character. However, it has arisen independently in a number of dissimilar species within even the genus *Ranunculus*, for example, *Ranunculus pedatifidus*, *Ranunculus glaberrimus* var. *glaberrimus* and var. *ellipticus*, and *Ranunculus ranunculinus*. In each of these species at least one apetalous form has been named as a new species because someone supposed apetaly to be an important character. In each case the new taxon was named despite the fact that apetaly was inconsistent in occurrence, being correlated with no other character.

3. *The limits of a taxon usually cannot be defined on the basis of the supposed course of evolution from one living taxon to another.* The gradual shifts of character emphasis within a taxon during geologic time result in one or more modified taxa and commonly in disappearance, at least in its original form, of the parental taxon. Sometimes the course of evolution may be reconstructed from series of fossils, as in the case of the closed-cone pines (see pp. 163–169), but in most instances fossils are lacking or inadequate. Thus, speculation as to which of two living taxa was derived from which is pointless unless there is evidence from fossils or from such phenomena as allopolyploidy. In most cases both were derived from an extinct common ancestor, rarely one from the other.

4. *The limits of a taxon are not necessarily confined to a single "line" or "branch" of evolutionary development.* One taxon may include fragments of several related branches, the limits being determined by the degree of differentiation of the branching lines and by the degree of isolation of their surviving segments (Fig. 9–2). Certainly white oaks and black oaks represent survivors of two branches of phylogeny. Nevertheless they are included in the genus *Quercus* by nearly all authors. This is true also of any two species in either group, of any two varieties of any species, and of minor groups within the varieties. All these represent segments of different branches of development.

5. *A single "line" of evolutionary development does not necessarily constitute only a single taxon.* The general trend of development which has given rise to the green plants,[2] that is, the green algae, the three major lines of bryophytes, the four divisions of pteridophytes, the four lines of gymnosperms, and a line of the angiosperms, does not represent a single division today (Fig. 10–1). Far back in Pre-cambrian, Cambrian, or early Silurian times doubtless it did, but now the derivatives of this trend of phylogeny are as diverse as *Chlamydomonas, Spirogyra, Anthoceros,* a moss, a fern, a pine, an oak tree, an orchid, and a sunflower. They differ in innumerable characters of both vegetative body and reproduction. They are isolated completely, and for the most part even the course

[2] Nearly all the plants with chlorophyll predominating over the associated carotenes and xanthophylls and with no fundamental accessory red or blue pigments.

of their evolution is no more than a matter of conjecture. Only the pigmentation and physiology of their cells remain as clear characters in common. A single division of the plant kingdom of the geological past has separated into several divisions and classes by strong differentiation and complete isolation of segments of branches of the evolutionary tree.

DEFINITION OF SPECIES

Definition of the term *species* is an elusive goal only if an attempt to limit the category is included. Leaving out criteria for distinguishing species from each other, the problem narrows down to the question of what kind of entity is being classified. A working definition must take into account the following elements:

1. *The species discussed in this book are composed of living organisms.* The definition adopted here is restricted arbitrarily to present-day species. Fossils represent pre-existing species of one geologic epoch or another, and it is not practical to include the remains of their members in the living species, for the reasons given on pages 160–163.

2. *A species is able to reproduce itself.* Thus, potentially it may persist in some form through an unlimited number of generations.

3. *A species is ordinarily a natural population or system of populations, rarely an individual.* Restriction of the definition to natural populations is somewhat arbitrary, but for the moment omission of transitory plant or animal types such as those produced through breeding controlled by man avoids unnecessary complications and fruitless argument about the status of these individuals or groups of individuals.

The expedient of putting horticultural forms aside does not solve the problems concerning them. Classification and nomenclature of cultivated plants present challenging and interesting questions in need of investigation (see Anderson, 1952). Many horticultural plants have survived for innumerable generations and form significant and outstandingly important artificially maintained populations. An example is wheat, a trigeneric hybrid derived in ancient times, as is shown by study of its chromosomes. In botany, minor horticultural forms such as the kinds of wheat are classified as cultivars, but classification and naming of the major forms, such as wheat itself, are more difficult.

Not every naturally occurring plant or animal belongs necessarily to a species. For example, F_1 hybrids or the heterozygous members of a hybrid swarm resulting from crossing of two species are members of neither. However, some plants of a hybrid group may be the precursors of new species, or, through backcrossing to one parental type, some of their genes may be absorbed into one parental species or the other.

In two instances a species may exist at least potentially as a single individual. These are as follows:

a. When an incipient species arises suddenly, as by formation of a natural allopolyploid. From the practical angle, a single individual in this category, about to give rise to a natural population, is not likely to be encountered by a taxonomist. In any event he has no way of knowing whether the individual will give rise to a natural population, and he is likely to solve the problem by pressing the plant. More often origin of new species is through gradual transition during geological time from populations emphasizing one set of characters to derived types emphasizing other sets.

b. When all individuals but one have died.

4. *The individuals composing a species are genetically closely related.* This implies derivation from a recent common ancestry, that is, a common phylogeny up to within relatively recent geological times.

A living natural species is a reproducing population or system of populations of genetically closely related individuals.

DEFINITIONS OF OTHER TAXA

Species, as opposed to variety, genus, family, order, etc., represents only one level among an infinite number of possible degrees of taxa. To facilitate reference to various levels of classification these are organized into only a few ranks.

A living natural taxon is a reproducing population or system of populations of genetically related individuals.

This definition of a taxon is the same as that for a species, except that the single word "closely" is omitted, the closeness of relationship being a relative matter. This modification of the definition stated above for species *may be applied with equal force to taxa of every rank.*

POLICY IN CLASSIFICATION

Since an infinite number of degrees would be required to express all the existing ranks of taxa but because only a few degrees can be used, each taxonomist must adopt a policy for determining the rank to be assigned to each taxon. In the past, policies have varied so much that botanists have applied epithets to each other. The botanical vernacular may be more or less codified as follows.

Splitters and Lumpers: Proposers of Unnatural Classification Systems. Obviously, the groups to be assigned scientific names must be natural. For example, they must not be so artificially finely subdivided that a similar system applied to human beings would call for a blue-eyed man to be considered of a different species from his brown-eyed mother.

Persons accepting narrow and unnatural divisions as "taxa" are known as "splitters." For example, in 1905 a particular author decided there were not just 6 or 8 species of *Eschscholtzia* but 112. Most of these were forms of the California poppy (*Eschscholtzia californica*). The California poppy varies somewhat, and there are minor local forms in which particular characters predominate, much as certain human genetic characters are more common in Ireland than in France although they may be found in both countries. Furthermore, the California poppy has a distinctive habit of its own (Fig. 9–3). In the perennial forms of the common var. *crocea*, the stems arising in early spring are robust, the leaves are green and relatively large, the flowers have a predominance of orange, and the torus (receptacle, in this case forming a platform) is large. As the season advances and the ground continues to dry in late spring and summer, the old stems die and the new ones are progressively more slender, the leaves are bluish and smaller, the flowers are smaller and more and more yellow, and the torus is disproportionately smaller. Furthermore, all forms of the species are affected by annual fluctuations of the moisture supply. The plants named in 1905 as different species were of no more stability and distinctness in their characters than the families of a middle-western town might be in theirs, and many of them were merely seasonal forms of the same population.

Persons accepting broad and unnatural divisions are known as "lumpers." The inclusive groups they recognize embrace elements not actually a part of the same genetic series, but exclude other elements of closer relationship.

Liberals and Conservatives: Proposers of Natural Classification Systems. Even though the taxa recognized by a given author are based upon distinctly natural population systems, in establishing policy there is still much to be settled by individual judgment.

Ever since a short time after Linnaeus (1753, 1754) put into effect the binomial system of naming plants according to genera and

Fig. 9–3. Seasonal variation in the characters of a single individual of the California poppy *Eschscholtzia californica* var. *crocea,* the common inland variety: (1) April 17, 1960—the flowers two to three inches in diameter and orange, the rim of the receptacle very broad, the stems robust, the leaves large, the plant green; (2) July 11, 1960—the same plant, the flowers less than one inch in diameter and pale yellow, the rim of the receptacle very narrow, the stems slender, the leaves small, the plant bluish (glaucous). Note the dried stems from the early season and the open capsules on the ground.

species, there have been differences of opinion concerning the breadth of the range of types to be included in each taxon. The taxa recognized by Linnaeus were inclusive, and commonly taxonomists with a tendency to follow him in accepting broad categories have been known in the botanical vernacular as "conservatives." Those tending strongly away from the policies of Linnaeus have been known as "liberals" (or, in extreme cases, "radicals"). There has been a continuous line of conservatives, and schools of liberals and radicals have arisen here and there at one time or another.

Probably there always will be both points of view and varying degrees of intermediate opinion, because all viewpoints are theoretically tenable as long as the classification system is natural. Setting a universal standard is not possible, because of the complexity of the problem and the individuality of human beings who work together by agreement and not by coercion. *The test of a taxonomist's work is not whether he is conservative or liberal but whether he evaluates and organizes well.* The same bit of research may be interpreted conservatively or liberally without theoretical loss of value. The following is an example.

The *Ranunculus occidentalis* complex includes the best-known buttercups occurring from Alaska to Baja California and some confined to the Rocky Mountain system (Figs. 9–4, 9–5). Within this complex there are six major groups, each with a separate geographical range but some having common frontiers with others. Along these boundaries it is possible to find here and there minor local populations displaying various recombinations of the characters of the two adjacent major population systems, but each of these minor groups represents only a minute percentage of the complex as a whole. Within the group commonly called *Ranunculus occidentalis* there are eight principal geographical populations distinguished by fewer or less stable characters than those segregating the six major members of the complex; within *Ranunculus acriformis* there are three; within *Ranunculus austro-oreganus,* one; within *Ranunculus hexasepalus,* one; within *Ranunculus californicus,* five; within *Ranunculus canus,* three.

To summarize, in addition to scores of minor variants, there are 21 population systems of sufficient distinctness and stability of associated characters to be accorded scientific names. Some might consider these to be a single species composed of 21 varieties; others might accept 6 species, each with the number of varieties indicated above; still others would recognize 21 separate species. Any of these three interpretations or others intermediate between them could be defended.

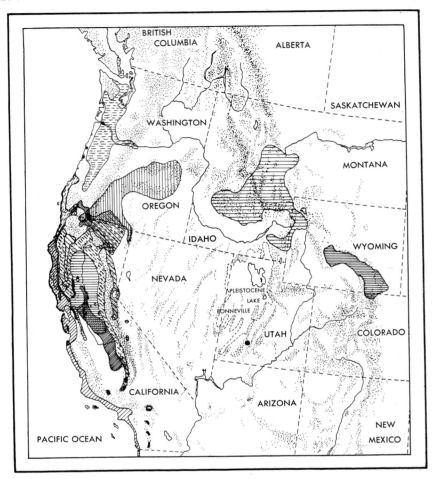

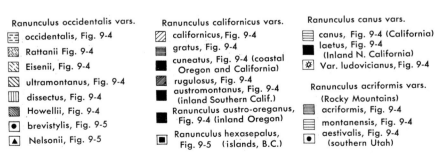

Ranunculus occidentalis vars.

occidentalis, Fig. 9-4

Rattanii Fig. 9-4

Eisenii, Fig. 9-4

ultramontanus, Fig. 9-4

dissectus, Fig. 9-4

Howellii, Fig. 9-4

brevistylis, Fig. 9-5

Nelsonii, Fig. 9-5

Ranunculus californicus vars.

californicus, Fig. 9-4

gratus, Fig. 9-4

cuneatus, Fig. 9-4 (coastal Oregon and California)

rugulosus, Fig. 9-4

austromontanus, Fig. 9-4 (inland Southern Calif.)

Ranunculus austro-oreganus, Fig. 9-4 (inland Oregon)

Ranunculus hexasepalus, Fig. 9-5 (islands, B.C.)

Ranunculus canus vars.

canus, Fig. 9-4 (California)

laetus, Fig. 9-4 (Inland N. California)

Var. ludovicianus, Fig. 9-4

Ranunculus acriformis vars. (Rocky Mountains)

acriformis, Fig. 9-4

montanensis, Fig. 9-4

aestivalis, Fig. 9-4 (southern Utah)

Fig. 9–4. See next page for legend.

Even though any of the three interpretations might be acceptable upon theoretical grounds, there is a practical question to be considered. As far as can be determined, which of the three interpretations is most nearly consistent with policies prevailing in the world as a whole for classifying the entire plant kingdom? It is not desirable to have the names of plants in constant turmoil as different scientific papers and books come out. Even though the ideal of absolute unity of opinion can not be attained, the nearer all taxonomists can come to achieving a common policy the better. Therefore, a system of classification of a particular group which is far out of line with the most generally adopted ones should be examined carefully to determine whether it possesses any particular merit which warrants its retention. Ultimately it should be either a contribution toward a consistent system of classification of the entire plant kingdom or it should be rejected. For example, in 1902 a conservative botanist proposed that all plants in the mustard family should be considered as a single genus, *Crucifera*. This would have required endless recombinations of names, creating an arrangement wholly unfamiliar to anyone. Adopting it would have required not only renaming all the plants of the mustard family but also, for the sake of consistency, the plants of all other families. As another example, from about 1906 to 1929 a very liberal botanist published

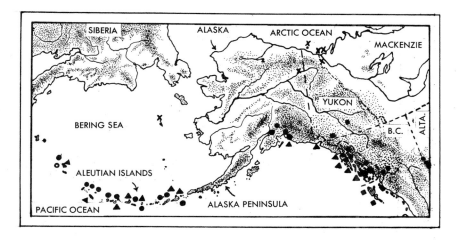

Fig. 9–5.

Figs. 9–4, 9–5. Two maps showing the geographical distribution of the members of the *Ranunculus occidentalis* complex—species and varieties as indicated for the two figures by the key under Fig. 9–4.

an arrangement recognizing 28 genera to represent the group commonly known as a single genus *Astragalus* (locoweeds). This required hundreds of new combinations of names, and, for the sake of consistency of policy, if the matter had been carried to its logical conclusion, it should have required hundreds of thousands or even millions more to bring the treatment of the other genera of the plant kingdom into harmony with the treatment of *Astragalus*.

On purely logical grounds, as long as the populations or groups of populations designated by scientific names are natural, a conservative, liberal, or any intermediate policy in delimiting them must be of equal value. *The choice must be based, therefore, upon practical considerations, including, especially, conformity to prevailing practice throughout the world in classifying the entire plant kingdom.*

The Case for Liberalism. GENERA. The liberal argues that many local species growing side by side and assigned by the conservative to the same genus do not resemble each other sufficiently to be associated quickly and certainly.

SPECIES. The traditional argument of the liberal rests on the need for proper emphasis on minor entities, especially those of local significance. He points out the differences in the related populations occurring in adjacent valleys and calls for describing them under formal specific names instead of burying them in the treatments of broadly defined species. He does not wish them to be described as varieties or taxa of other ranks requiring a trinomial, because he considers combinations of three names awkward to use and not significant in a limited local flora. His interest is in simple reference to the few local or regional forms.

The Case for Conservatism. According to the conservative, usually the liberal viewpoint is primarily a local one—a concern with the plants of a restricted area for their own sake rather than an interest in their relationship to the flora of the earth as a whole. Often the conservative takes a broader view, attempting to correlate elements of the flora on a world-wide basis.

GENERA.[3] Some years ago, even one of the greatest American conservative botanists was so impressed by a highly specialized species collected on the eastern edge of the Sierra Nevada that he

---

[3] Altering the status of a single genus may upset common reference to many included species by changing the binomial combinations of their scientific names. Consequently, stability is of even greater importance on the generic level than on the specific, where each change affects only a single species.

proposed the genus *Beckwithia* to include it. This plant, long known as *Ranunculus Andersonii* [Fig. 9–6 (1)], has red flowers and does not look like a buttercup. It is related closely to *Ranunculus glacialis* [Fig. 9–7 (1)], common in Arctic and Alpine Europe and near enough in its characters to some other *Ranunculi* in the region not to be questioned as a member of the genus. A proposal to use *Beckwithia* for *Ranunculus glacialis* is likely to be taken seriously by only a few European botanists. Nevertheless, any natural segregation of a "genus" *Beckwithia* must include *Ranunculus glacialis*, together with two other species (one, less specialized than *Ranunculus Andersonii*, growing in and near Utah, the other in central Asia) (Figs. 9–6, 9–7, 9–8). This generic segregation has been followed for local purposes by several western-American authors, but on a world-wide basis the proposition is not as attractive as it seems for a restricted area. In local floras often representatives of only a few extreme species may be present, the "connecting links" occurring elsewhere.

SPECIES. Consideration of each local element as a separate species makes it difficult to carry over knowledge from one region to another. The flora of each locality is given the aspect of a local independent unit rather than a phase of the general flora of the continent and of the world as a whole. For individuals concerned with the flora of only a limited geographical region, the need for reconciling the plants of one area with those of another is not encountered, and use of a trinomial, for example, *Prunus virginiana* var. *demissa* for the chokecherry of the Pacific states, may seem cumbersome (Figs. 9–9, 9–10). However, for those who have known elsewhere a closely similar plant such as *Prunus virginiana* var. *virginiana*, the chokecherry of the East and Middle West, it is helpful to know that the plant encountered in a new situation is similar to the one known earlier. This is true even though it differs in some not wholly stable characters occurring through a particular geographical area. If the Pacific-region chokecherry, for example, appears simply under the binomial *Prunus demissa*, there is no ready correlation with its near relatives. Several books written by members of the American "liberal" school of the early twentieth century cover one or another of the states or larger portions of the Far West. In each manual one or two chokecherries are described; in some books *Prunus demissa* appears; in some, *Prunus melanocarpa*; in some, both. Nowhere in these books is there a statement of close relationship to *Prunus virginiana*. Except that the chokecherries are among the small percentage of plants with well-established English names, all

Fig. 9–6. Ranunculus, subgenus Crymodes—I, a pair of related species occurring in a markedly disjunct pattern (see Figs. 9–7, 9–8): (1) Ranunculus Andersonii (Bishop, California); (2) Ranunculus juniperinus (east of Zion National Park, Utah).

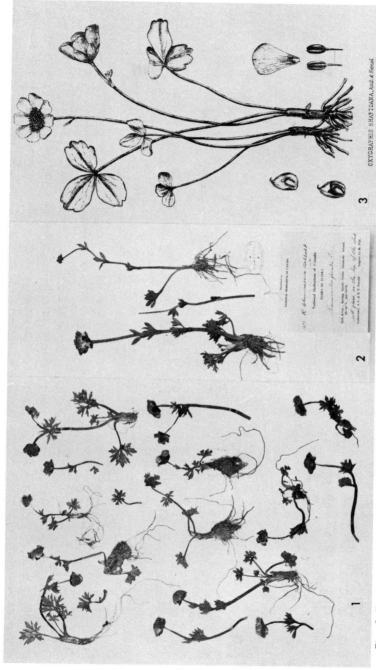

Fig. 9–7. *Ranunculus*, subgenus *Crymodes*—II, a group of related relict species occurring in a markedly disjunct pattern (see Figs. 9–6, 9–8): (1) *Ranunculus glacialis* var. *glacialis* (Snoritjakko, Lake Torneträsk, Swedish Lapland); (2) var. *Chamissonis* (Little Diomede Island, Bering Strait, Alaska); (3) *Ranunculus Shaftoanus* (Afghanistan). [Item (3) from James Edward Aitchison and William B. Hemsley, Journal of the Linnaean Society, London 19: 149, Fig. B, 1882. Used by permission.]

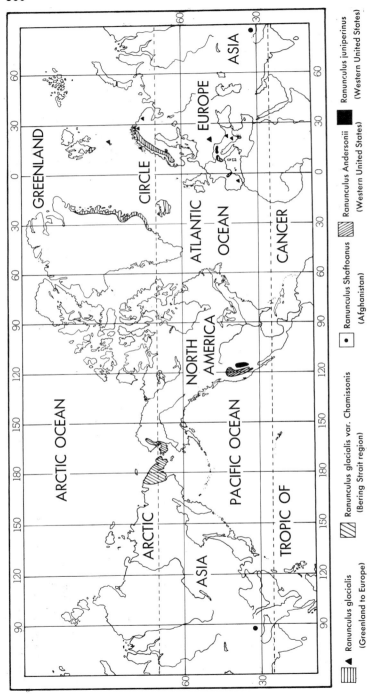

Fig. 9–8. *Ranunculus*, subgenus Crymodes, distributional map of the species and varieties, as indicated. This subgenus is remarkable for disjunction in occurrence of its members, which probably are remnants of once much more widely distributed populations.

Fig. 9–9. Chokecherries, in flower (see map, Fig. 9–10): (1) the Pacific-coast and Great Basin chokecherry, *Prunus virginiana* var. *demissa* (Santa Cruz Mountains, California); (2) the Rocky Mountain black chokecherry, var. *melanocarpa* (Las Vegas, New Mexico); (3) the eastern chokecherry, var. *virginiana* (East Northfield, Massachusetts).

evidence of their transcontinental relationship and of their intergradation in and near the northern Rocky Mountains is obliterated. According to the conservative position, it is far better to consider these incompletely differentiated geographical units as follows: *Prunus virginiana* var. *virginiana* of the East and Middle West, *Prunus virginiana* var. *melanocarpa* of the Rocky Mountains and the Great Basin, *Prunus virginiana* var. *demissa* largely of the Pacific

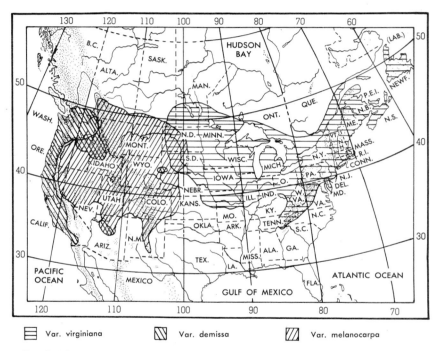

Fig. 9–10. Geographical distribution of the chokecherries, varieties of *Prunus virginiana*, as indicated. (Base map copyright Denoyer-Geppert Co., Chicago. Used by permission.)

Slope but occurring far inland in some areas. Adoption of such a policy makes **variety** a strong and useful category of value in improving organization (for **subspecies** see pp. 350–352).

Many fairly well-marked natural populations or groups of populations lack single characters of sufficient stability or consistency of association to make feasible their segregation by keys. In the conservative view, these are considered more effectively as varieties than as species, because subordinate status removes the necessity of attempting to segregate them by keys and it leaves for separation within the keys only the major populations with relatively clear and stable diagnostic characters. Varieties, then, may be segregated in a table, (see Table 9–1 for the varieties of *Ranunculus Gmelinii*, Figs. 9–11, 9–12, 9–13), thus throwing the burden of identification on the whole complex of characters rather than on one or two, as in a key, and furnishing a ready means of character comparison from one variety to the next. The point becomes clear with an attempt

TABLE 9–1
Varieties of *Ranunculus Gmelinii*

Var. *Gmelinii*	Var. *limosus*	Var. *Hookeri*
Sparsely to markedly hirsute.	Markedly pubescent.	Glabrous or essentially so.
Stems 0.5–2 dm. long, 0.5–1 mm. in diameter.	Stems mostly 1–2 dm. long, 0.7–1 mm. in diameter.	Stems 1 or usually 2–5 dm. long, 1.5–3 dm. in diameter.
Leaf blades 0.8–1.2 or 1.5 cm. in diameter, 3-parted or -divided and again 3-lobed to -parted, usually finely dissected into linear, acute divisions.	Leaf blades 0.8–1.5 mm. long, 1–1.7 cm. broad, usually 3-parted and again once or twice lobed, the segments usually entire and apically broad and rounded or obtuse but sometimes dissected.	Leaf blades 1–2 cm. long, 1.5–2.5 cm. broad, very rarely larger, deeply 3-parted or -divided, the divisions again 2–3 times forked or sometimes dissected into ribbon-like divisions.
Sepals 2.5–3 mm. long.	Sepals about 2.5–3.5 mm. long.	Sepals 4–6 mm. long.
Petals obovate-oblanceolate to obovate, 3.5–4 mm. long, 1.5–2 or 3 mm. broad.	Petals broadly obovate to orbicular, 4–5 mm. long, 3.5–5 mm. broad.	Petals orbicular or obovate, 4–7 mm. long, 3–6 mm. broad.
Northern and central Alaska to Keewatin and to Peace River, Alberta; rare in northern Minnesota; northern European Russia and Siberia.	Eastern British Columbia and Alberta and rare eastward to Manitoba and adjacent North Dakota; rare in Washington, Idaho, Montana, Utah, and Colorado.	Central Alaska and the Yukon to Newfoundland (including Labrador) and Nova Scotia; southward to eastern Oregon northern Nevada, Utah, New Mexico, North Dakota, Iowa, Michigan, and Maine.

to identify species according to the keys appearing in floras and manuals in which a markedly liberal policy has been followed. Despite the care with which a genus may have been studied and despite penetrating research, fine division of species inevitably yields a key which at many points breaks down just above the "species" level.

Thus, according to the conservative viewpoint, the local units of interest to the liberal are treated best not as species but as varieties

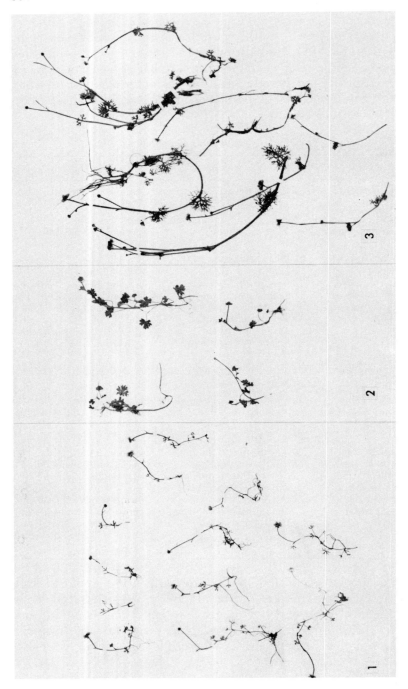

Fig. 9–11. Varieties of *Ranunculus Gmelinii* (Figs. 9–12, 9–13: (1) var. *Gmelinii* (Lake Noluk, Brooks Range, Alaska); (2) var. *limosus* (Marble Mountains, British Columbia); (3) var. *Hookeri* (Cecil Bay, Emmet County, Michigan).

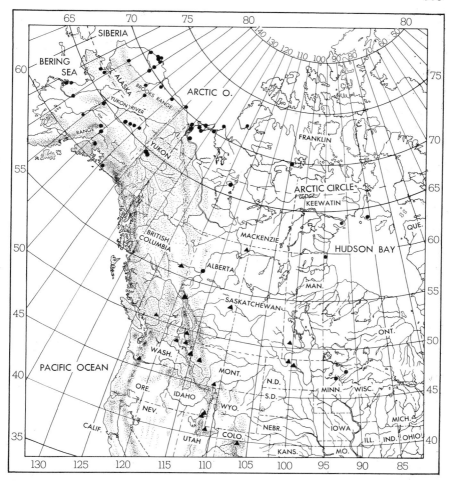

Fig. 9–12. Distribution in North America of the varieties of *Ranunculus Gmelinii*—I: circles, var. *Gmelinii*, mostly Asian; triangles, var. *limosus*, an endemic variety.

or subspecies (to be given formal scientific names) and minor forms or variants (to be described and discussed but not necessarily named formally). If minor taxa are treated as species, the important outlines of classification within the genus are obscured in a mass of detail.

As was pointed out above, if classification is to attain stability, conformity with prevailing practice is necessary. The traditional policy is conservative, and the various schools of liberalism which

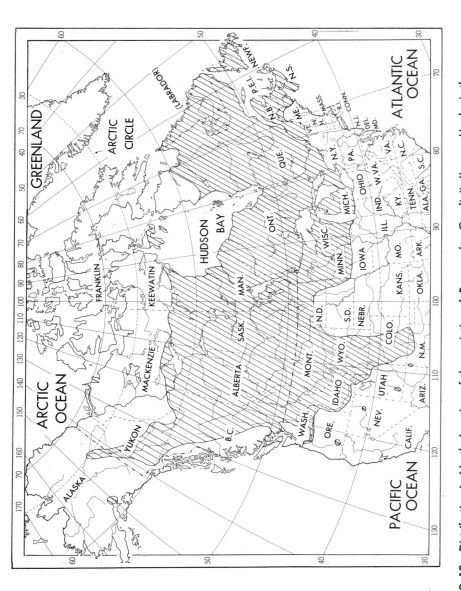

Fig. 9–13. Distribution in North America of the varieties of *Ranunculus Gmelinii*—II: var. *Hookeri*, the common and well-known endemic variety. (Base map, Goode Map Series, copyright by the University of Chicago. Used by permission.)

have arisen from time to time have been localized and discontinuous. Each of these liberal or often radical schools has produced works not in harmony with prevailing practice in classification in the world as a whole.

For example, the principal book on the cactus family represents a local liberalism endemic in the United States in the period from about 1900 to 1930. This series of volumes, representing a great deal of research, has not been matched by a complete comparable treatment of the cacti according to conservative policy, and the result is retention in popular, semitechnical, and technical works of microgenera and microspecies of a degree not recognized by botanists for other families. To classify the rest of the plant kingdom according to a policy comparable to that current in many books on the Cactaceae would require more than 1,000,000 changes or additions of plant names.

In this instance, conformity with prevailing practice presents a special problem. Common usage among non-botanists interested in the cactus family is recognition of many generic and specific names for finely divided taxa. Thus the botanist is confronted with the choice of conformity with prevailing horticultural practice in the study of one group of plants or with botanical practice in interpretation of all groups.

SUMMARY

Both differentiation and isolation of natural population systems occur in an infinite number of degrees. However, the taxonomic ranks into which they are classified must be few. Consequently, assignment of natural populations or of population systems to taxa involves judgment.

A living natural species is a reproducing population or system of populations of genetically closely related individuals. The question of *how closely* cannot be answered in precise terms, and definition of the term *species* is possible only if no attempt is made to limit the category.

Taxa of lower or higher ranks are defined in exactly the same words as species, except that the word "closely" is omitted from the definition. A species is a group of related varieties; a genus, of related species; a family, of related genera; an order, of related families; etc.

On purely logical grounds, a liberal or conservative interpretation of taxa, or any intermediate between these two extremes, is of equal value. The choice must be based, therefore, upon practical considerations, including conformity with prevailing practice through the world as a whole for classification of the entire plant kingdom. The liberal point of view tends to be adopted by those who are interested in localized forms such as the plants occurring in a single state. Segregation of these may be fairly simple, and the chief concern is to recognize each one. The interest of the conservative is more likely to be broad. His primary object may be to correlate floral elements on a world-wide basis. Thus he tends to include more forms within each category, for example, within each species. Recognition of local forms as infraspecific taxa makes possible a readier correlation of plants growing in distant areas. For example, the chokecherries of the East, the Rocky Mountain Region, and the Pacific coast are three taxa which the liberal would consider three independent species, while the conservative would consider them local varieties of the same broad species. Thus, under a conservative policy, distant floras are correlated.

Since no arbitrary standards are possible and since classification depends ultimately upon human judgment, the goal of a uniform policy in classification is difficult to attain.

SUGGESTED READING

BAKER, H. G. 1952. Preference is for special biosystematic terminology instead of taxonomic species (see TURESSON, 1922a; CLAUSEN, KECK, and HIESEY, 1939; and CLAUSEN, 1958). For a review of this subject, see CONSTANCE, 1953.

BURMA, BENJAMIN H. 1949a. The view that "species" have only a subjective existence and that the real biological unit is the breeding population (see papers below and DUNBAR, 1950; ELIAS, 1950; MAYR, 1949a; and SIMPSON, 1951).

———. 1949b. See above.

———. 1954. The view that the term "species" should be overthrown and a new one coined for phyletic-line segments.

BUXBAUM, FRANZ. 1951. A textbook covering the general field of taxonomy.

CLAUSEN, JENS. 1958. The value of the concept of ecotypes for evolutionary and experimental studies (see TURESSON, 1922a; CLAUSEN, KECK, and HIESEY, 1939; and, for a review of the subject, CONSTANCE, 1953).

CONSTANCE, LINCOLN. 1953. See Suggested Reading, Chapter 6.

CRONQUIST, ARTHUR. 1955. Discussion of species.

DAVIDSON, J. F. 1954. The view that the "species problem" is not so much what constitutes a species as what are the attributes of the individuals included in the species.

DUNBAR, CARL O. 1950. See BURMA, 1949a, 1949b; ELIAS, 1950; MAYR, 1949a, 1949b; and SIMPSON, 1951. Paleontological vs. zoological points of view.

ELIAS, MAXIM K. 1950. See BURMA, 1949a, 1949b; DUNBAR, 1950; MAYR, 1949a, 1949b; and SIMPSON, 1951.

EPLING, CARL. 1939. An analysis of the nature of taxa and of the background of their classification.

———, and W. CATLIN. 1950. The processes affecting adaptation or development of a character in relation to individuals in the breeding population and the effective environment.

FÆGRI, KNUT. 1935. See below.

———. 1937. Discussion of the fundamental concept of species and other taxa, with emphasis on the studies and viewpoints of Scandinavian authors.

GRANT, VERNE. 1949. This and the following paper gave a strong impetus to revival of the neglected study of pollinating mechanisms and pointed out their significance in speciation and taxonomy. Isolation resulting from mechanical features of the flower and of the body of the insect and from the habits of insects which exhibit degrees of flower constancy.
————. 1950. See above.
————. 1952.
————. 1956a. A thorough exposition and a critical evaluation of the species problem.
————. 1957. A thorough and important general review of the species problem in terms of (1) population systems only partly differentiated and not yet at the species level, (2) reproductively isolated populations without obvious distinguishing characters, (3) hybrid populations, and (4) apomixis.
HALL, HARVEY MONROE. 1926.
————, and FREDERICK E. CLEMENTS. 1923. A classic work with examples of monographs.
HEDBERG, OLAV. 1958. See Suggested Reading, Chapter 3.
HESLOP-HARRISON, J. 1954. See Suggested Reading, Chapter 8.
INGER, ROBERT F. 1958. Taxa are conceived as based on genetics, developmental mechanics, behavior, and ecology, which are likely to lead to an understanding of phylogeny, which, in turn, must be the foundation of classification.
KECK, DAVID D. 1957. See Suggested Reading, Chapter 8.
LAWRENCE, GEORGE H. M. 1951. A textbook, covering several areas of the field.
LEWIS, HARLAN. 1955. Definition of taxa of specific and infraspecific rank.
LÖVE, ÁSKELL. 1954. Definition of species based on intersterility and the view that groups with differing chromosome numbers must be classified as different species.
MAYR, ERNST. 1949a. The view of a zoologist as opposed to a paleontologist, the difference arising partly from the types of data available in the two fields and partly from recent developments in botany and zoology.
————. 1949b. See above.
————. 1951. An example of species of animals sharply defined in some areas and highly irregular and intergrading in others, a phenomenon common in plants but more unusual in vertebrate animals.
OWNBY, MARION. 1950. Discussion of three European diploid species introduced as weeds in the United States, of sterile diploid hybrids, and of tetraploid hybrids which have formed small populations (raises the issue of whether these populations are to be named as species).
ROLLINS, REED C. 1952. See Suggested Reading, Chapter 8.
————. 1957. See Suggested Reading, Chapter 8.
ROTHMALER, WERNER. 1950. A general textbook of taxonomy and plant distribution.
SIMPSON, GEORGE GAYLORD. 1951. The difficulty of distinguishing species in paleontology in (1) the basic genetic and evolutionary sense and (2) the sense of subdivisions in a continuous line of ancestors and descendants through geological time. Paleontological "species" may be of either sort (See BURMA, 1949a, 1949b; DUNBAR, 1950; ELIAS, 1950; and MAYR, 1949a, 1949b).
STEBBINS, G. LEDYARD, JR. 1942. The lack of direct correlation between the genetic isolating mechanisms which produce hybrid sterility and the genetic changes which make species visibly different.
————. 1956. The view that genera are differentiated by a continuation of the processes leading to speciation, but with a greater degree of extinction of intermediate populations.
STRAW, RICHARD M. 1955. Sympatric speciation in flowering plants pollinated by essentially flower-constant insects.
————. 1956. Isolation through differing groups of pollinating insects.
VALENTINE, D. H., and ÁSKELL LÖVE. 1958. The view that species (1) known only from herbarium specimens, (2) known and studied in the field, and (3) studied cytologically and experimentally may be classified differently according to the state of knowledge concerning them. A compromise between "taxonomic" and "biosystematic" points of view is sought.

chapter
10

Classification of
the Higher Taxa

Not even the kingdoms of plants and animals are clearly distinct. In many minute living organisms characters commonly considered to be the special distinctive features of the plant kingdom may be combined with those of the animal kingdom. These borderline creatures are claimed by both botanists and zoologists and are described in the textbooks of both fields.

Plants and animals have been distinguished from each other on many bases, including presence or absence of each of the following: (1) power of locomotion, (2) green color, (3) ability to digest and absorb solid foods, (4) cellulose cell walls, (5) terminal as opposed to other growth. Although these criteria seem obvious, each fails in some or many instances, as will be shown in the following discussion.

Power of locomotion in plants seldom is apparent to the naked eye, but many simple plants are motile, and only some very simple plants and the seed plants (and even these with exceptions) do not move rapidly during some special phase or phases of the life cycle. Movement is a common and obvious animal character, but some animals spend most or all of their lives fastened in one place. Thus, although a stationary existence is usual among the best-known plants and motion is the tendency among animals, motility is not an absolute criterion serving to separate the two kingdoms of living organisms.

Green color is a characteristic plant feature, and most plants have chlorophyll, but many do not. Examples of the latter include the bacteria, slime molds, fungi, and even some flowering plants, for example, dodder in the morning-glory family and some members of the orchid and heather families. All undoubted animals lack chlorophyll, but a few intermediate organisms possess it. An example is *Euglena*, which may be assigned to either kingdom.

Ability to digest and absorb solid foods from external sources is not the rule among plants, and it is nearly universal in the animal kingdom. This ability is unnecessary for green plants, but for the non-green ones it is fundamental. Some of the plants mentioned in the preceding paragraph are **saprophytes**, that is, they digest dead organic matter such as the leaf mold of forest floors. The most striking examples of plants which digest and absorb food from external sources are the ones (particularly in the Sarraceniaceae) which trap and digest animals, usually insects. One of the more elaborate of these is the cobra plant (*Darlingtonia*), the pitcher plant of California. An insect is attracted into the hood at the top of the tubular leaf. When the visitor is ready to leave, it flies toward the most obvious source of light, an area of transparent window-like cells opposite the entrance. For a time the captive beats against these windows, but finally it falls into a funnel-like tube formed by the petiole and the basal portion of the leaf. The tube is lined with downward-directed hairs which prevent escape. Here the insect dies and then decays by bacterial action. The plant may absorb the liberated substances. In the less elaborate pitcher plants (*Sarracenia*) of the eastern United States, the basal portion of the leaf secretes digestive juices. In the Venus flytrap of the southern states the two halves of the leaf behave somewhat like the jaws of a steel trap, snapping together and enclosing the insect, which then is digested and absorbed. In insectivorous plants of the sundew group occurring in northern and eastern North America the sticky hairlike glands on the upper side of the leaf catch the insect by the feet, and in some cases other leaves move over and surround the victim. In all these examples the food material is digested essentially outside the body of the plant. Fundamentally, however, the same is true for most animals because the alimentary canal is merely a tube enclosing an area technically outside the body.

Cellulose cell walls are typical of plants. Cellulose is a basic material of wood and paper, and cotton fibers are nearly pure cellulose. However, many plant cell walls are largely of other substances, many algae lack cellulose, and often its presence is open to question. Thus, the presence or absence of cellulose is not a reliable criterion, even though this substance is always or nearly always absent in animals.

Terminal growth is common in the bryophytes and the vascular plants, but it is not the only type in these, and it is not necessarily characteristic of algae or fungi.

No single character always occurs in the plant kingdom and never in the animal kingdom or vice versa. However, the vast majority of plants and animals may be segregated by a combination of the characters mentioned above, accompanied by others, and the intermediate types are relative few.

THE HIGHER PLANT TAXA

On even the highest level of taxonomic ranks, the problem of classification is the same as on the level of genera, species, and varieties. This principle applies to divisions, classes, orders, and families, and to such intercalated additional taxonomic categories as subclasses, subfamilies, and tribes.

Divisions. For many years North American textbooks of botany have divided the plant kingdom into the classical divisions of Eichler, as follows:

Thallophyta—thallus plants: the algae and fungi
Bryophyta—moss plants: the hornworts, liverworts, and mosses
Pteridophyta—fern plants: the club mosses, psilotums, horsetails, and ferns
Spermatophya—seed plants: the gymnosperms and flowering plants

Many authors have proposed alteration of these classical divisions into a greater number of divisions of lesser scope. In view of the wide diversity of plants included within some of the divisions of Eichler, this has seemed justified. However, fossil plants form connecting links which have made separation difficult. An example is classification of the groups included by Eichler in his broad division Pteridophyta. The *Psilotum*, club moss, horsetail, and fern lines of development are connected relatively clearly by series of fossil plants, and, if these fossils are included in the classification system, retention of all pteridophytes within a single division of the plant kingdom is justified. This raises the question discussed in the beginning of Chapter 5: "Are the limits of taxa to be determined in accordance with inclusion of extinct organisms as well as the living ones?"

Any two taxa derived from a common ancestor may have diverged, as shown by the circles in Fig. 9–1. Each pair of circles represents the degree of isolation of the two taxa in a later unit of geological time. Thus, classification of the taxa represented by the circles could not have remained unchanged through two long geological periods. They began as a single unit which became less homogeneous; in time they became differentiated as two units difficult to segregate; finally they became two clearly distinct units. The usual course of history of taxa parallels this series of diagrams, their limits having changed with the passage of geological time.

As was pointed out in the beginning of Chapter 5, an attempt to include plants of the past with those of the present must always, if enough fossils are known, bring about the amalgamation of the units of the plant or animal kingdom. Knowledge of the past course of evolution is nevertheless fundamental to understanding the relationships of living organisms and therefore to construction of the taxonomic system.

Among the major taxa known only from fossils are various extinct orders of pteridophytes, as used in the broad sense to include Psilophyta, Lycophyta, Sphenophyta, and Pteridophyta. Among these are the Psilophytales, Lepidodendrales, Lepidocarpales, Hyeniales, Sphenophyllales, and Coenopteridales. The families Pleuromeiaceae and Calamitaceae resembled the living families Isoëtaceae and Equisetaceae so closely that, if the two in either pair had lived at the same time, they would have been included in the same order. The following orders of gymnosperms also are known only from fossils: Cycadofilicales, Bennettitales, and Cordaitales. Although innumerable groups of flowering plants must have lived before the present ones, they are known only imperfectly. This is because either soft floral parts are not preserved or their remains are inadequate for showing structural details.

Figure 10–1 indicates the known living and extinct pteridophytes and spermatophytes and their possible classification at various times from the Cambrian or Silurian periods and the early Devonian period to the present. Probably through divergent evolution the ancient division Psilophyta has become gradually modified into the four modern divisions of pteridophytes and one division of seed plants. By middle Devonian times it may have become indistinctly divided into four inconsistently differentiated units. In upper Devonian times these were more clearly segregated, and other groups leading ultimately to the chief groups of seed plants probably were in existence. Since Carboniferous times four major units, the Psilophyta, Lycophyta, Sphenophyta, and Pteridophyta, have represented the *Psilotum* line, club moss line, horsetail line, and fern line of development. Certainly the living members of these groups now represent different divisions of the plant kingdom.

Some have argued that the fern division should include both the pteridophytes and the spermatophytes, as classified here. In the past these constituted a single division, but this has divided into two modern units as distinctive and significant as any of the three other entire surviving lines of development among vascular plants.

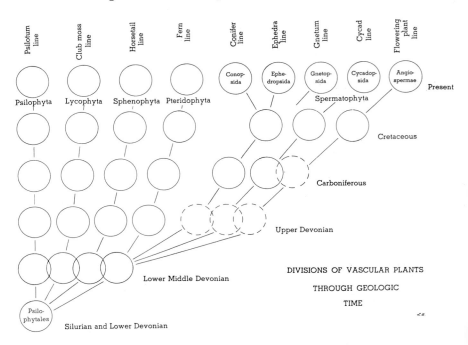

Fig. 10–1. Diagram indicating the possible divergence of the major taxa of vascular plants through geologic time. Uncertainties and gaps in the record are numerous. (From Lyman Benson, *Plant Classification*, D. C. Heath & Co., 1957, p. ix. Used by permission.)

Imperfect series of fossils connect the five divisions of vascular plants, but in classification of most groups they are lacking for the following reasons: (1) The plants may not have grown in marshes or other habitats favorable to formation of fossils; (2) they may have lacked hard parts readily fossilized; or (3) they may not have occurred in the more carefully explored regions of the earth and may not be known.

Classes. The five living groups of Spermatophyta, representing the flowering-plant, conifer, *Ephedra, Gnetum,* and cycad lines of development, were not derived from each other. The interrelationships of the classes of flowering plants and gymnosperms are based upon inference of underlying phylogenetic relationship, as indicated by many characters occurring in all of them. Probably their common ancestry is remote, for the gaps between them are great. As far back as each line can be traced in geological history it has been separate from each of the others. Lines of development from which the conifers and cycads arose have been segregated since at least Carboniferous times and probably since middle Devonian. The origins of the flowering-plant, *Ephedra*, and *Gnetum* lines in Mesozoic or possibly Paleozoic times are not documented by fossils. Probably all these lines of development originated from early members of the fern line, but data are inadequate for determination of this point. Thus these five groups must be classified as relatively high-ranking taxa at either the division or the class level. As classes they may be known as Conopsida, Ephedropsida, Gnetopsida, Cycadopsida, and Angiospermae.

Subclasses. The rank of subclass is used only rarely as an extra category between class and order. Commonly it is employed to differentiate dicotyledons from monocotyledons (Dicotyledoneae and Monocotyledoneae).

The line between these two groups is fairly sharp. However, the flower patterns of two orders, one in each group, are identical insofar as general structure is concerned (Figs. 1–1, 1–3). Some of the six more obvious characters ordinarily distinguishing the subclasses break down between the Ranales and the Alismales. The herbaceous Ranales have a fibrous root system like that in the Monocotyledoneae. Although the "vascular bundles" of the Ranales are arranged as in the other Dicotyledoneae, their internal structure is reminiscent of the Monocotyledoneae. Cambial activity does not occur in the stems of many herbaceous Ranales. The leaf venation of the Alismales may be somewhat netted. Parts of the flowers in half the families of the Ranales are in threes, as in the Monocotyledoneae. *Ranunculus Ficaria* develops only one cotyledon, the other being abortive. Probably some of these characters represent parallel development, but some tend to weaken the distinction of dicotyledons and monocotyledons. Furthermore, the pollen (Fig. 10–11) of all monocotyledons is monocolpate; that of dicotyledons in general is tricolpate. However, monocolpate pollen appears among presumably primitive woody Ranales.

The two orders Ranales and Alismales have retained probably primitive characters which may have existed among the plants ancestral to the present angiosperms.

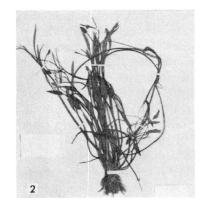
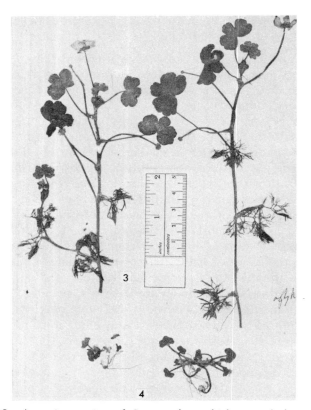

Fig. 10–2. Aquatic species of *Ranunculus*, which may belong to widely differing subgenera and sections of the genus (see also the varieties of *Ranunculus Gmelinii* [subgenus *Ranunculus*, section *Hecatonia*], Figs. 9–11, 9–12, 9–13): (1) *Ranunculus aquatilis* var. *capillaceus* (subgenus *Batrachium*), a Eura-

The surviving Alismales are composed of two families of highly specialized aquatic plants with a relatively primitive flower structure. The Ranales include a great diversity of plants which have evolved in many directions. Among them are as highly specialized aquatics as those in Alismales, for example, the Nymphaeaceae, or water lily family, and the Ceratophyllaceae, or hornwort family. Aquatics are to be found also in several groups of the Ranunculaceae, or buttercup family. Even within the genus *Ranunculus* there are several groups of aquatics, not closely related to each other and specialized in different ways (Fig. 10–2). Some of these are similar in form, others are not. Parallel development in vegetative features of the subgenus *Batrachium* (for example, *Ranunculus aquatilis*) and of the only remotely related species of the subgenus *Ranunculus* section *Hecatonia* (for example, *Ranunculus flabellaris* and *Ranunculus Gmelinii*) is remarkable. Similarities in appearance of these two groups to other aquatic species such as *Ranunculus Pallasii*, *Ranunculus hydrocharoides,* and forms of *Ranunculus Cymbalaria* are relatively much less. Thus specialized aquatics have evolved a number of times within the Ranales and particularly within the genus *Ranunculus.* Probably the aquatic Alismales are survivors from a once much more highly developed group which may have included terrestrial as well as aquatic and marsh plants. The fact that the survivors are specialized aquatics does not preclude the possibility that the Alismales have retained more other features of the ancestral groups of monocotyledons than any other order or that they are related at least remotely to the Ranales. Neither does the presence in their roots of the most highly developed type of monocotyledonous vessels (Cheadle, 1942), but these factors show that the Alismales are not in themselves a strictly primitive group.

Certainly neither the Ranales nor the Alismales can be considered ancestral to the other orders, and neither is necessarily the starting point for classification of flowering plants. Nevertheless, their similarity to each other is significant in classification of the dicotyledons and monocotyledons and in gaining some idea of the likely interrelationships of the various orders in both groups.

---

sian and North American plant (Modoc County, California); (2) *Ranunculus hydrocharoides* var. *natans* (State of Mexico, Mexico) (subgenus *Ranunculus* section *Flammula*); (3) water buttercup (*Ranunculus aquatilis* L.), material possibly to be designated as a lectotype; (4) *Ranunculus hederaceus* L. [(3–4) photograph (larger scale than the others) courtesy of Carl G. Alm and Library of the Institute of Systematic Botany, University of Uppsala. Used by permission.] An aquatic species, *Ranunculus Pallasii,* of the subgenus *Pallasiantha* occurs in the Arctic regions of North America.

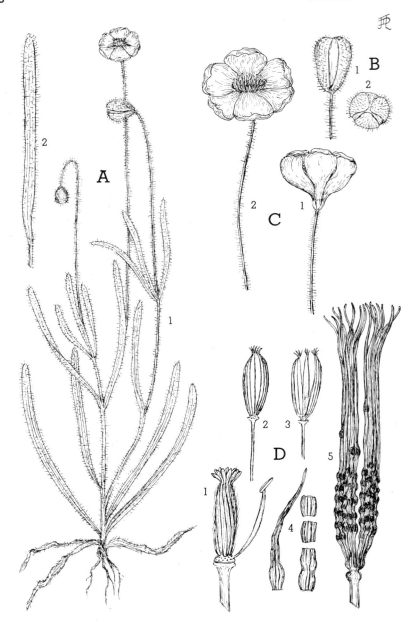

Fig. 10–3. A species on the border line between the Ranales and Papaver-ales, the cream cup (*Platystemon californicus*) (Papaverales, Papaveraceae or poppy family)—a plant whose sepals and petals are trimerous, as are those of many Ranales and a few other Papaveraceae, and whose carpels are lightly

Orders. Classifying the orders of flowering plants is particularly difficult. The Angiospermae are a rapidly developing class of relatively recent origin. During the last 100,000,000 to 150,000,000 years and particularly the last 50,000,000, the members of the class have occupied nearly all the favorable habitats of the earth. They have undergone an explosive type of evolution resulting in at least 175,000 species in intricately interrelated genera, families, and orders. The evolutionary or phylogenetic gaps between taxa at all levels are irregular and often slight or non-existent.

Some lines of development are segregated clearly in their extreme forms, but some members of one order are related more closely to members of another than to the opposite extremes of their own. An example of this is the genus *Platystemon* (Fig. 10–3) (cream cup) of the poppy family. There is no question of its close relationship to similar poppies; neither is there any doubt of its close affinity to some members of the order Ranales. Flower structure of the Papaveraceae and many Ranales is nearly identical, and the genus *Platystemon* and a few related genera of the Papaveraceae are the only members of the Papaverales having sepals and petals in cycles of three. This character occurs in about half the members of the Ranales, and, as was pointed out above, it is one of the characters in common with the monocotyledons. The character most sharply distinguishing the Papaverales from the Ranales is the usually small number (4 to 9) of coalescent carpels in the former and the usually though not necessarily large number of separate carpels in the latter. The cream cup has a relatively large number of carpels (6 to 17 or sometimes 20). These are lightly coalescent at flowering time, and they separate of their own accord as the fruit reaches maturity. Although the border zone between the two orders is not sharp, the Papaverales as a whole form a consistent unit nearly all of whose members are strongly different from the Ranales. At the opposite extreme within the Papaverales from the poppy family, the mustard family (Cruciferae) is much farther removed from the cream cup than are some members of the Ranales. Thus,

---

coalescent in flower but separate at fruiting time, the characters of the plant placing it within the Papaverales but very near in relationships to the Ranales: (A)(1–2) habit; (B)(1–2) buds, showing the sepals which fall early (are caducous) as in the Papaveraceae; (C)(1–2) flowers after falling of the sepals; (D)(1–3) stages in separation of the carpels, (4) carpel with its segments enlarged, (5) old carpels no longer clearly coalescent, with conspicuous bulges in the areas of the seeds. (By J. D. Laudermilk for Lyman Benson, *Plant Classification*, D. C. Heath & Co., 1957, p. 136. Used by permission.)

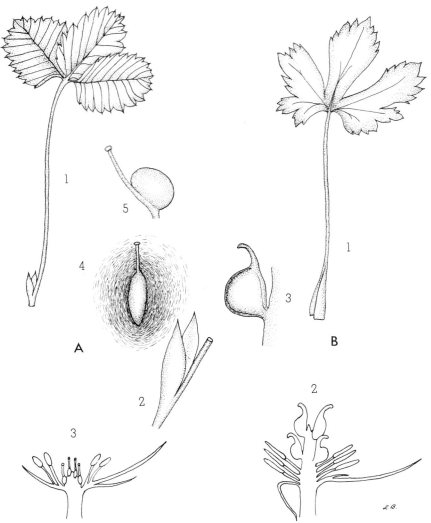

Fig. 10–4. Similar members of the Rosales and the Ranales: (A) a wild strawberry, *Fragaria californica*—(1) leaf with stipules, a characteristic of the Rosales, (2) stipules, enlarged, (3) longitudinal section of the perigynous flower, perigyny or epigyny being characteristic of many though not all Rosales, (4) the true fruit (achene) in a depression in the surface of the red, edible receptacle, (5) achene removed from the receptacle, showing the stigma, style, and ovary; (B) a buttercup, *Ranunculus occidentalis*—(1) leaf, with an expanded leaf base but, as in nearly all Ranales, with no stipules, (2) longitudinal section of the hypogynous flower, characteristic of the Ranales, (3) one of the fruits (achenes) developed from a pistil of the type in (2).

if emphasis is placed upon the order as a whole rather than upon the border zone, segregation of the Papaverales from the Ranales is reasonable.

Distinction of the Rosales from the Ranales is justified similarly, though the case is less clear. The best-known members of the Rosales are those occurring in the temperate regions of the Northern Hemisphere, including the areas of Europe and North America in which most of the study of plant classification has centered. The Rosales of these areas are mostly with perigynous or epigynous flowers and with stipules, and these two characters have been supposed to segregate the two orders (Fig. 10–4). Nevertheless, in the world as a whole about half the families of Rosales have hypogynous flowers; and some families of the Rosales do not have stipules, while several members of the Ranales do. The actual segregation of the two orders, as with most pairs of taxa, is **not** upon the basis of character pairs taken singly, but of a group of differentiating characters. In this instance no single character in the complex is infallible in itself. The effectiveness of every distinguishing feature segregating the two groups has been broken down, often by parallel evolution.

There have been many attempts to subdivide the Rosales and other orders into smaller, more consistent units. However, the connecting forms between the extremes are so numerous that there are no obviously reasonable dividing lines. Proposals include segregation of one order centered about the Rosaceae and another about the Saxifragaceae. Often a third group, based primarily upon the Hamamelidaceae is segregated from the one based upon the Saxifragaceae. If such segregations are to be made, a clear distinction between the Rosaceae and the Saxifragaceae must be found. These two families are not keyed apart simply, and their relationship is close. Characters in the parallel list are the most reliable found so far for segregation of the two families, but inspection shows the separation to be difficult. In many books the families are distinguished on the basis of presence or absence of endosperm in the seeds, and this is extended to the orders based upon the families. As recorded in various books, occurrence of this character is inconsistent. Dissection of a relatively small number of seeds bears this out, but far more investigation is necessary before the applicability of the distinction can be shown to be either valid or invalid. Determination of the occurrence or absence of any one of these characters in a considerable number of members of each family is the work of a large part of a lifetime. Table 10–1 merely summarizes the data available.

TABLE 10–1

Characters Differentiating the Saxifragaceae from the Rosaceae

Rosaceae	Saxifragaceae
Fruit indehiscent, except when there are 3 or more follicles per flower (these sometimes barely coalescent basally but splitting lengthwise at maturity). (Note: When the ovary is inferior, in fruit it becomes a pome with 2–5 chambers and axile placentae.)	Fruit dehiscent, a capsule (the carpels rarely 5–7 and nearly separate, then dehiscent horizontally and forming a pyxis) or in *Ribes* indehiscent and a berry which is inferior, 1-chambered, and with parietal placentae.
Stipules present, except in *Spiraea* and *Holodiscus,* but often early deciduous.	Stipules none, except sometimes in *Heuchera* and sometimes in *Ribes.*
Stamens usually numerous, more than 10, except (a) in herbs with pinnate or 3-foliolate leaves (*Alchemilla, Acaena,* and some species of *Agrimonia, Potentilla,* and *Sanguisorba*) and (b) in shrubs or trees with alternate leaves which are not palmately veined or lobed (10 in *Photinia* and 5–10 in some species of *Crataegus* and perhaps *Spiraea* and *Adenostoma*); leaves alternate.	Stamens 3–10, except in shrubs with opposite leaves (*Carpenteria, Philadelphus, Decumaria,* and sometimes *Whipplea* in the *Hydrageoideae*).
Carpels sometimes 1 or rarely 2–4, commonly 5–many.	Carpels usually 2, rarely 3–10.
Seeds with little or no endosperm.	Seeds with endosperm.

Families. The table (Table 10–2) of the characters of the families of the Rosales points up the necessity for investigating a great many members of each family not only for the obvious and conspicuous characters but also for the obscure ones. In many instances the difficulty of classifying families (and their ultimate segregation or joining) can be clarified by securing additional data and particularly data from fields so far neglected. These include all the features of microscopic morphology described in Chapter 4. Recent studies of individual families, especially of their microscopic structure and development, have contributed to advancement of understanding of the families and the orders they compose.

Hutchinson (1934) proposed reclassification of the orders and families of monocotyledons. Among his suggestions was removal of the century plants and the yuccas from the *Amaryllis* family and the lily family, respectively, and formation of a family Agavaceae composed of these plants and their immediate relatives (Fig. 10–5). The artificial distinction of the Amaryllidacae and the Liliacae is the subject of a long-standing controversy, and the Agavaceae in the sense of Hutchinson have been one of the centers of this argument.

The usual segregation of the two large families on the basis of an inferior or superior ovary probably is not natural, and it has been adopted by many authors only to afford a convenient means of distinction until sufficient information becomes available for reclassification.

Hutchinson's proposal received immediate support from an unexpected source. Almost simultaneously McKelvey and Sax (1933) had published cytological evidence of the close interrelationship of *Yucca* and *Agave* and some of their relatives. In both genera the chromosome complement consists of 25 small chromosomes and 5 large ones (Fig. 10–6). This is a distinctive set of chromosomes little duplicated, so far as is known, among unrelated plants, and it is an almost certain indicator of relationship. The *Yucca-Agave* karyotype occurs in the rather diverse elements of *Yucca* and in the related *Hesperaloë*. It occurs not only in *Agave,* in the broad sense, but also in the related *Furcraea* and *Beschorneria.* Three of the tribes included by Hutchinson in the family Agavaceae have the *Yucca-Agave* karyotype. These are the Yucceae, Agaveae, and Polyantheae.

Three other tribes were included in the Agavaceae. These were (1) Dracaeneae, including such well-known genera as *Dracaena, Sansevieria,* and *Cordyline;* (2) Nolineae, including *Nolina, Dasylirion,* and *Beaucarnea;* and (3) Phormieae, including a single genus of two species restricted to New Zealand.

The chromosome complements of these groups, insofar as they have been studied, are variable and include large and small chromosomes in combinations not obviously derivatives of the *Yucca-Agave* karyotype. This factor complicates the question of segregation of the family Agavaceae. Some structural characters of the fruits and seeds indicate the desirability of excluding the Dracaeneae and Nolineae from the Agavaceae. Furthermore, the dissimilar genera of Liliaceae, *Hosta,* the plantain lily of China and Japan, and *Hesperocallis,* the desert lily of the southwestern United States and adjacent Mexico, have chromosome complements essentially like those of *Yucca* and *Agave.*

Thus chromosomes offer strong evidence of relationship of genera frequently considered to be in different families, but the investigation has not indicated absolutely clear lines of segregation. Additional information from a new source contributes a better understanding of the problem of classification, but it does not necessarily provide a final and absolute solution.

The following authors have contributed to knowledge applicable to this problem: Whitaker (1934), Granick (1944), Moran (1949), and Wunderlich (1950).

TABLE

Occurrence of Some Distinguishing

		Hypogynous, Perigynous, or Epigynous	Stipules	Endosperm
Group 1 (Based upon the Rosaceae as typical)	2. Connaraceae	Hypogynous	None	Present or absent
	3. Leguminosae	Mostly perig- ynous; some hypogynous	Present	None or scanty
	4. Crossosomaceae	Perigynous	None	Thin
	5. Rosaceae	Perigynous or epigynous	Present (except rarely)	None (usually)
	6. Platanaceae (Group 1 or 2)	Hypogynous	Present	Thin
Group 2 (Based upon the Hamamelidaceae as typical)	7. Myrothamnaceae	Hypogynous	Present	Present
	8. Bruniaceae	Epigynous	Present	Present
	9. Hamamelidaceae	Epigynous or sometimes hypogynous	Present	Thin
Group 3 (Based upon the Saxifragaceae as typical)	1. Crassulaceae	Hypogynous	None	Scanty or none
	10. Brunelliaceae	Hypogynous	Present	Present
	11. Cunoniaceae	Hypogynous	Present	Present
	12. Byblidaceae	Hypogynous	None	Present
	13. Pittosporaceae	Hypogynous	None	Present
	14. Cephalotaceae	Perigynous	None	Present
	15. Saxifragaceae	Perigynous or epigynous or rarely hypogynous	Rare	Present

10–2

Characters Among Families of the Rosales

Carpels Free or Coalescent	Carpel Number	Fruit Type	Stamen Number
Free	5	Follicle	10 or sometimes 5
Free	1	Legume or loment (usually)	10 or rarely fewer
Free	2–9	Follicle	15–50
Free or sometimes coalescent	5–many (or rarely 1–4)	Indehiscent or follicle or pome	Numerous (rarely 10 or fewer)
Free	3–5 or 9	Achene	3–7
Coalescent	3	Capsule	5 (sometimes 4–8)
Coalescent	4–5	Capsule	8–10
Coalescent	2	Capsule	2–8
Free or barely coalescent	5 (or rarely 3–30)	Follicle or barely a capsule	5 (or 3–30, same as other parts)
Free	4–5	Follicles	8–10
Coalescent	2–5	Capsule or fleshy	4–5 or numerous
Coalescent	2–3	Capsule	5
Coalescent	2–5	Berry or capsule	5
Free	6	Follicular (1-seeded)	12
Coalescent or rarely free	2 or rarely 3–12	Capsule or berry	3 or commonly 5–10 or sometimes numerous

Fig. 10–5. Similarities in the appearance of some species of *Yucca* and *Agave*: (1) *Yucca Whipplei* (Claremont, California); (2) *Agave americana* (escaped from cultivation in the same area). In both species the main stem is underground, and a rosette of leaves produced aboveground manufactures food for several seasons before appearance of the flowering stem (scape). After fruiting time the whole plant (or in some species of either genus only the underground branch and the rosette of leaves associated with the scape) dies. In both illustrations the scapes are bearing fruit, and the plants are dying. In some species of *Yucca* the stems are aboveground, the plants being trees.

Fig. 10–6. The *Yucca-Agave* karyoptype, or complement of chromosomes, consisting in both genera of 25 small chromosomes and 5 large ones: (1–3 *Yucca*; (4–6) *Agave* (century plants). (From Susan D. McKelvey and Karl Sax, Journal of the Arnold Arboretum, 81, *pl. 25,* 1933. Used by permission.)

THE SPECIAL SIGNIFICANCE OF OBSCURE STRUCTURES

In addition to the chromosomes discussed in the preceding paragraphs, many others of the obscure features of plants have been applied recently to classification of the higher taxa as well as the lower (see Chapter 4). Constance (1955) has summarized the literature of flowering-plant classification, and his paper includes an extensive bibliography. The following examples of investigations of particular importance to delineation of orders or families are of special interest because of the obscurity or the neglect of the char-

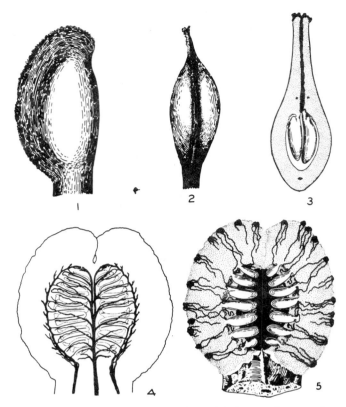

Fig. 10–7. The primitive conduplicately folded carpel: (1) side view, the midrib on the right, the margins on the left; (2) ventral view showing the margins appressed against each other and forming specialized stigmatic crests receptive to pollen; (3) the carpel in cross-section, the midrib below, the stigmatic margins above, a pollen tube having traveled through the network of hairs on the ventral (infolded) surface of the carpel to the micropyle of an ovule; (4) carpel unfolded and cleared, showing the vascular bundles and, by dotted lines, the positions of the ovules; (5) carpel unfolded, showing the placentae, ovules, glandular hairs (indicated by stippling), and pollen tubes. (From Irving W. Bailey, American Journal of Botany 38: 374, *Figs. 1–5*, 1951; and *Contributions to Plant Anatomy* [A Chronica Botanica Publication], The Ronald Press Co., 1954, p. 167. Used by permission.)

acter concerned. Obviously investigations of this sort may apply to taxa at any level of rank, and this includes suborders, subfamilies, and tribes.

The nature of carpels and of stamens has been the subject of long debate and the basis of many theories. The argument usually has centered about possible origin of these structures from stems or from leaves. The following recent studies have supplied new information.

Bailey and Smith (1942) described and named the family Degeneriaceae based on the new genus *Degeneria* composed of a single species restricted to the Fiji Islands. The carpels (Fig. 10–7) of this plant are composed fundamentally each of a single folded leaf, the margins of which are not coalescent. There is no style or stigma, but the margins of the leaf are stigmatic. The ovules are not produced at the margins but on the ventral infolded surface of the leaf, somewhat nearer the midrib than the margins. Pollen germinates on the stigmatic margins, and the pollen tubes grow among the hairs of the upper surface of the leaf toward the ovules. Discovery of this type of carpel was the fuse which ignited almost explosive research by Bailey and his co-workers upon the fundamental structure and development of the carpels of other woody members of the order Ranales (Bailey and Nast, 1943b, 1945; Nast and Bailey, 1945, 1946; Bailey, 1949; Bailey and Swamy, 1951). These studies and others on the evolution of carpels (Fig. 10–8) in cooperation with the taxonomist A. C. Smith lead to a realignment of the families of the woody members of the Ranales. The group previously was too little understood for effective classification, and it was inadequately studied, primarily because of its occurrence in remote regions of the tropics, especially on the islands of the Pacific Ocean.

Along with investigation of the carpels, there developed a review of the stamens of the woody Ranales (Bailey and Smith, 1942; Bailey and Nast, 1943a, 1945; Bailey, Nast, and Smith, 1943; Bailey, 1949; Bailey and Swamy, 1951; Canright, 1952). The stamens of *Degeneria, Himantandra,* and others of the woody Ranales (Fig. 10–9) resemble small leaves, and they have a vascular system based upon three traces as do the leaves of the same plants. There is no division into anther and filament, and the sporangia or pollen chambers are imbedded in the tissue of the upper side of the leaflike structure at a considerable distance from the margins. The stamens, like the carpels, seem to be homologous with leaves.

Canright (1952) made a detailed investigation of the stamens of members of the *Magnolia* family. He found series, apparently representing gradual specialization, ranging from apparently primordial types similar to *Degeneria* and *Himantandra* stamens to others typical of the more specialized Magnoliaceae and similar to those of flowering plants in general. (Fig. 10–10).

Thus, characters of the woody Ranales, neglected largely be-

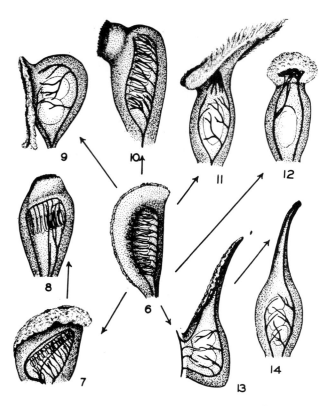

Fig. 10–8. Trends of modification of the primitive conduplicate carpel (stig-matic margins to the left in all figures; numbers from the original publication): (6) the primitive conduplicate carpel (Fig. 10–7); (7–8), (9), (10), (11), (12), (13–14) differing lines of specialization, the last one (13–14) resulting in a style and stigma. (From Irving W. Bailey, American Journal of Botany 38: 374, Figs. 6–14, 1951. Also from Contributions to Plant Anatomy [A Chronica Botanica Publication] the Ronald Press Co., 1954, p. 168. Used by permission.)

cause the plants are tropical in occurrence and therefore not easily available, have provided the basis for reclassification of the families of a large order and at the same time provided solid evidence con-cerning the fundamental origin of the two most significant parts of the flower. The preponderance of evidence from the work of Bailey and his co-workers supports the thesis that carpels and stamens are specialized leaves. This may not prove the point, but it provides the best evidence available so far. Under most systems of classifica-tion the Ranales are considered to be the group of angiosperms retaining the greatest number of primitive characters, and occur-

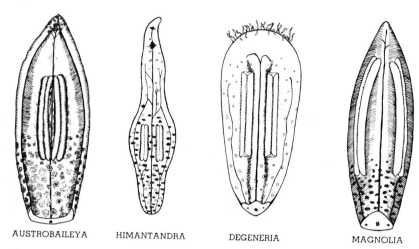

AUSTROBAILEYA   HIMANTANDRA   DEGENERIA   MAGNOLIA

Fig. 10–9. Stamens in the primitive woody Ranales—a comparison of microsporophylls of the genera indicated. The microsporangia (pollen chambers) are embedded in the dorsal or ventral surface of the sporophyll, frequently nearer the midrib than the margins. There is no distinction of anther and filament. (From James E. Canright, American Journal of Botany, 39: 488, Fig. 13, 1952. Also from Lyman Benson, *Plant Classification*, D. C. Heath & Co., 1957, p. 478. Used by permission.)

rence of primitive carpels and primitive stamens in this order is of first significance to the still unsolved problem of the phylogeny of angiosperms.

Except in the study of hay fever, pollen grains have been neglected until relatively recently because their small size makes them obscure. They are useful for dating changes of vegetation and climate and certain events in human prehistory because the accumulation of layers of pollen indicates the plants which have grown in the vicinity of bogs at various times over the course of thousands of years. For this reason pollen has been studied intensively in recent decades. In some instances, as was shown in Chapter 4, the characteristics of pollen grains have been useful in segregation of taxa such as species or genera.

The most significant contribution of pollen studies to classification of the higher taxa is the establishment of the occurrence of the single-furrowed (monocolpate) type in the extinct Cycadofilicales and Bennettitales and in the living Cycadales, Ginkgoales, and Monocotyledoneae (Fig. 10–11). Dicotyledons normally have tricolpate, or three-furrowed, pollen or specialized forms of it, but monocolpate pollen occurs in a number of families of woody mem-

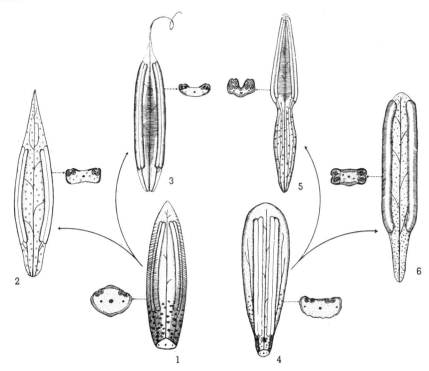

Fig. 10–10. The chief trends of specialization of the stamens of various genera of Magnoliaceae (Ranales) (ventral view, the pollen chambers of the family, except those of the tulip-tree [Liriodendron], being ventral): (1) Magnolia Maingayi, the arrows running from this to more specialized types; (2) Magnolia nitida; (3) Magnolia Hamorii; (4) Manglietia Forestii, the arrows running to more specialized types; (5) Magnolia hypoleuca; (6) Magnolia fuscata. (From James E. Canright, American Journal of Botany 30: 489, Fig. 14, 1952. Also from Lyman Benson, Plant Classification, D. C. Heath & Co., 1957, p. 479. Used by permission.)

bers of the order Ranales. Of particular significance is the Ranalian genus *Schisandra*, which has in the same pollen grain a vestige of the triradiate crest characteristic of the ferns and in general absent from all the groups just mentioned except the Cycadofilicales, at the opposite end three short furrows homologous with those of tricolpate pollen, and on the side an area homologous with the single furrow of monocolpate pollen. Thus, again, the woody Ranales are indicated to be a possible connecting link between monocotyledons and dicotyledons and perhaps more especially with the primitive ancestors of both (Wodehouse, 1936).

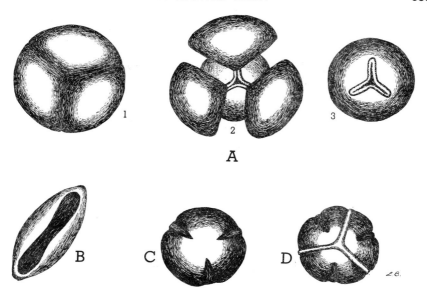

Fig. 10–11. Evolution of pollen grains: (A) (1) young fern spores in a group of four just formed by the reduction divisions (meiosis), only three being visible in any one view; (2) spores separating; (3) single spore showing the three crests (triradiate crest) formed along the margins of the spore which were tightly appressed against the other three spores; (B) the monocolpate (single-furrowed) pollen of a gymnosperm; (C) the tricolpate (three-furrowed) pollen of all dicotyledons except some species of primitive woody Ranales; (D) pollen grain of *Schisandra* (Ranales) with the triradiate crest of ferns, the three furrows of dicotyledons, and an area (at the opposite end and not showing) homologous with the single furrow of gymnosperms. (Redrawn, with modification, from Roger P. Wodehouse, Botanical Review 2: 67–84, *Figs. 1, 2a, b, c, 8a, b, c,* 1936. Also from Lyman Benson, *Plant Classification,* D. C. Heath & Co., 1957, p. 480. Used by permission.)

Bailey (1949, 1953a) considered possession of conducting tissues such as xylem and phloem to be the significant feature of land plants. Xylem not only serves this function but is also a mechanical support.

Xylem cells during most of their existence are actually cell remnants, that is, the walls remaining after the early death of the cells and disintegration of the internal structures. They are of two types (Fig. 10–12): *tracheids,* which are elongated and usually spindle-shaped, and *vessel segments,* which tend to be proportionately shorter and of greater diameter, with blunt ends and no end walls. The end walls of long series of cells have been dissolved away, leaving elongated tubes or vessels as pipelike conducting elements.

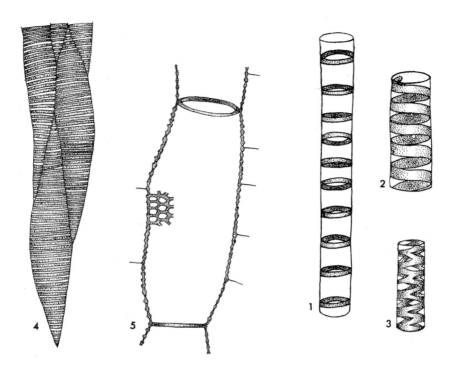

Fig. 10–12. Xylem elements—vessels and tracheids—and types of thickening
of xylem cell walls: (1–3) segments of tracheids; (4) tracheids of a shorter type;
(5) portion of a vessel, each wall of a single cell (minus the end walls, which
have been dissolved away) forming a vessel segment; (1) annular (ringed)
thickening of the wall; (2) spiral thickening; (3) scalariform (ladder-like) thickening; (4) ringed or spiral thickening (only one side of the cell showing); (5) pitted
thickening, the wall having minute window-like thin parts.

According to Bailey, the chief trends of evolutionary modification
of xylem among land plants involve an equilibrium between the
two functions of these cells. For the most part those trends are in
a single direction of development, and in any line of evolution they
are irreversible. The course of evolution of xylem is preserved fully
among living flowering plants in complete series without missing
links. Thus, it is unnecessary to depend upon fossil plants for

phylogenetic series, these being observable by studying living dicotyledons and monocotyledons. The classic work in this field is that of Bailey and Tupper (1918). Frost (1930a, 1930b, 1931) constructed a phylogenetic sequence of the types of pitting in the walls of xylem elements. Subsequent studies added series of characters of the vascular rays, fiber-tracheids, and other features of wood anatomy. Analysis of wood anatomy has been applied to many families of flowering plants, and the basic sequences have been summarized by Vestal (1937, 1940), Tippo (1938, 1946), Moseley (1948), and J. W. Hall (1952). The applications of these features to individual families, to groups of families within an order, or to pairs of families suspected of being related to each other appear in many papers (see Constance, 1955).

Features of wood anatomy must be considered in relationship to the entire character complex of one taxon as opposed to another. In some cases, anatomical study has indicated the impossibility of derivation of a taxon from one group but not from another. An example of this is the normal developmental sequence of thickening in the walls of xylem elements of flowering plants, the earliest type to appear in maturing cells, being followed by different types in cells maturing in later stages of development of the root or stem. Types of xylem-wall thickening appear in the following order: *annular, spiral, scalariform,* and *pitted.* The cycad line of development, including the living Cycadopsida and the extinct Cycadofilicales, and the most primitive extinct members of the conifer line of gymnosperms (Cordaitales) had or have the same developmental series of xylem elements as the flowering plants. Consequently, wood anatomy does not rule out any of these groups as possible ancestors of the angiosperms. In the living gymnosperms, except the cycad line, the sequence is *annular, spiral, pitted*; typical scalariform elements do not occur. Bailey argues that this trend among the gymnosperms could not have been reversed and that therefore the flowering plants could not have been derived from any of these groups. Thus, the recent members of the conifer line, the *Ephedra* line, and the *Gnetum* line are ruled out as ancestors of the Angiospermae.

Investigation has included all features of the plant, but in all fields the amount accomplished is relatively small in comparison with the quantity remaining to be done. The chromosomes, pollen or microgametophytes, ovules, megagametophytes, embryos, vegetative portions of the plant, fruits, and seeds are sources of potential information. From a combination of data of all types, a greater knowledge of the classification of the plant kingdom may ultimately emerge, and this must be based upon a better understanding of individual orders and families.

SUMMARY

Classification of the higher taxa does not differ in any fundamental way from classification of those of lower rank. Likewise, it is dependent upon a balancing of similarities and differences on the supposition that these reflect underlying genetic and phylogenetic relationships. The goal is a phylogenetic system of classification, but attaining this quickly to more than a limited degree is unlikely because of the relatively small amount of evidence available and in particular because of the lack of adequate series of fossils.

Because the groups are vast, and because in all likelihood a much smaller percentage of their included members may be studied, accuracy in classifying the higher-ranking taxa may be more difficult to attain than in classification of genera and species. On the other hand, intergradation between groups is likely to be restricted, that is, to involve only certain species of certain genera of certain families. It is not likely to cut across the whole taxon, and this is in contrast to the possibility that any element of one species may hybridize with any element of another, as with *Quercus dumosa* and *Quercus Engelmannii* (see pp. 270–271). Nevertheless, several families included within one order may intergrade through some of their members with certain elements of each of several families in another order. This of course strikes at the foundations of distinction of the two orders and complicates the problem of classification.

The great need is for knowledge of minute structural characters, especially those connected closely with the life history and development of all groups of plants. Many of these have been neglected because of obscurity or for other reasons, and their thorough investigation may contribute to a better foundation for classification of the plant and animal kingdoms and the border zone between them, and of divisions, classes, orders, and families. As in all classification, there is a need for wealth of data combining the fields of taxonomy, morphology, paleobotany, and ecology with many others. This provides a challenge to work in the border zones between fields.

SUGGESTED READING

BAILEY, IRVING W. 1944b. Independent origin of vessels in the Selaginellales, Filicales, Gnetales, monocotyledons, and dicotyledons, the trends of specialization in each case being considered irreversible.
———. 1949. A plea for application of data from many fields to study of the origin and phylogeny of angiosperms.

———. 1951. The values of anatomical data and the dangers of their overemphasis as opposed to other data; the need for combined methods of study through co-operation of workers in various fields.

———. 1953a. A brief but thorough summary.

———, and B. G. L. SWAMY. 1951. A significant paper on the origin and nature of the carpel, based on studies of primitive woody Ranales.

BARGHOORN, E. S., JR. 1940, 1941a, 1941b. Presence of large heterogeneous multi-seriate rays and conspicuously high-celled uniseriate rays considered to be a primitive condition; ray tissue may be eliminated completely from the secondary xylem by transformation of ray initials to fusiform initials.

CANRIGHT, JAMES E. 1952. Series of stamens from primitive foliar types to those with anther and filament (see p. 329).

CHALK, L. 1937. Scalariform perforation plates, fiber-tracheids, libriform wood fibers, septate fibers, storied structure, types of parenchyma.

———. 1944.

CHEADLE, VERNON I. 1942. A brief summary of the problem of the origin and phylogeny of monocotyledons, and of divergence in anatomical characters.

———. 1943. Origin and development are stated to parallel these features in the Dicotyledoneae, but vessels have arisen independently.

———. 1953. Evidence of independent origin in the two subclasses.

CONSTANCE, LINCOLN. 1955. A thorough survey of the literature.

CRONQUIST, ARTHUR. 1957. A realignment of the dicotyledons.

FROST, F. H. 1930a, 1930b, 1931. Formulation of ideas of sequences of progression in vessel specialization; sequence of specialization of end and lateral walls.

GILBERT, S. G. 1940.

GREGUSS, P. 1955. A remarkably detailed application of wood anatomy to classification.

KRIBS, D. A. 1935. A summary of types and of transitions between types of wood rays.

———. 1937. Correlation between vessel type and wood-parenchyma type. The evolutionary sequence of wood-parenchyma types is stated as follows: diffuse, diffuse-aggregate, vasicentric scanty, metatracheal, vasicentric abundant.

METCALFE, C. R. 1944.

MORAN, REID. 1949. A summary of the problem of recognition of the Agavaceae.

SPORNE, K. R. 1959. Fossils as the key to a phylogenetic classification of plants.

THORNE, ROBERT F. 1958. A brief summary of principles.

TIPPO, OSWALD. 1946. A summary of the significant points of wood anatomy and of their use in establishing phylogenetic sequences.

VESTAL, PAUL A. 1940. Brief resumé of the application of the anatomical approach to classification of some families of dicotyledons.

Part III
CHOICE OF NAMES

Popular and Scientific Names

NAMES IN COMMON LANGUAGE

At first thought, scientific names seem formidable; often, they are long and their pronunciation is unfamiliar. Despite these drawbacks they are indispensable for precision. Vernacular names cannot replace them for the following reasons:

1. Names in common language are ordinarily applicable in only a single language; they are not universal.
2. In most parts of the world relatively few species have common or vernacular names in any language.
3. Common names are applied indiscriminately to genera, species or varieties.
4. Often two or more unrelated plants are known by the same name, and frequently even in one language a single species may have two to several common names applied either in the same or different localities.

Well-chosen common-language names may and should be added to the public vocabulary whenever the opportunity arises, but there is no way of making application of vernacular names wholly consistent. If rules are applied, these designations become no longer common or folk names but book names. Codification of names in modern languages not only requires different combinations in every language, but, carried to extremes, it may result in combinations at least as difficult as scientific names.

Attempts to coin "vernacular" names and translation of scientific names into "common" names must be undertaken with restraint.

341

The need for restraint, however, does not reduce the importance of developing a set of modern-language names useful to the public.

An impetus toward standardization of common names may be given by choosing for manuals the names of a given plant which are best established, omitting others less well known. This selection should not be carried too far, and it is sometimes necessary to retain more than one common name for a single species. This is for example, true if the geographical range overlaps regions in which more than one language is in use, for instance, in North America the areas near the international boundary between the United States and Canada, and that between the United States and Mexico. In the eighth edition of *Gray's Manual of Botany,* Fernald (1950) retained for *Sanguinaria* the well-known English name bloodroot, but he included also two names used in Quebec, *sanguinaire* and *sang-dragon.* These were retained for the genus. Another vernacular name, red puccoon, applied to the single local species, *Sanguinaria canadensis,* has been retained as well. *Cereus giganteus* occurs in both the United States and Mexico. Its English name is giant cactus; its Spanish name is *saguaro* (spelled also *sahuaro,* according to the way in which the original Indian name has been transliterated into Spanish). In Arizona "giant cactus" is heard only rarely among even the English-speaking population; the name is used chiefly in other parts of the United States, where the saguaro does not occur.

In *Gray's Manual,* Fernald adopted an excellent device for indicating the meaning of scientific names. In parenthesis after each Latin name he placed an English translation of the specific or varietal epithet. Examples are as follows:

Sassafras albidum (Nutt.) Nees (whitish)
Vitis aestivalis Michx. (of summer). The names summer grape and pigeon grape are given, also.

SCIENTIFIC NAMES

Classification is determined by ***judgment*** of many complex factors indicating the degrees of differentiation and isolation of taxa. ***Nomenclature*** follows rules which are ***automatic*** in their application.

However, application of scientific names is not simple, and confusion may exist in scientific as well as popular naming. There are many more scientific names than plants. For example, the 4,000 species of grasses have received perhaps 10,000 or 20,000 names during the course of the last two centuries. These have been applied by workers in various parts of the world who often were ignorant of one another's work, were unaware that the populations being named were mere phases of previously known groups, or were in disagreement about classification or rules of nomenclature. One foxtail millet, *Setaria geniculata,* has been named 22 times, and the epithets have been used in 74 combinations to represent classification under species or varieties of 7 genera. Obviously such confusion and difference of opinion, combined with the vastness of the task of naming the 300,000 or more members of the plant kingdom, create a problem in need of settlement according to rules.

In the time of Linnaeus, about two centuries ago, rules for naming plants seemed unnecessary because the works of Linnaeus (1753, 1754, 1764) constituted a complete review of the relatively small number of plants known at the time. Botanical works multiplied, and by the middle of the nineteenth century confusion reached such a degree that an International Botanical Congress meeting at Paris formulated rules (Anonymous, 1867) to guide taxonomists in their choice of scientific names. This body adopted the Paris Code, which set forth simple and seemingly obvious principles, essentially as follows, together with many detailed regulations:

1. One plant may not have more than one name.
2. No two plants may have the same name.
3. If more than one name has been applied to a plant, the valid one shall be the earlier or earliest, but priority begins with 1753 because the binomial system was used only inconsistently and by few authors before Linnaeus.
4. The author's name shall be cited with each scientific name in order that confusion may be avoided in referring to duplicated names. For example, *Yucca macrocarpa* Engelmann (published in 1881) and *Yucca macrocarpa* (Torrey) Coville (published in 1893), two combinations applied to different species, are identical except for authors' names.

The present universally accepted International Code of Botanical Nomenclature (Lanjouw and Stafleu, 1956, revised slightly at Montreal in 1959) is a complete and complicated guide for the systematic botanist to follow in application of names. The primary objectives of the rules are as follows (Preamble):

The purpose of giving a name to a taxonomic group is not to indicate its characters or history, but to supply a means of referring to it and to indicate its taxonomic rank. This Code aims at the provision of a stable method of naming taxonomic groups, avoiding and rejecting the use of names which may cause error or ambiguity or throw science into confusion. Next in importance is the avoidance of the useless creation of names. Other considerations, such as absolute grammatical correctness, regularity or euphony of names, more or less prevailing custom, regard for persons, etc., notwithstanding their undeniable importance are relatively accessory.

In order that jealousy may be avoided and that the rules may be universally acceptable, the scientific names of all groups are taken from the ancient language Latin. Sometimes the names are derived from Greek, from modern languages, or from arbitrary combinations of letters, but, if so, they are treated as if they were Latin. Latin terminations are used as far as possible.

A TYPICAL NOMENCLATURAL PROBLEM

When manuals covering the same flora or including the same species are studied, discrepancies are obvious. For example, the creosote bush appears in Jepson's *Manual of the Flowering Plants of California* (1923–1925) as *Larrea tridentata* (DC.) Cov. var. *glutinosa* (Engelm.) Jepson; in Munz's *Manual of Southern California Botany* (1935) and Munz and Keck's *A California Flora* (1959) the same plant appears as *Larrea divaricata* Cav.; in Wooton and Standley's *Flora of New Mexico* (1915) it is called *Covillea glutinosa* (Engelm.) Rydb.; in other works it is listed as *Larrea mexicana* Moric.; in Kearney and Peebles' *Flowering Plants and Ferns of Arizona* (1942) and *Arizona Flora* (1951) it is called *Larrea tridentata* (DC.) Cov. The reasons for these discrepancies may be summed up under four headings, as follows:

1. *Complexity of the Group To Be Classified.* As was shown in preceding chapters, the problem of classification is complex, and some disagreement is inevitable. Examination of specimens of the creosote bush collected in Chile indicates that there is no material difference between the South American plants and the North American desert forms and that the earliest specific epithet applied to either one (*Larrea divaricata*, based on South American specimens) must be used. However, not all authors have agreed with this point of view. Neither have they agreed that there is only a single taxon in North America.

2. *Differences in Policy.* Although most of the authors of the books mentioned above are conservative, and in this particular example there is less than the usual variation in viewpoint from author to author, frequently such differences from book to book are explainable on the basis of author policy in classification (see pp. 290–307).

3. *Limitations of Knowledge.* It is not possible for the author of any manual or flora to see all the herbarial material available to every other author or to visit exactly the same localities within the range of the species. Consequently, although each author bases his conclusions on all the available data, no two have exactly the same data. Obviously, in this case, each author has made a fairly extensive study of the problems involved. However, often one author may be ignorant of what another has done, for the botanical literature of the world is extensive, the indices are not completely adequate, and not every book or journal is available universally. No matter how thorough an investigator may be in writing such an elaborate work as a manual of the plants of a large region, he is almost certain to overlook some papers which would have bearing on his problems.

4. *Variation in Rules of Nomenclature.* Use of the generic name *Larrea* is dependent upon the list of *nomina conservanda* (names of genera conserved in spite of lack of priority over others) in the present International Code of Botanical Nomenclature. During the period from 1908 to 1930 many American botanists followed the American Code of Botanical Nomenclature (Anonymous, 1907). Under this code there were no exceptions to priority, that is, no names were conserved. Wooton and Standley, who followed the American Code, did not accept the name *Larrea* for this genus, because the name had been used earlier for another (in the pea family). Because under the American Code it was not available for the genus of the creosote bush, they described the creosote bush under *Covillea*.

Discussion of the International Code of Botanical Nomenclature

The following is a simplified (and unofficial) exposition and explanation of the major principles and practices specified in the International Code of Botanical Nomenclature (Lanjouw and Stafleu, 1956, slightly revised in Montreal in 1959). It is set up in the same form as the code, and it is designed to aid in developing appreciation of the nature and scope of the nomenclatural [1] problems involved in systematic botany, but it is not a complete guide. For revision of a group of plants, the code, itself, must be consulted.

PRINCIPLES

PRINCIPLE I

Botanical nomenclature is independent of zoological nomenclature, in the sense that the name of a plant must not be rejected merely because it is identical with the name of an animal [e.g., *Corydalis*, a flowering plant, and *Corydalis*, a lark].

PRINCIPLE II

The application of names of taxonomic groups is determined by means of nomenclatural types.

PRINCIPLE III

The naming of taxonomic groups is based on priority of publication.

[1] **Nomenclatorial** refers to a **nomenclator,** a person or book giving names to objects.

PRINCIPLE IV

Each taxonomic group can bear only one correct name, the earliest that is in accordance with the Rules, except in specified cases.

PRINCIPLE V

Scientific names of plants are Latin or are treated as Latin.

PRINCIPLE VI

The Rules of nomenclature are retroactive except when expressly limited.

RANKS OF TAXA

A taxon is a taxonomic group or unit. Each plant belongs to a series of taxa of consecutive rank. The basic botanical taxa are the following, proceeding from highest rank to lowest: *division, class, order, family, genus, species*. The list may be increased to 23 degrees by addition of subordinate categories usually with the prefix *sub-*. This expanded list (Article 4), translated into English, is as follows: plant kingdom, division, subdivision, class, subclass, order, suborder, family, subfamily, tribe, subtribe, genus, subgenus, section, subsection, series, subseries, species, subspecies, variety, subvariety, form, subform. This order must not be altered, but the list may be augmented still further by supplementary categories, provided these do not lead to confusion or error.[2]

NAMES OF TAXA

Names of the Higher Taxa. The choice of names of taxa of ranks higher than order is not governed by rules similar to those applying to taxa of ordinal rank or lower (Article 16), but there are definite recommendations concerning the forms of the names) (see Recommendation 16A in the code).

NAMES OF ORDERS (Article 17).

The name of an order is taken from that of its type family and has the ending *-ales*. [E.g., Urticales, Ranales, Rosales, Liliales, Pinales (Article 17).]

NAMES OF FAMILIES (Article 18).

The name of a family is a plural adjective used as a substantive [noun]; it is formed by adding the suffix *-aceae* to the stem of the name of its type genus or of a synonym of this name, even if [it is] illegitimate. . . .

---

[2] Note that the zoological term **phylum** is not included in the list. It may be introduced only as a supplementary term if division and subdivision have been used and if further categories are necessary. It may be introduced as an intermediate category between subdivision and class, but it may not be substituted for division or subdivision.

Examples: *Rosaceae* (from *Rosa*), *Salicaceae* (from *Salix*), *Plumbaginaceae* (from *Plumbago*), *Caryophyllaceae* (from *Caryophyllus*, a pre-linnaean generic name), *Winteraceae* (from *Wintera* Murr., a synonym of *Drimys* J. R. & G. Forst.) . . .

. . . The following names [of families], sanctioned by long usage, are treated as exceptions to the rule: *Palmae, Gramineae, Cruciferae, Leguminosae, Guttiferae, Umbelliferae, Labiatae, Compositae.* . . .

Botanists are authorized, however, to use as alternatives the appropriate names ending in *-aceae*. [These are Arecaceae, Poaceae, Brassicaceae, Fabaceae, Clusiaceae and the segregated Hypericaceae, Ammiaceae, Lamiaceae, and Asteraceae.]

Those who regard the *Papilionaceae* [a name not derived from a generic name] as constituting an independent family [from the pea family, known in the broader sense as Leguminosae or Fabaceae] may use that name, although it is not formed in the prescribed manner.

Names of Genera (Article 20).

The name of a genus is a substantive, or an adjective used as a substantive, in the singular number. [Generic names are commonly Latin or Greek nouns, although they] . . . may be taken from any source whatever, and may even be composed in an absolutely arbitrary manner. . . . [According to Recommendation 20A,] Botanists who are forming generic names should comply with the following [and other listed] suggestions:

(a) To use Latin terminations insofar as possible.
(b) To avoid names not readily adaptable to the Latin tongue.
(c) Not to make names very long or difficult to pronounce. [However, relatively few possible combinations of fewer than ten letters including some vowels are still available.]
(d) Not to make names by combining words from different languages [nomina hybrida]. . . .
(h) Not to dedicate genera to persons quite unconnected with botany or at least with natural science [and not to dedicate taxa of lower rank, e.g., species, to persons who had nothing to do with their discovery or characterization].
(i) To give a feminine form to all personal generic names, whether they commemorate a man or a woman. (See Rec. 73B).

When a new name for a genus, subgenus, or section is taken from the name of a person, it should be formed in the following manner [Recommendation 73B]:

(a) When the name of the person ends in a vowel, the letter *a* is added (thus *Bouteloua* after Boutelou; *Ottoa* after Otto; *Sloanea* after Sloane), except when the name ends in *a*, when *ea* is added (e.g. *Collaea* after Colla).
(b) When the name of the person ends in a consonant, the letters *ia* are added [e.g., *Ramondia* after Ramond], except when the name ends in *er*, when *a* is added (e.g. *Kernera* after Kerner). In latinized names ending in *-us*, this termination is dropped before adding the suffix (*Dillenia* [from Dillenius]).

Names of Species (Article 23).

The name of a species is a binary combination consisting of the name of the genus followed by a single specific epithet [which may be an adjective or a substantive. The **epithet** (a descriptive word used to characterize the species, e.g., *alba*, or a noun in the genitive [possessive] form, e.g., *Smithii*, or the adjectival form, e.g., *Smithiana*) must be either a single word or a compound joined by hyphens, e.g., *Adiantum capillus-veneris* for the maidenhair fern. It must not consist of two or more separate words].

The specific epithet, when adjectival in form and not used as a substantive, agrees grammatically [e.g., in gender] with the generic name. [Most frequently the feminine ending is **-a**, the masculine **-us**, and the neuter **-um** or **-on**, but this is by no means always true. Examples: *Mentzelia reflexa*, *Linanthus dichotomus*, *Geranium incisum*. Trees are feminine. Some names ending in **-us** are feminine, e.g., *Quercus*. Examples: *Quercus rubra, alba, nigra, velutina,* or *agrifolia*.]

The following are recommendations for formation of specific epithets from the names of persons (Recommendation 73C):

When a new specific or infraspecific epithet is taken from the name of a man, it should be formed in the following manner:

(a) When the name of the person ends in a vowel, the letter *i* is added (thus *glazioui* [or *Glazioui*] from Glaziou, *bureaui* [or *Bureaui*] from Bureau), except when the name ends in an *a*, when *e* is added (thus *balansae* [or *Balansae*] from Balansa).

(b) When the name ends in a consonant, the letters *ii* are added (thus *ramondii* [or *Ramondii*] from Ramond), except when the name ends in *-er*, when *i* is added (thus *kerneri* [or *Kerneri*] from Kerner) [those who follow this recommendation may treat the termination *-i* as an orthographic error and correct it (e.g., *Smithi* may be changed to Smithii)]. . . .

(d) When epithets taken from the name of a man have an adjectival form they are formed in a similar way (e.g., Geranium *robertianum* [or *Robertianum*], *Verbena hasslerana* [or *Hasslerana*]).

The same provisions apply to epithets formed from the names of women. When these have a substantival form, they are given a feminine termination (e.g., *Cypripedium hookerae* [or *Hookerae*], *Rosa beatricis* [or *Beatricis*], *Scabiosa olgae* [or *Olgae*], *Omphalodes luciliae* [or *Luciliae*]).

Until 1950, initial letters of certain specific epithets (e.g., *Vitis Baileyana*) were recommended to be capitalized, all others to begin with a small letter (e.g., *Disporum trachyandrum, Limonium carolinianum, Quercus marilandica*). Many botanists prefer to capitalize the initials of no specific epithets, and the rules did not specifically forbid this practice. At the International Botanical Congress at Stockholm in 1950, the **recommendation** (now 73F) (**not a rule**) was reversed, favoring decapitalization of all specific epithets but specifically permitting (if preferred) capitalization of epithets as follows:

1. Direct forms of names of actual or mythical persons, e.g., *Disporum Hookeri, Ranunculus Jovis*

2. Former generic names, e.g., *Dianthus Caryophyllus, Papaver Rhoeas, Daucus Carota, Ranunculus Populago*
3. Vernacular (or non-Latin) names, e.g., *Olneya Tesota (Tesota* being an Indian name), *Diospyros Kaki* (a Japanese word).

At the Paris Congress in 1954, this was held to be a question of typography rather than of nomenclature (Article 73, Note 1).

Names of Varieties and Other Infraspecific Taxa (Articles 24–27). Species are not subdivided further if they include no significant partly segregated populations, but they may consist of two or more varieties or other infraspecific taxa. "For nomenclatural purposes, a species or any taxon below the rank of a species is regarded as the sum of its subordinate taxa, if any" (Article 25). If there is more than one variety, one receives the name of the species as a whole, e.g., *Viola pedata* var. *pedata*. Until 1950, in accordance with the earlier rules, some authors designated this "typical" [3] variety by an epithet such as *typica, genuina,* or *originaria;* since 1950, it is designated automatically by repetition of the specific epithet, as above. No publication is needed; author references are not cited. The other varieties of the same species are given epithets similar to specific epithets, e.g., *Viola pedata* var. *lineariloba*.

Varietal epithets in adjectival form agree in gender with the generic name, as do specific epithets.

A potential category of higher rank than variety is subspecies, and ones of lower rank are subvariety, forma, and subforma. Some botanists attempt to distinguish several or all of these ranks. This leads to such names as *Saxifraga Aizoön* subsp. *Aizoön* var. *Aizoön* subvar. *brevifolia* forma *multicaulis* subforma *surculosa* with an author's name or two inserted after each epithet in the chain. However, in informal treatments it is possible at times to omit all the infraspecific epithets but the last.

Common practice is use of a single infraspecific category, usually variety or, if preferred, subspecies. If variety is adopted as the only named taxon below the rank of species, the full name of a plant may appear as follows: *Fragaria virginiana* Duchesne var. *illinoensis* (Prince) A. Gray, *Meconella oregana* Nutt. var. *californica* Jepson. If subspecies is adopted, a name may appear as follows: *Orthocarpus faucibarbatus* A. Gray subsp. *albidus* Keck.

Interpretations of the two ranks vary; frequently what a particular botanist interprets as one is exactly what another person ac-

---

[3] Typical only in the sense of including the type specimen for the name accepted for the species as a whole.

cepts as the other. Both terms have been used ambiguously—subspecies to indicate (as used mostly in Europe) a taxon of a rank between species and variety and (as used mostly in the United States) a geographically segregated type, theoretically a major one but in practice often a minor one; variety to indicate both botanical variety and horticultural variety (i.e., minor variants of commercial or aesthetic value). Actually the botanical term is *varietas*, and there should be no confusion of this with the former horticultural use of the term *variety* now abandoned, anyhow, in official nomenclature for horticulture. Horticultural names are preferably (compulsorily since January 1, 1959) in modern languages according to the International Code of Nomenclature for Cultivated Plants (Anonymous, 1958).

Varietas is the classical botanical category below the rank of species, and its use requires infinitely less formal changing of names than does use of *subspecies* in all but the relatively few groups studied intensively by recent authors favoring subspecies over variety. For example, among the 99 species of North American *Ranunculi* there are, in addition to the numerous typical varieties, 79 significant populations of lower rank than species. Until recently none had been named as a subspecies, and even now only 4 or 5 have been so designated, but all have been named as varieties. The nomenclatural usage of varietas as opposed to subspecies in the Cactaceae and most other plant families is identical.

The question of subspecies or variety is far too complicated for a complete discussion here, and taxonomists have argued it freely (see J. Clausen, Keck, and Hiesey, 1939, 1940; R. Clausen, 1941; Fernald, 1936, 1940; Fosberg, 1942; Hall, 1926; Rosendahl, 1949; Weatherby, 1942; Meikle, 1957).

Many authors believe two ranks of taxa below species to be useful, and they either recognize both *subspecies* and *variety*, e.g., *Vochysia rufa* Mart. subsp. *sericea* (Pohl) Stafleu var. *fulva* Stafleu, or they add *forma* after one or the other, e.g., *Convolvulus sepium* L. var. *sepium* f. *coloratus* Lange.

In practice, *forma* often has been applied to any commonly occurring type set off by a single usually conspicuous character. Consistent application of the category to all genetic variants in every species regardless of the obviousness of the distinguishing character would require, of course, millions of names, and this is not practical. Furthermore, a high percentage of individuals marked by a single qualitative character may be heterozygous but not detectably so to the eye. To many botanists it seems better practice to describe and discuss such forms but not to give them formal names, but this opinion is not universal and other botanists employ *formae* as a means of designating minor infraspecific populations.

Citation of Authors' Names (Articles 46–50)

The name of at least one author (or combination of joint authors) follows the name of a plant. This is to avoid confusion in referring to duplicated names (see p. 343). The author's name constitutes a brief reference to the original publication which offers a means of determining which specimen is the type (see pp. 357–365).[4]

In other cases, when two personal names follow the plant name, the first (in parentheses) refers to the publication of the earliest use of the epithet. The author of this publication supplied the basic name, or **basionym,** and a reference to the type specimen upon which the currently accepted name combination is based. The author's name following parenthesis is used for reference to publication of the accepted combination of names. For example, a plant in the pea family was originally named *Hosackia strigosa* Nutt. (the basionym), and its identity is established in Nuttall's original publication. Later, *Hosackia* was referred by Greene to *Lotus,* and the name of this species became *Lotus strigosus* (Nutt.) Greene, based upon *Hosackia strigosa* Nutt. If a single author has both proposed a name and altered its status, custom permits omitting the first usage of his name, which normally appears in parentheses.

If a name of a taxonomic group was proposed but not validly published by one author, but subsequently was published validly and ascribed to him (or her) by another author who supplied the description, the name of the later author may be appended to the citation with the connecting word *ex.* For example, *Cercidium floridum* was described by Gray and ascribed to Bentham. It is written as *Cercidium floridum* Benth. ex A. Gray. Had Bentham supplied the description as well as the name, the connecting word would be *in* instead of *ex* (Recommendations 46A–46B).

Effective Publication of Names (Articles 29–45)

When new names are necessary or when names are recombined in harmony with reclassification of natural populations, certain rules

---

[4] The necessity of the name of the author is open to question, except as it may distinguish between identical combinations used for different plants. However, for taxonomists, the author's name often provides a quick method of finding directly the original publication without consulting an index.

of publication are required to establish their valid status. Publication of names is effected (Article 29) only by distribution (sale, exchange, or gift) of printed matter. No other kind of communication is accepted as effective.

In order to be validly published, a name of a taxon of recent plants must be both (1) effectively published . . . and . . . (2) accompanied by a description of the taxon or by a reference (direct or indirect) to a previously and effectively published description of it [Article 32]. In order to be validly published, a name of a new taxon of recent plants, the bacteria and algae excepted, published on or after 1 Jan. 1935 must be accompanied by a Latin diagnosis or by a reference to a previously and effectively published Latin diagnosis [Article 34].

Names published before 1935 with diagnoses in modern languages are accepted, and this makes legitimate much of the work done under the American Code, which did not require Latin descriptions (see Anonymous, 1907).

Requirement of a Latin diagnosis serves a twofold purpose. First, Latin is a language known among scholars throughout the world, whereas many modern languages are known to relatively few persons outside the country in which they are used. Substitution of a choice among specified "leading" modern languages would raise the question of which ones enjoy this distinction. Second, since January 1, 1935, casual or accidental publication of names in obscure non-botanical journals and in periodicals, such as newspapers and trade catalogs which are not intended to be of a permanent nature, has been nearly always invalidated by lack of a Latin diagnosis. Occasionally, names published long ago in obscure or ephemeral publications are brought to light, and frequently these have priority over well-established names published as the result of careful research. For example, the plants of an until recently little-known grove of California fan palms native in an Arizona desert mountain range received a formal and valid name as a species because in 1923 they were discussed and described in a local newspaper. The intention of a specialist in palms to apply the name was stated, but this is doubtful because the purpose announced for him has not been followed up. Had a Latin description been required in 1923, casual newspaper publication of the name (*Washingtonia arizonica*) could not have been ignored. Beginning with January 1, 1953, new names appearing in tradesmen's catalogs or newspapers are *not* considered as effectively published even with a Latin diagnosis (Article 29).

Handwriting, no matter how it is reproduced, is ineffective. Microfilm from typewriting is *not* effective (Article 29).

Names proposed provisionally and not clearly accepted by their author as representing new taxa are *not* published validly. For example, publication of one name and another new name as an alternative for use of those who prefer it is not valid. This does not apply to use of question marks to indicate doubt about the *status* in classification of an *accepted* taxon, e.g., concerning the position of a new species under one genus or another (Article 33).

The Eighth International Botanical Congress, meeting at Paris in 1954, adopted the requirement, "Publication on or after 1 Jan. 1958 of the name of a new taxon of recent plants of the rank of order or below is valid only when the nomenclatural type is indicated (see Arts. 7–10)" (Article 35) (see discussion of the type method, pp. 357–365).

Rejection of Names (Articles 62–72)

A name or epithet must not be rejected, changed, or modified merely because it is inappropriate or disagreeable; because another is preferable or better known; or because the earlier name has lost its original meaning. It is obvious that to throw the names of plants into disputes over which has the more pleasant sound would result in chaos, even in a single country, let alone in the world as a whole.

Illegitimate Names. The following kinds of names or epithets are the most common illegitimate types:

1. SUPERFLUOUS NAMES. A name is illegitimate if it was nomenclaturally superfluous when published. For example, *Ranunculus terrestris* is a superfluous name for *Ranunculus Gormanii*, published much earlier. Admittedly, it was applied to a species already having a legitimate name given to a form, which, although unusual, was retained by the later author within the species.

2. LATER HOMONYMS. A name is illegitimate if it is a later homonym, that is, if it is identical with a properly published name previously applied to another group, e.g., *Astragalus rhizanthus* Royle (1835) and *Astragalus rhizanthus* Boiss. (1843). The second species is known properly as *Astragalus cariensis* Boiss. (1849).

NAMES BASED ON DISCORDANT ELEMENTS. A name applied to a supposed group of plants with the characters derived from two or more entirely discordant elements appearing in the type specimen (e.g., a host and parasite taken to be a single specimen) must be rejected unless one of the elements can be selected as a satisfactory type. For example, John C. Frémont accidentally mixed specimens of the coiled pods of the screw bean (*Prosopis pubescens*) with leaves and flowers of the western honey mesquite (*Prosopis juliflora* var. *Torreyana*). When John Torrey based a described species, *Prosopis odorata,* upon this material he did not realize, as he stated later, that parts of two species were involved. Subsequent authors have attempted to establish the name *Prosopis odorata* for the screw bean and for the velvet mesquite (*Prosopis juliflora* var. *velutina*). If it were not possible to separate these elements, the name would be necessarily rejected. In this instance a satisfactory choice can be made; in some others it cannot (see Article 66).

A name or epithet to be rejected is replaced by the oldest available **legitimate name** or **epithet,** which in the new position will be in accordance with the code. If none exists, a new name or epithet must be chosen. An old and well-known illegitimate epithet may be preserved sometimes by validly publishing it in a new position where there is no obstacle to its use. For example, under a different genus the well-known illegitimate epithet may be applied as part of a new name. This is treated as having occurred even when a transfer was intended. For example, *Talinum polyandrum* Hook. (1855) is a later homonym of *Talinum polyandrum* Ruiz & Pav. (1798). Bentham transferred *Talinum polyandrum* Hook. to another genus as *Calandrinia polyandra* Benth. (1863). This is treated as a new publication of the epithet despite the fact that it was intended only as a transfer. Hooker's name is dropped from the author reference (Article 72).

Antedated Names, or Metanyms. Two or more names may be applied to seemingly different taxa. If a later author considers these plants to represent different phases of a single taxon, only the earliest name can be the **correct name** for the taxon. *According to this classification of the plants,* the later names are **metanyms.** Their use is not permitted so long as the classification is accepted. However, if it is modified, any of the names may become the correct name for a segregated taxon. Thus, even though according to a particular idea of classification certain names are metanyms and therefore are superfluous, they are not necessarily permanently so, and they are not illegitimate.

Priority of Names (Articles 12–15)

Not all plant groups have the same starting point for priority among the names applied to them. It is natural that the seed plants and ferns should have been studied first, because most are con-

spicuous and some are useful. The starting point for the spermatophytes, pteridophytes, and most other plants is the first edition of
Linnaeus's *Species Plantarum*, May 1, 1753, and it is agreed that
the generic names appearing in that book shall be associated with
the descriptions published by Linnaeus in the fifth and sixth editions
of *Genera Plantarum* (1754, 1764). For the fungi, certain groups
of algae, most mosses, and fossil plants, which were not well understood in the time of Linnaeus, the starting points are with later
authors or later dates.

The rule of priority holds in all cases except for certain generic
names which are conserved in spite of the rule (*nomina conservanda*). These are listed in Appendix III of the code (see also Rickett and Stafleu, 1959–). It is obvious that, occasionally, names
proposed in obscure or non-botanical publications will be overlooked
and therefore will not be found in their proper places in the botanical indices (Hooker and Jackson, 1885– ; Gray Herbarium,
1885–). Occasionally these have priority over well-known names,
despite not having been used by anyone. Adoption of such generic
names may require recombination of names for all the subordinate
taxa. For example, under the American Code of Botanical Nomenclature (Anonymous, 1907), much used on this continent from 1908
to 1930, strict priority was followed, and it was necessary to substitute the generic name *Larrea* for *Hoffmanseggia*, a genus of the
pea family, and to replace *Larrea* with *Covillea* for the creosote bush
and its relatives (as mentioned above, pp. 344–345). This involved
numerous recombinations of names and no end of confusion.
Nomina conservanda have been set up to avoid such occurrences.

Modification, Division, and Union of Groups (Articles 51–72)

A taxonomist, upon completing the organization of a group of
plants, may find that his treatment differs from previously published
ones. The fact that he has altered a group, expanded its scope, or
circumscribed it ". . . does not warrant a change in its name, except
as this may be required (1) by transference of the taxon (Arts.
54–56) . . .", for example, a species to another genus, ". . . (2) by its
union with another taxon of the same rank, (Arts. 57–58A), or (3)
by a change of its rank (Art. 60)."

"When a genus is divided into two or more genera, the generic
name must be retained for one of them. . . ." (Article 52), and
"When a species [or a taxon of lower rank] is divided into two or
more species [or taxa of lower rank], the specific [or other] epithet
must be retained . . . for the species [or other taxon] including . . .
[the] type specimen . . ." (Article 53). Determination of which

taxon is to bear the original name is dependent, then, upon the type method described below.

The Type Method (Articles 7–10). For nomenclatural purposes each species or variety is based upon a *type specimen* (*holotype* [Figs. 12–1, 12–2, 12–4 (2), 15–1, 15–4 (2), (3)]) designated by the author at the time of publication of the name. The *type* is the collec-

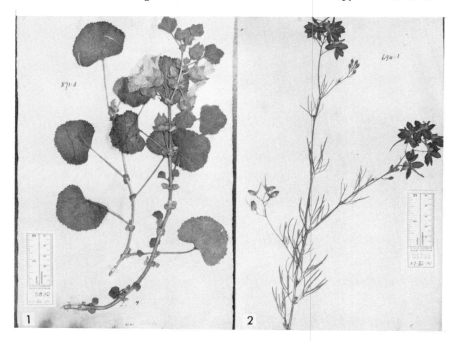

Fig. 12–1. Type and historically important specimens in the herbarium of Linnaeus: (1) *Lavatera triloba*, Malvaceae or mallow family; specimen sheet No. 871.3. (2) *Delphinium consolidum*, Ranunculaceae or buttercup family; specimen sheet No. 694.1. (Courtesy of George H. M. Lawrence, the Bailey Hortorium of Cornell University, and the Linnaean Society, London.)

tion with which the epithet denoting a species or a taxon of lower rank is associated permanently, and it affords a means of determining exactly which plant the author was naming.

The name of each genus is based upon a *type species* and, there-fore, actually upon its type specimen. Each family name is based upon a type genus and indirectly, therefore, upon the type specimen of the type species of the type genus. Each ordinal name is based upon a type family, etc.

Unfortunately, the type method is a recent development (the great contribution of the American Code), and *types* were not

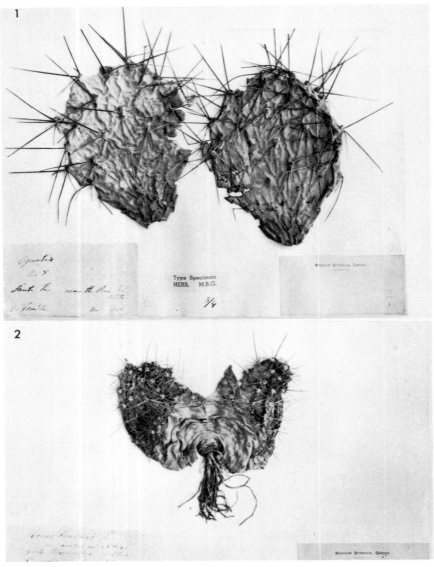

Fig. 12–2. Type specimens: (1) *Opuntia phaeacantha* (var. *phaeacantha*), a common prickly pear of the plateau region of southeastern Utah, southern Colorado, northeastern Arizona, and northern New Mexico. The specific epithet, written in pencil, is pale in the photograph. "Santa Fe, near the Rio Del Norte [Rio Grande], A. *Fendler*, 20 Nov. 1846." (New Mexico.) Engelmann Herbarium, Missouri Botanical Garden. (2) *Echinocereus triglochidiatus* var. *melanacanthus* (described first as *Cereus coccineus* var. *melanacanthus*). "Santa Fe, A. *Fendler*, 20 Nov. 1846." (New Mexico.) Engelmann Herbarium, Missouri Botanical Garden.

designated in the earlier botanical literature. However, in most cases a particular specimen (to be considered as the type) or a group of specimens (each a *syntype*, Fig. 12–3) was cited. Sometimes only the general range of the plant was given, and application of the name may depend upon finding, usually in the herbarium where the author of the species studied, plants which fit the original

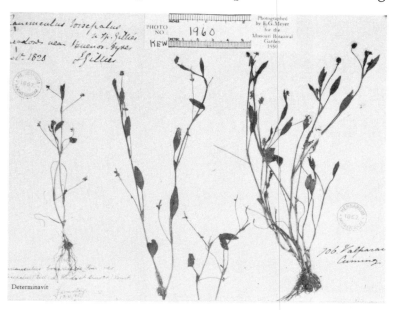

Fig. 12–3. Two syntypes, one designated as a lectotype. The proposed species *Ranunculus trisepalus* Gillies ex Hooker (the equivalent of *Ranunculus bonariensis* var. *trisepalus*) was based on collections from "Buenos Ayres. J. Gillies, Valparaiso, Cuming. (No. 706)." Thus the two specimens mounted on the same sheet are syntypes. The better specimen by Cuming has been designated as a lectotype (Lyman Benson, American Midland Naturalist 52: 361, 1954). Once published, such a choice is binding, and in effect the lectotype is the type specimen for the epithet. (Photograph by Frederick G. Meyer, courtesy of the Missouri Botanical Garden.)

description of the taxon or which may be associated with the name for other reasons. In some cases, application of the name is dubious.

At the 1950 congress, a clear rule for settling most doubtful cases was adopted: "If no holotype has been indicated by the author who described a taxon, or when the holotype is lost or destroyed, a substitute for it may be chosen ... The author who makes this choice must be followed unless his choice is superseded under the provi-

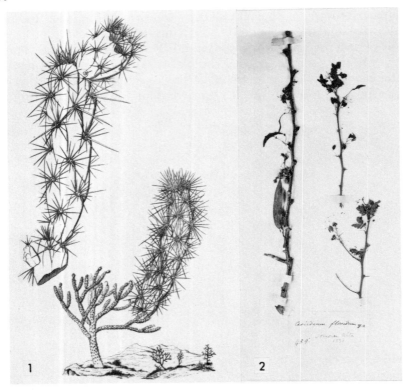

Fig. 12–4. Problems concerning type collections: (1) *Opuntia acanthocarpa*, a dry-fruited staghorn cholla, the species composed of several varieties occurring in the southwestern deserts. The type specimen collected by Bigelow and carried by pack horse from Cactus Pass in northwestern Arizona to California and thence sent to Washington, D.C., and later to George Engelmann in St. Louis, has disappeared, but the excellent drawing of a branch and an immature (still fleshy) fruit shows the nature of the described taxon (U.S. Senate Report of Explorations and Surveys for a Railroad Route to the Pacific Ocean. Botany. Cactaceae by George Engelmann. 4: 51, *pl. 18, Figs. 1–3,* 1856). This is not the plant (Fig. 12–7) commonly supposed to be *Opuntia acanthocarpa* var. *acanthocarpa,* but a more rare and localized variety occurring from southern Utah to Yavapai County, Arizona, where it was rediscovered 85 years after its first collection by Bigelow. Either a collection such as the one in Fig. 12–6 may be designated as a neotype to stand in place of the original or the figure may be designated as a lectotype; (2) The type specimen of *Cercidium floridum* Benth., the blue palo verde of the southwestern deserts in California, Arizona, and Sonora. This specimen in the herbarium of Trinity College, Dublin, Ireland, was collected near Hermosillo, Sonora, Mexico, by Thomas Coulter in 1830, and it is labeled "Cercidium floridum, sp. n." American botanists have not seen the specimen, but this photograph established the

sions of Article 8." The choice may be superseded if it is found to have been based upon a misinterpretation of the original description of the taxon or if the original specimens are rediscovered. The substitute for a *holotype* (*type*) [Figs. 12–3, 12–4 (1)] must be as follows:

1. A *lectotype* (Fig. 12–5) selected from the original specimens designated or studied by the publishing author. This is a substitute for a holotype if one was not designated or if it is missing.

2. A *neotype* [Figs. 12–4 (1), 12–6, 12–7] ". . . selected to serve as a nomenclatural type for so long as all the material upon which the name of the taxon was based is missing."

A lectotype always has precedence over a neotype.

Other recognized terms concerning types are the following (see Recommendation 8A):

An *isotype* [Figs. 15–4 (1), 15–5] is a duplicate specimen of the holotype (the same taxon collected at the same time and the same place and by the same person and not indicated to be considered as different). This useful term has been employed widely in North America for many years, but it must be used with caution; the isotype must be truly a duplicate of the type. For example, the supposed isotypes of *Ranunculus Lemmonii* A. Gray include specimens of four species collected by Lemmon. Duplication of field numbers should mark duplicate specimens, but this indication is not necessarily trustworthy. The number series of professional collectors are usually reliable; other series may or may not be dependable. This is soon determined from experience with collections.

A *paratype* is a specimen or element other than the holotype cited with the original description.

A *syntype* (Fig. 12–3) is either (1) one of two or more specimens cited by the author when no holotype was designated, or (2) one of two or more specimens designated together as the type. For example, one specimen including flowers and another including fruits may have been specified simultaneously as the type. This procedure ordinarily is not recommended, because the specimens may not be actually of the same taxon.

---

correctness of the name *Cercidium floridum* for the blue palo verde occurring west of the Continental Divide instead of for a palo verde occurring in southern Texas and adjacent Mexico, to which the name had been applied. The type specimen establishes the proper usage, despite the confusion in the botanical literature. [Item (2) from Lyman Benson, American Journal of Botany 27: 187, 1940; and *Plant Classification*, D. C. Heath & Co., 1957, p. 397. Used by permission.]

Fig. 12–5. Lectotype of *Quercus MacDonaldii* var. *elegantula*, the basis for the name combination *Quercus dumosa* var. *elegantula* (cf. Fig. 7–7). The lower two branches are clearly from *Quercus Engelmannii*; the upper possibly was from a hybrid tending slightly toward *Quercus dumosa*, but very near *Quercus Engelmannii*. The plants (Fig. 7–7) to which the epithet *elegantula* have been applied most commonly are forms frequent in the hybrid swarms of *Quercus dumosa* and *Quercus Engelmannii*. This specimen was designated as a lectotype by Ewan, *Bulletin of the Torrey Botanical Club*, 64: 511–513, *Fig. 1*, 1937. The choice is binding.

A *topotype* (see Figs. 15–2, 15–3), which is a specimen collected at the same place as the type (holotype) but at a different time or by a different collector or both, may be useful, but it has no official status. Its value must be assessed by careful comparison with the holotype (if possible) and with the original description.

When a comprehensive taxon is divided, the segregated taxon retaining the original name or epithet is the one of which the plant

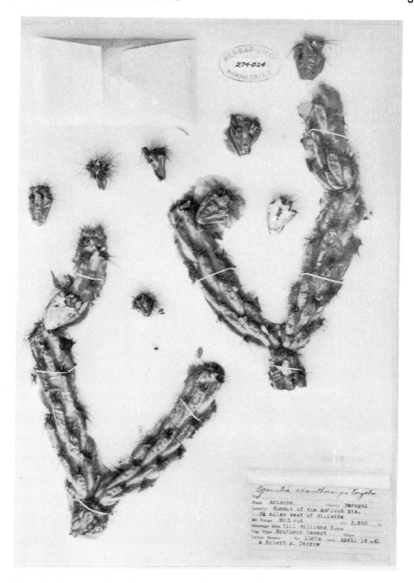

Fig. 12–6. A relatively recent collection of *Opuntia acanthocarpa* var. *acanthocarpa* [cf. Fig. 12–4 (1)]. Two more collections were made in other localities in 1959 and 1960, supporting the belief that the type of var. *acanthocarpa* is from a geographically restricted population and not from the common plant (Fig. 12–7) heretofore known by that epithet.

364   CHOICE OF NAMES

Fig. 12–7. The most common and widespread variety of *Opuntia acanth-ocarpa* (cf. Figs. 12–4, 12–6). Its proper varietal epithet is not yet determined (1961).

forming the type specimen was a member. For the other taxa, names or epithets must be chosen if they exist; otherwise, new ones must be applied. If a valid name or epithet of the proper rank (e.g., the rank of a species, subspecies, or variety) previously has been based upon any plant falling within one of these taxa, then it (converted if necessary into the proper form) must be used. If more than one have been applied, a choice must be made, according to the rule of priority, among the epithets applied to the taxon.

The following is an example of invalid alteration of the name of a previously and validly described species. In 1930, an author concluded that a particular species occurring in Oregon had been described originally from unusual specimens, differing slightly from any of the populations he had found in the field. The taxon was given a name as a new species with the remark, "Since Greene's plant [the type upon which the original name was based] is here regarded as merely an abnormal form of this proposed new species we would include it as a synonym." Following such a policy as this to its logical conclusion would result in renaming thousands upon thousands of plants, for the original or type specimen is ". . . not necessarily the most typical or representative element of a taxon; it is merely that element with which the name of the group is permanently associated" (Article 7, Note 1). *It is not uncommon for the type specimen to represent a minor phase of a species or variety, but, so long as the holotype represents any element whatever* [5] *within the taxon, the name applied to it applies to the entire population.* Had the author in question considered the plant described previously by Greene to be a separate species, it would have been legitimate to propose a new species with a new name to encompass the population with which he was familiar, but to apply a new name to cover the original species in its expanded scope was not legitimate.

Application of the rules above to modification, division, and union of groups gives rise to various nomenclatural complications, as follows.

Union of Groups.

When two or more taxa of the same rank are united, the oldest legitimate name or (for taxa below the rank of genus) the oldest legitimate epithet is retained. . . . K. Schumann . . . uniting the three genera *Sloanea* L. (1753), *Echinocarpus* Blume (1825) and *Phoenicosperma* Miq. (1865), rightly adopted the oldest of these three generic names, *Sloanea* L., for the resulting genus.

The names *Acacia cuspidata* Schlecht. (1838) and *Acacia texensis* Torr. and Gray (1840) were applied to members of the same popu-

---

[5] An exception is a name based upon a monstrosity (Article 67).

lation. If the group is to be treated as a species, its name must be *Acacia cuspidata.* If the names or epithets are of the same date, the author who unites the groups has the right to choose one of them. The author who first adopts one, definitely treating another as a synonym or referring it to a subordinate group, must be followed. Union of *Dentaria* and *Cardamine,* published simultaneously by Linnaeus, must result in a genus called *Cardamine*

. . . because this name was chosen by Crantz . . . , who was the first to unite the two genera. . . . Robert Brown . . . appears to have been the first to unite *Waltheria americana* L. . . . and W. *indica* L. . . . [published simultaneously]. He adopted the name *Waltheria indica* for the combined species, and this name must accordingly be retained [Article 57].

Change of Rank. When a tribe becomes a family, when a subgenus becomes a genus, when a subdivision of a species becomes a species, or when the reverse of these changes takes place, and in general when a group changes its rank, *the earliest legitimate name or epithet given to the group in its new rank is valid,* unless that name or the resulting association or combination is a later homonym, that is, unless it is identical with a name used previously for another plant. Example: *Magnolia virginiana* L. var. *foetida* L. (1753) must be called *Magnolia grandiflora* L. (1759), instead of *Magnolia foetida* (L.) Sarg. (1889), because *grandiflora* has priority in specific rank. However, if the group were transferred to varietal status under another species, it would be var. *foetida,* because this epithet has priority in varietal rank. *"In no case does a name or an epithet have priority outside its own rank"* (Article 60, boldface type ours). *The important rule is to adopt the oldest usable epithet published in the proper rank.*

According to Recommendation 60A, when a taxon is changed in rank (as subgenus to genus or the reverse, or variety to species or the reverse) and no epithet of the new rank has been published, the original epithet should be retained by transferring it to the proper rank. For example, reducing *Cercidium floridum* Benth. to varietal status under another species should be as var. *floridum* instead of under a new varietal epithet. This is not mandatory, but it is good practice.

"When a species is transferred to another genus (or placed under another generic name for the same genus) without change of rank, the specific epithet, if legitimate, must be retained. . . ." (Article 55) unless the resulting combination is a *later homonym* (a duplicate of a name previously used for another plant) or a *tautonym* (the generic and specific names being exact duplicates). Examples: Under *Linaria, Antirrhinum spurium* L. becomes *Linaria spuria* (L.)

Mill. Transferred to *Cytisus, Spartium biflorum* Desf. does not become *Cytisus biflorus,* because that name was applied to a different species of *Cytisus* at an earlier date. Consequently, the transferred species is known by the next legitimate epithet in order of priority, that is *Cytisus Fontanesii* Spach. *Spiraea Aruncus* when it is considered to form the type species of a segregate genus, *Aruncus,* can not be called *Aruncus Aruncus* (L.) Karst. (a tautonym); it must receive a later name, e.g., *Aruncus sylvester* Kostel. (see Article 55).

"When an infraspecific taxon is transferred without change of rank to another genus or species [or placed under another name], the original epithet must be retained . . ." unless the resulting combination previously has been published validly for a subdivision based upon a different type. Examples: *Helianthemum italicum* Pers. var. *micranthum Gren.* and *Godr.,* after transfer to another species, may become *Helianthemum penicillatum* Thib. var. *micranthum* (Gren. and Godr.) Grosser; *Parosela Schottii* (Torr.) Heller var. *puberula* Parish under the generic name *Dalea* becomes *Dalea Schottii* Torr. var. *puberula* (Parish) Munz (see Article 56).

Each epithet must be retained for the plants on which the group was based originally. In other words, no matter who may have misinterpreted the application of a name or an epithet, it is associated permanently with the type specimen upon which it was based. It is always applied to the original population or population system; no amount of misuse can change this.

An example of misapplication of a name is found among the palos verdes of the southwestern deserts. *Cercidium floridum* Benth. ex A. Gray was described in 1852, and Gray, who supplied the description, interpreted the species as including primarily a palo verde growing east of the Continental Divide in Texas and northeastern Mexico, although two collections from along the Gila River (Arizona), west of the Divide, were cited. The type specimen, named by Bentham and deposited at the Herbarium of Trinity College, Dublin, Ireland, has not been inspected by American authors. However, a photograph [Fig. 12–4 (2)] shows it to be a collection of the blue palo verde of California, Arizona, and northwestern Mexico. The type specimen came from Hermosillo, Sonora, just south of Arizona. Consequently, when this point was established, *Cercidium floridum* replaced the later name *Cercidium Torreyanum* for the western plant, and the Gulf-coast tree became known by a new name, *Cercidium macrum* I. M. Johnston.

SUGGESTED READING

SMITH, ALBERT C. 1957. Historical sketch of development of the present code through years of controversy.

Application of the Code

EXAMPLES AND PROBLEMS

The cresosote bush (see p. 344 and Fig. 13–1) occurs in the deserts of both North and South America but consists of a single only slightly variable population system to be considered as one species. It has received the following names based on the type specimens indicated:

1. *Larrea divaricata* Cav. in 1800. Buenos Aires, Argentina, *Née.* Probably actually from Chile. *Covillea divaricata* Vail in 1895.
2. *Zygophyllum tridentatum* Moc. and Sessé in 1824. Mexico.
   Larrea tridentata Cov. in 1893.
   Schroeterella tridentata Briq. in 1925.
   Neoschroetera tridentata Briq. in 1926.
3. *Larrea mexicana* Moric. in 1839. San Luis Potosí, Mexico, *Berlandier 1362* (the collector's specimen number).
4. *Zygophyllum californicum* Torr. & Frem. in 1845. Walker Pass, Mojave Desert, Kern County, California. *Frémont.*
5. *Larrea glutinosa* Engelm. in 1848. "Ola and Fray Cristobal, in New Mexico, to Chihuahua and Saltillo; also about Presidio (Dr. Gregg). . . ." The first-mentioned collections and observations above were by Wislizenus.

Covillea glutinosa Rydb. in 1910.
Larrea tridentata var. *glutinosa* Jeps. in 1925.
Schroeterella glutinosa Briq. in 1925.
Neoschroetera glutinosa Briq. in 1926.

The list of names and their recombinations is imposing, but, under the interpretation as a single taxon of the rank of species, the nomenclatural case is relatively simple.

Fig. 13–1. The creosote bush (*Larrea divaricata*), the characteristic woody plant of the southwestern desert flora. The plant has been given a variety of names (see text, p. 368). (1) a creosote bush on sand in the Mojavean Desert near the line between California and Nevada west of Las Vegas (photograph by Frank Salisbury); (2) characteristically widely spaced creosote bushes in the Arizona Desert near Ajo, Arizona. [(2) From Lyman Benson, *Plant Classification*, D. C. Heath & Co., 1957. Used by permission.]

The first question is choice of a name for the genus. *Larrea*, the correct name, was used first for a genus in the pea family (known under the present code as *Hoffmanseggia*), but its use for the creosote bush is conserved. *Schroeterella* was applied by Briquet in the belief that the creosote bushes should be separated from the other South American species of *Larrea*, which he considered a different genus. A year later he substituted *Neoschroetera* because he found *Schroeterella* had been used earlier by Hertzog in 1916 as the name for a genus of mosses. *Zygophyllum* is another genus in the family; confusion with *Larrea* is not likely in the present state of knowledge. *Covillea* was substituted for *Larrea* because, under the American Code, *Larrea* could not be used for the creosote bush.

The choice of one of the five epithets applied in specific rank is simple because *divaricata* (*-us, -um*) (1800) has clear priority over the others, all of which are metanyms. This means only that they are not to be used so long as the North American population system (species) they represent is considered to include also the South American plants upon which *Larrea divaricata* was based.

Any shift of opinion concerning classification requires nomenclatural changes. For example, if the plants forming the basis for each of the five epithets are thought to represent five different species of *Larrea*, it becomes necessary to use in each case the combination of the specific epithet under *Larrea*. For *Zygophyllum californicum*, No. 4, this requires a new combination as *Larrea californica* (Torr. and Frem.), followed by the name of the combining author. The other species become as follows:

1. *Larrea divaricata* Cav.,
2. *Larrea tridentata* (Moc.) Cov.,
3. *Larrea mexicana* Mor., and
5. *Larrea glutinosa* Engelm.

If the five epithets are considered each to have been applied to a variety of the single species, each must have an epithet in varietal rank. Variety 1, *divaricata*, the "typical" variety, is indicated simply by repetition of the specific epithet (without citation of the author's name and without publishing a new combination). It is written as follows:

Larrea divaricata Cav. var. *divaricata*.

For var. 5, the epithet *glutinosa* (already once used in varietal rank) must be employed, though recombined under *Larrea divaricata*. In the other three varieties, 2, 3, and 4, the best practice is recombination of the existing specific epithets in varietal rank as vars. *tridentata, mexicana,* and *californica* under *Larrea divaricata.* This is not mandatory under the code, but supplying new epithets would not reflect credit upon the author.

Problem 1. The following list of name combinations has been applied to a grass taxon. For practice, the exercise at the end of each list should be carried out. Authors' names (references) as well as plant names should be included in the answers.

> *Avena flavescens* L., 1753
> *Trisetum pratense* Pers., 1805
> *Trisetum flavescens* Beauv., 1812
> *Trisetaria flavescens* Baumg., 1816
> *Rebentischia flavescens* Opiz, 1854, as synonym

Write the correct name combination and citation of authors for this plant, under each of the following conditions: [1]

1. The taxon is classified as a species of *Trisetum.*
2. The taxon is classified as a species of *Trisetaria.*
3. The taxon and *Trisetum interruptum* Buckl. 1862 are classified as two varieties composing a single species of *Trisetum.*

The answers should be as follows:

1. *Trisetum flavescens* (L.) Beauv. Priority is clear because the epithet *flavescens* was used in specific rank long before any other.
2. *Trisetaria flavescens* (L.) Baumg. Ordinarily, no matter under what genus the taxon may be classified, the earliest epithet of the proper rank published under any genus is used. However, there may be some definite obstacle to its use, for example, in this case, possibly an earlier use of the combination *Trisetaria flavescens* for another species. If an earlier homonym exists, the next oldest specific epithet (the oldest usable one) must be taken up.
3. *Trisetum flavescens* (L.) Beauv. var. *flavescens* and var. *interruptum* (Buckl.) Author, that is, the word "Author" may be substituted here for your own name as the author of the new combination. This is done only for the purpose of solving practice problems.

Problem 2. The following list should be used in the same way as the first one for practice in illustration of principles:

> *Bromus spicatus* Nees, 1829
> *Diplachne spicata* Doell, 1878
> *Triodia Schaffneri* S. Wats., 1883
> *Diplachne Reverchonii* Vasey, 1886

[1] For purposes of practice problems, assume that no other names or combinations of names have been applied.

Leptochloa spicata Scribn., 1891
Sieglingia Schaffneri Kuntz, 1891

Write the correct name combination and citation of authors for this taxon under each of the following conditions, depending upon various judgments as to its classification:

1. As a species of *Tripogon* recombined by Eckman in 1912.
2. As a species of *Diplachne*.
3. As a species of *Bromus*.
4. As a species of *Agropyron*. The combination *Agropyron spicatum* was published for another species by Scribner and Smith in 1900.
5. As a variety of *Tridens pulchellus* (H. B. K.) Hitchc. (note: *Tridens* is masculine).

The following are the proper combinations:

1. *Tripogon spicatum* (Nees) Eckman.

2. *Diplachne spicata* (Nees) Doell. Unless indicated otherwise, in such lists as these it is understood that *two or more usages of the same epithet with no indication of changes* except minor ones in the terminations (which vary according to the gender of the genus) *are based on the same type specimen.* For example, *Bromus spicatus, Diplachne spicata,* and *Tripogon spicatum* are based upon the same type, later authors having recombined Nees's epithet *spicatus* under other genera. Other epithets such as *Schaffneri* are based upon different type specimens, unless they are followed by the abbreviation *nom. nov.,* which stands for *nomen novum,* or a new name applied to replace an old epithet which cannot be used (e.g., a later homonym).

3. *Bromus spicatus* Nees.

4. *Agropyron Schaffneri* (S. Wats.) Author. Since the combination *Agropyron spicatum* has been used for another plant, the combination is preoccupied. Consequently, the next epithet in order of priority is taken up, provided there is no obstacle to its use.

5. *Tridens pulchellus* (H. B. K.) Hitchc. var. *spicatus* (Nees) Author. Since no epithet has been published previously in varietal rank, it is necessary to supply one. Although there is no specific requirement, it is good practice to retain by recombination of names the epithet having priority in another rank in order to make as little change as possible.

Problem 3. The evergreen Californian cherries discussed in Chapter 3 (Figs. 3–9, 3–10, 3–11) may be classified, according to point of view, either as two species or as two varieties composing a species.

The following name combinations have been applied to the holly-leaved cherry, which grows on both the mainland and Santa Rosa and other islands:

Cerasus ilicifolia Nutt. in 1832,
Prunus ilicifolia (Nutt.) Walp. in 1843, and
Laurocerasus ilicifolia (Nutt.) Roem. in 1847.

The single epithet, *ilicifolia,* applied to the holly-leaved cherry presents no nomenclatural complications. By simple transfer it has appeared in three combinations under different generic names. *Prunus* is an inclusive genus which some authors have preferred to divide into several genera, one of these being *Cerasus,* including only the cherries and not the plums, prunes, apricots, peaches, almonds, etc. Some have divided *Cerasus* further, segregating the evergreen cherries as *Laurocerasus.* The name combinations reflect only differences in opinion as to classification. Priority of the epithet under any genus to which the species is likely to be transferred dates from 1832.

Naming of the Catalina cherry, which is restricted to the islands, has had a complex history. Three epithets have been applied to it, and each of these has been recombined in specific and varietal rank under various genera, as shown in the lists below. The history of the epithets is as follows:

1. OCCIDENTALIS. *The epithet occidentalis is legitimate for use for the Catalina cherry interpreted as a species under any genus so far suggested, except* **Prunus.** *It is the correct epithet for use in varietal rank under any genus or species.*

Lyon named the Catalina cherry in 1886, but in naming it *Prunus occidentalis* he overlooked an earlier use of the same name combination for a West Indian cherry (*Prunus occidentalis* Swartz in 1788). Thus, the combination *Prunus occidentalis* Lyon is a later homonym and therefore illegitimate.

In 1887, Greene published a recombination of the epithet as *Cerasus occidentalis.* Since the combination published by Lyon is illegitimate, the epithet cannot be recombined, but Greene's combination is treated as though he had published the epithet as a new one under *Cerasus,* and its priority in specific rank, to be employed under *Cerasus* or any other genus where there is no obstacle to its use, begins with 1887. This case is parallel to the second example under Article 72 of the International Code of Botanical Nomenclature (see p. 355).

The epithet *occidentalis* was employed in varietal rank by

Brandegee in 1888, and priority of the epithet in this rank dates from then. This epithet is treated also as newly published. Priority in varietal rank is effective under any genus, including *Prunus*, because the combination *Prunus ilicifolia* var. *occidentalis* was not preoccupied.

2. INTEGRIFOLIA. *The epithet* integrifolia *is illegitimate in all the situations in which it has been used.*

In 1891, Sudworth, finding the epithet *occidentalis* preoccupied under *Prunus* because of the West Indian *Prunus occidentalis* Swartz, supplied a new epithet, based upon *Prunus occidentalis* Lyon, which he published in varietal rank. He named the Catalina cherry *Prunus ilicifolia* (Nutt.) Walp. var. *integrifolia* Sudw. This combination was not based upon a different type specimen from that of var. *occidentalis* (see above) but was offered simply as a *nomen novum*, that is, as a substitute for the older epithet. Since the epithet *occidentalis*, with the same type specimen, had been published legitimately for use in varietal rank, this name was superfluous when published and therefore illegitimate.

In 1905, Sargent recombined *integrifolia* in specific rank under *Prunus*. However, the combination *Prunus integrifolia* was a later homonym because it had been used for another species of *Prunus* by Walpers in 1852–1853. Consequently *Prunus integrifolia* (Sudw.) Sarg. is illegitimate, that is, a later homonym.

In 1906, C. K. Schneider recombined *integrifolia* as *Laurocerasus integrifolia*. Inasmuch as the combination was superfluous when published, because the epithet *occidentalis* based upon the same type specimen was available for use in specific rank under any suggested genus but *Prunus*, the name was illegitimate.

3. LYONII. *If the Catalina cherry is considered a species of* Prunus, *it must be named* Prunus Lyonii Sarg.

In 1905, Alice Eastwood provided still another epithet intended to replace *integrifolia*, naming the Catalina cherry *Cerasus Lyonii* Eastw. Had she applied the epithet under *Prunus*, it would have been legitimate, but under *Cerasus* there was no obstacle to use of *occidentalis*, published earlier and based upon the same type specimen (see above), so *Cerasus Lyonii* (based upon *integrifolia*, which was based upon *occidentalis*) was superfluous and therefore illegitimate.

The epithet was recombined by Britton in 1908 as *Laurocerasus Lyonii*, this, too, being superfluous and illegitimate.

In 1911, the epithet was published in the combination *Prunus Lyonii* Sarg. Sargent's use was legitimate under *Prunus* because, in this genus alone, there was an obstacle to the use of the original epithet *occidentalis* in the rank of species. Consequently the name was not superfluous. The combination is treated as a newly published name, and it is cited as *Prunus Lyonii* Sarg., **not** as *Prunus Lyonii* (Eastw.) Sarg.

In summary, if the Catalina cherry is classified under *Prunus,* the names must be as follows:

1. As a species, it is *Prunus Lyonii* Sarg.
2. As a variety, it is *Prunus ilicifolia* (Nutt.) Walp. var. *occidentalis* Brandegee.

As in the case of the creosote bush, interpretations in various books differ. Abrams' *Illustrated Flora of the Pacific States* (2: 1944), Munz's *Manual of Southern California Botany* (1935), and Munz and Keck's *A California Flora* (1959) contain a treatment of the Catalina cherry as *Prunus Lyonii.* Jepson's *Manual of the Flowering Plants of California* (1923–1925) names the same plant *Prunus ilicifolia* (Nutt.) Walp. var. *integrifolia* Sudw.; Jepson's *A Flora of California* (2: 1936) names it *Prunus ilicifolia* (Nutt.) Walp. var. *occidentalis* Brandegee.

The differences in treatment are due chiefly to variation in classification, though in one instance the difference is due to a question of nomenclature. All three authors considered the holly-leaved cherry and the Catalina cherry separate taxa, two writers according them specific rank and one varietal (that is, as two varieties of the same species).

Let us assume that the cherries are varieties of a single species. The specific epithet *ilicifolia* was the first applied to either element of the species. It is not surprising that the holly-leaved cherry should have been discovered and named first, because it occurs near the four mainland seaports where early visitors to Alta California stopped, while the Catalina cherry grows in restricted areas, then and now (except for Santa Catalina Island) little visited. Since the type specimen for *Cerasus ilicifolia* Nutt. is a collection of the holly-leaved cherry, that variety automatically becomes the typical one. This is indicated by automatic repetition of the specific epithet, that is, *Prunus ilicifolia* Nutt. var. *ilicifolia.*

The difference in the two treatments of the Catalina cherry by Jepson was nomenclatural. Apparently, when he was preparing his *Manual of the Flowering Plants of California* he overlooked the earlier epithet published in varietal rank by Brandegee, and for the manual he chose var. *integrifolia* published in 1891. In his later work, *A Flora of California,* Jepson corrected this error and chose properly the earliest epithet published in the rank he accepted, that is, *occidentalis,* as a variety.

In order to illustrate the working of the rules, let us suppose that a search of botanical literature shows the epithet *Prunus ilicifolia* to have been used for another species named in 1820. The same name may not be used for two species. However, if by chance they receive the same combination, then according to the rule of priority it may be used only for the first to receive it. According to the assumption above, *Prunus ilicifolia* (Nutt.) Walp., based upon *Cerasus ilicifolia* Nutt. (in 1832), cannot be used for the holly-leaved cherry, because it is assumed here to be a later homonym (preoccupied name). The next usable epithet of specific rank to be applied to any member of the species must be taken up. Under the supposition here, the earliest remaining usable specific epithet applied to members of either variety is *Prunus Lyonii* Sarg., as is shown in the discussion above. Since this epithet was applied to the Catalina cherry, that taxon becomes the typical variety, that is, *Prunus Lyonii* var. *Lyonii*. *Determination of which variety is the typical one has nothing to do with which is more abundant or better known; it depends solely upon which variety includes the type specimen upon which the accepted specific epithet was based.*

Under the suppositions in these paragraphs, the holly-leaved cherry must be supplied with an epithet of varietal rank, for none has been applied to it. Applying a new one is a required procedure, but it is possible to preserve the epithet already applied in another rank, that is, by using *ilicifolia* in varietal status. Since the combination *Prunus ilicifolia* was illegitimate (under the supposition above, a later homonym), the epithet *ilicifolia* may be applied in varietal rank as a new name, not as a new combination.

Problem 4. In the following example two lists are given. These apply to grasses which have been considered by some as a single taxon and by others as two taxa, A and B. Both lists will enter into consideration in carrying out the exercise.

LIST A

Panicum laevigatum Muhl., 1816, not Lam. in 1778 (meaning there is an earlier application, by Lamarck of the same name, *Panicum laevigatum*, to a different species)

Panicum medium Muhl., 1816, as syn. (i.e., merely cited as a synonym and therefore not published validly)

Panicum glaucum var. *purpurascens* Ell., 1816

Setaria affinis Schult., 1824

Panicum imberbe var. *dasyurum* Doell, 1877

Setaria perennis Hall, 1892

LIST B

Panicum fuscescens Willd., 1829, as syn.
Panicum penicillatum Willd., 1829, not Nees in 1826
Setaria Ventenatii Kunth., 1830
Chamaeraphis glauca var. *perennis* Beal, 1896

Write the correct name combination(s) and citation(s) of authors under each of the following conditions and judgment as to classification.

1. All the epithets of both lists are found to apply to a **single** recognizable taxon—a species of *Setaria*.
2. The epithets of List A and List B represent two varieties constituting a species of the genus *Panicum*. Name the typical variety. Name the other variety.
3. Taxa A and B are two species of *Chamaeraphis*. Name Taxon A. Name Taxon B.

The following are the answers for the exercises above:

1. *Setaria affinis* Schult. The oldest legitimate epithet in either list validly published in specific rank and not preoccupied under *Setaria* is *affinis*. *Panicum laevigatum* Muhl. (in 1816) is permanently illegitimate because a duplicating combination (earlier homonym) was published by Lamarck in 1778. There is no obstacle to use of the epithet under *Setaria*. However, because *Panicum laevigatum* Muhl. was illegitimate, a combination of *Setaria* with *laevigata* would have to be published as a new name, and a usable one (*affinis*) already exists and has priority. *Panicum medium* was cited as a synonym (without intention of naming a new entity), and this is not considered as valid and effective publication.

2. The typical variety is *Panicum affinis* (Schult.) Author var. *affinis*. The other variety is var. *perennis* (Beal) Author. Since (under *Panicum*) *affinis* is the oldest usable epithet in specific rank in either list, it is combined under *Panicum* to form the name of the species. Since it is in List A, the taxon represented by this list is the typical variety, as is indicated by repetition of the specific epithet. The other variety is designated by the oldest epithet in varietal rank appearing in List B, representing the other taxon. This is *perennis*, published in 1896. Although *purpurascens* (1816) is much older, it was applied to the taxon of List A, not B. Since *perennis* is the first varietal epithet in List B, it has precedence over the older epithets published in specific rank. The epithet *perennis* of List B is not to be confused with *Setaria perennis* Hall, applied to the taxon of List A and based on a different type.

3. Species A is *Chamaeraphis affinis* (Schult.) Author. Species B is *Chamaeraphis Ventenatii* (Kunth) Author. The oldest usable epithet in specific rank in List B is *Ventenatii*. *Panicum fuscescens* was cited as a synonym instead of published as a new name. The epithet *penicillatum* cannot be used for Taxon B, because there is an older combination, *Panicum penicillatum*, published by Nees in 1826. This is not an obstacle to use of the combination *Chamaeraphis penicillata* as a new name because it does not duplicate any previously published combination, but there is already a validly published legitimate epithet (*Ventenatii*) of the proper rank.

Problem 5. The following name combinations have been applied to the taxa listed below. In this case full references to the publications are given in order to illustrate the form in which lists of this type may appear under species in the more elaborate botanical works such as Abrams' *Illustrated Flora of the Pacific States* (1923, 1944, 1951, 1960), Britton and Brown's *Illustrated Flora of the Northern States and Canada* (1896–1898, 1913–1914), the *North American Flora*, or other technical works such as monographs of genera.

TAXON A

Bigelovia graveolens (Nutt.) A. Gray var. *latisquamea* A. Gray, Proc. Amer. Acad. 8: 645. 1873

Crysothamnus speciosus Nutt. var. *latisquameus* Greene, Erythea 3: 110. 1895

Chrysothamnus speciosus Nutt. var. *arizonicus* Greene, Erythea 3: 110. 1895

Bigelovia graveolens (Nutt.) A. Gray var. *appendiculata* Eastw. Proc. Calif. Acad. III. 1: 74. *pl. 6.* 1897

Chrysothamnus latisquameus Greene, Pittonia 4: 42. 1899

Chrysothamnus nauseosus (Pall.) Britt. var. *latisquameus* H. M. Hall, Univ. Calif. Publ. Bot. 7: 167. 1919

Chrysothamnus nauseosus (Pall.) Britt. subsp. *latisquameus* H. M. Hall, Carnegie Inst. Wash. Publ. (326): 212, 221. 1923

TAXON B

Bigelovia leiosperma A. Gray, Syn. Fl. N. Amer. 1(2): 139. 1884

Aster leiospermus Kuntze, Rev. Gen. 1: 318. 1891

Bigelovia leiosperma A. Gray, var. *abbreviata* M. E. Jones, Proc. Calif. Acad. II. 5: 693. 1895

Chrysothamnus leiospermus Greene, Erythea 3: 113. 1895

Chrysothamnus nauseosus (Pall.) Britt. var. *leiospermus* H. M. Hall, Univ. Calif. Publ. Bot. 7: 173. 1919

Crysothamnus nauseosus (Pall.) Britt. subsp. *leiospermus* H. M. Hall, Carnegie Inst. Wash. Publ. (326): 217, 221. 1923

Chrysothamnus nauseosus (Pall.) Britt. var. *abbreviatus* Blake, Jour. Wash. Acad. Sci. 27: 377. 1937

TAXON C

Chrysothamnus graveolens Nutt. Gen. N. Amer. Pl. 2: 136. 1818

Bigelovia graveolens A. Gray, Proc. Amer. Acad. 8: 644. 1873

Linosyris graveolens (Nutt.) A. Gray var. *glabrata* Engelm. ex A. Gray, Proc. Amer. Acad. 8: 644. 1873, as syn.

Chrysothamnus virens Greene, Pittonia 5: 61. 1902

Chrysothamnus laetevirens Greene, Pittonia 5: 61. 1902

Chrysothamnus nauseosus var. *graveolens* Piper, Contr. U.S. Nat. Herb. 11: 559. 1906. (see footnote 2 on p. 381)

Chrysothamnus graveolens (Nutt.) A. Gray var. *glabrata* A. Nels, in Coult. and Nels. New Man. Rocky Mt. Bot. 496. 1909

Chrysothamnus nauseosus (Britt.) Pall. subsp. *graveolens* H. M. Hall, Carnegie Inst. Wash. Publ. (362): 214, 221. 1923

Assuming there are no other taxa or published names in the group, write the proper name combination and author references for each taxon, taking into account the following assumptions:

1. In your research you have found that the three taxa above are distinct species of *Chrysothamnus*.
2. In your research you have found that these taxa are three varieties composing a species of *Chrysothamnus*.
3. The same assumptions as in 2 above, plus the assumption of application of the name *Chrysothamnus graveolens* Smith (in 1807) to a species not a member of the complex included in the list of taxa above (the name combination is fictitious and is introduced here only to illustrate a rule).
4. Your study shows that these plants are not *Chrysothamnus* but *Gutierrezia* and that A and B are varieties composing one species while C is another.
5. Your study shows that only two taxa are represented, A and B being the same, that is, a species of *Chrysothamnus* not divisible into varieties, and C being a species of *Bigelovia*.

The following is a list of answers for the exercise above.

1. A. *Chrysothamnus latisquameus* (A. Gray) Greene. This is the oldest specific epithet. It is to be noted that *graveolens* as an epithet was not applied to this taxon and that *latisquameus* was merely classified by Gray as a variety under it. *Graveolens* is another taxon based upon another type specimen (see Taxon C). The same is true for *speciosus*.

B. *Chrysothamnus leiospermus* (A. Gray) Greene.

C. *Chrysothamnus graveolens* Nutt.

2. *Chrysothamnus graveolens* Nutt. is the name of the species. Since the type specimen as indicated by the list is a collection of Taxon C, the third taxon becomes the typical variety, as is indicated by a repetition of the specific epithet in varietal status (see below, under C).

A. *Chrysothamnus graveolens* (Nutt.) var. latisquameus (A. Gray) Author.

B. *Chrysothamnus graveolens* Nutt. var. *abbreviatus* (M. E. Jones) Author. The oldest usable epithet of varietal rank is chosen.

C. *Chrysothamnus graveolens* Nutt. var. *graveolens.*

3. In view of the (fictitious) combination *Chrysothamnus graveolens* Smith applied to another species, *Chrysothamnus graveolens* Nutt. becomes a later homonym. With *graveolens* removed from the field, the next oldest epithet of specific rank is *leiosperma.* This was published by Gray under *Bigelovia* and applied to Taxon B, which becomes the typical variety. Since the epithet *leiosperma* was based upon a collection of Taxon B, the species is *Chrysothamnus leiospermus* (A. Gray) Greene.

A. *Chrysothamnus leiospermus* (A. Gray) Greene var. *latisquameus* (A. Gray) Author.

B. *Chrysothamnus leiospermus* (A. Gray) Greene var. *leiospermus.*

C. *Chrysothamnus leiospermus* (A. Gray) Greene var. *graveolens* (Piper) Author. Var. *glabrata,* as indicated, was cited merely as a synonym the first time it was used and therefore was not published validly. Its valid publication dates from 1909, when, as *Chrysothamnus graveolens* A. Gray var. *glabrata* (A. Gray) A. Nels., it was supplied with a description. *Graveolens* is treated as having been published as a new variety by Piper in 1906.

4. In this case the oldest usable specific epithet applied to either Taxon A or B (now combined) is *leiosperma.* Consequently, the species becomes *Gutierrezia leiosperma* (A. Gray) Author.

A. *Gutierrezia leiosperma* (A. Gray) Author var. *latisquamea* (A. Gray) Author.

B. *Gutierrezia leiosperma* (A. Gray) Author var. *leiosperma.*

C. *Gutierrezia graveolens* (Nutt.) Author.

5. A. and B. *Chrysothamnus leiospermus* (A. Gray) Greene.

C. *Bigelovia graveolens* (Nutt.) A. Gray.

The five numbered problems above have been provided for purposes of illustration. The lists of names are correct, but the suppositions made in regard to classification are hypothetical.

The following, however, is a real case. Three taxa are involved, and they are considered to be three varieties constituting a species. The following list of name combinations includes all known to have been applied at the time of appearance of a publication in 1941.

TAXON A

Ranunculus tenellus Nutt. in Torr. and Gray, Fl. N. Amer. 1: 23. 1838, not Viviani in 1831, not *R. Andersonii* var. *tenellus* S. Wats. in 1871

Ranunculus Nelsonii DC. var. *tenellus* A. Gray, Proc. Amer. Acad. 8: 374. 1872 (this is not invalidated by *Ranunculus Andersonii* var. *tenellus,* based on a different type and classified under another species)

Ranunculus occidentalis Nutt. var. *tenellus* A. Gray, Proc. Amer. Acad. 21: 373. 1886

Ranunculus Bongardii Greene var. *tenellus* Greene, Erythea 3: 54. Apr. 1, 1895

Ranunculus Nelsonii glabriusculus[2] Holzinger, Contr. U.S. Nat. Herb. 3: 210. Nov. 23, 1895

Ranunculus Douglasii Howell, Fl. N. W. Amer. 1: 18. Mar., 1897

Ranunculus arcuatus Heller. Bull. Torrey Club 24: 319. June 29, 1897

Ranunculus Bongardii Greene var. *Douglasii* Davis, Minn. Bot. Studies 2: 479. 1900

TAXON B

Ranunculus occidentalis Nutt. var. *parviflorus* Torr. Bot. Wilkes Exped. 17: 214. 1874

Ranunculus occidentalis var. *Lyallii* A. Gray, Proc. Amer. Acad. 21: 373. 1886

Ranunculus Bongardii Greene, Erythea 3: 54. Apr. 1, 1895

Ranunculus tenellus var. *Lyallii* Rob. in A. Gray, Syn. Fl. N. Amer. 1: 33. 1895

Ranunculus Greenei Howell, Fl. N. W. Amer. 1: 18. 1897

Ranunculus Lyallii Rydb. Mem. N. Y. Bot. Gard. 1: 166. 1900

Ranunculus Bongardii Greenei[3] Piper, Contr. U.S. Nat. Herb. 11: 275. 1906

TAXON C

Ranunculus Earlei Greene, Pittonia 4: 15. 1899

Ranunculus Bongardi Greene var. *Earlei* L. Benson, Bull. Torrey Club 68: 479. 1941

As the matter stood in 1941, after study of the Ranunculi occurring in North America north of Mexico, it was necessary to name

---

[2] Some authors have not indicated the rank for taxa of infraspecific status, e.g., variety or subspecies. Epithets applied without designation of rank have no priority in any rank. Epithets published in infraspecific rank and preceded by a Greek letter, e.g., "α *hirsuta*" or "β *glauca*" are considered to have been proposed for varietal rank.

[3] See footnote 2.

this species as *Ranunculus Bongardii* Greene, because *Bongardii* was the oldest known specific epithet for any of the three taxa. *Ranunculus tenellus* Nutt. published in 1838 is not usable (a later homonym), because Viviani had used an exactly duplicating combination in 1831. Taxon A, therefore, was considered as *Ranunculus Bongardii* Greene var. *tenellus* Greene (considered to have been published as a new use of the epithet, not as a recombination based on the illegitimate name applied by Nuttall); Taxon B was the typical variety *Ranunculus Bongardii* Greene var. *Bongardii;* Taxon C, reduced to varietal status, was given the epithet *Earlei* transferred to varietal rank, as shown above, that is, *Ranunculus Bongardii* Greene var. *Earlei* (Greene), a new combination having been required.

In studying the Mexican Ranunculi in 1944, an amazing specimen came to light. In the last years of the eighteenth century and the first years of the nineteenth, Mociño, Sessé, and their associates traveled widely in Mexico collecting plant specimens. These were sent to Spain, and duplicates of some of them were distributed to herbaria in other European countries. One collection is clearly Taxon A above, despite the fact that all other known collections of this taxon and of the other two were made somewhere in the triangle having Alaska, California, and Colorado as its corners. Probably no species having a distributional pattern of this type has outposts of occurrence far southward in Mexico in the areas travelled by Mociño and Sessé. The label of the "Mociño and Sessé" collection of *Ranunculus* bears only the one word "Mexico" to describe the locality from whence it came.

After a considerable amount of research in Mexico on the itinerary of the expedition, Rickett (1947) described the travels of Mociño and Sessé in detail. He found that Mociño had taken ship to Alaska from a west-coast port. Spain then considered Alaska to be a part of Mexico. He spent some time at Nutka and then returned to Mexico (proper). Probably during his stay in Alaska or at some point at which the ship may have touched along the northwest coast Mociño must have collected Taxon A.

In 1831, Taxon A was named *Ranunculus uncinatus* by D. Don. The epithet *uncinatus,* published in specific rank and based upon the Mociño collection from "Mexico," antedates *Bongardii* by 64 years and even antedates *tenellus* as published by Nuttall, although this is unimportant because *tenellus* is a later homonym. Consequently, a nomenclatural shift has been necessary. Taxon A has become the typical one, the species as a whole becoming *Ranunculus uncinatus* D. Don. Taxon A is *Ranunculus uncinatus* D. Don var.

uncinatus. Taxon B is designated by the oldest usable epithet in varietal rank, that is, *parviflorus;* it is *Ranunculus uncinatus* D. Don var. *parviflorus* (Torr.), which required a new combination. Taxon C is *Ranunculus uncinatus* D. Don var. *Earlei* (Greene), which also required a new combination.

APPLICATION OF THE RULE OF PRIORITY

Such shifts in the names of individual species as the one described above are unfortunate, and practical means of avoiding them are much needed. The following proposals have been made.

Voting. Some have suggested abolishing the complex system of nomenclature based upon priorities and substituting a "simple" system based upon voting to determine the name for each plant. The advocates of this procedure are mostly laymen and those working in botanical fields other than taxonomy. Although the use of ballots may at first seem plausible, this procedure has not been considered seriously by botanists with experience in critical classification and naming of plants. Since the problem of classification is bound up intimately with application of names, only the individual who has conducted the research leading to classification of the taxa in question is able to define them clearly enough to vote intelligently. The machinery necessary for conducting such votes would have to be elaborate and world-wide, and, because there are at least 300,000 plant species, the ballot, even though restricted to dubious nomenclatural cases, would be a very long one. Because probably no botanist has even seen more than a few thousand species and not many are familiar with more than a few hundred, and because few have investigated the classification and nomenclature of any one problem in question, no one could comprehend the whole list. Determining who is qualified to vote on a technical question would be a delicate matter.

Another question is: "Who would be willing to do jury duty of this sort?" Nearly all qualified botanists hold teaching or research positions from which sufficient time for such a vast clerical undertaking cannot be spared. Still another difficulty is financing such a venture, even if the time of the jury were donated. Like most simple answers to complex problems, this one does not seem practical.

Limiting the Period of Priority. A similar suggestion is to determine the names of plants according to the length of time each one has been in general use, substituting usage for priority as the basis for determination of which name is to be used. In the most frequently proposed form of this proposition, priority requires evidence of use of a name within 50 years, or within the twentieth century. This proposal would require settling some difficult points. In the case involving *Ranunculus uncinatus* there is little doubt that the epithet *uncinatus* was unused, or practically so, from 1831 to 1948, while *Ranunculus Bongardii* was in various states of use and disuse from 1895 to 1948. Consultation of the books and papers published prior to 1948 and even since 1895 shows that the three taxa have appeared under a variety of names, *Bongardii* (and the various combinations of varieties under it) having come into clear usage only in 1936. During the period from 1895 to 1936, one book presented one name and the next any of half a dozen others. The only nearly definite point is the probable disuse of *uncinatus*. In most similar cases, none of the competing names has clear status as having been used for any definite length of time to the exclusion of all other combinations. Few cases are clear-cut, and each individual problem would require even far more bibliographic investigation than it does under the present International Code of Botanical Nomenclature. In all cases it would be necessary to attempt the impossible, that is, to prove the negative proposition that one epithet had not been used in any of the vast number of publications during a stated period. Even approaching proof of such a proposition would require endless clerical work; it could be accomplished in no single library and in few combinations of several libraries.

Conservation (or Rejection) of Specific Combinations. The lists of *nomina conservanda* have not been applied to the names of taxa of ranks lower than genera. Offhand, it would seem desirable in a few cases to conserve the names of species, provided it were possible to draw the line between names sufficiently important to receive such treatment and those barely not so significant. An example is the name of the giant sequoia or big tree of California, long known as *Sequoia gigantea*, a name clearly invalid because it was used first for the coast redwood, a tree with a still earlier name, *Sequoia sempervirens*. The name *Sequoia gigantea* has appeared in a large number of publications, and the necessity for upsetting this widely used combination is unfortunate. However, although selection of a few such epithets for retention either by conservation or rejection of the earlier combinations displacing them seems to the uninitiated to be a good idea, the problem is not simple. There are not a few but thousands of such cases, their merits ranging without a break from clear to unclear.

Even the list of conserved generic names has become unwieldy, and it is threatening to burst all bounds. Such a list for species would be many times more complicated, and each item would be much less useful, because in each case it would save the well-known combination for only one species instead of for several to many.

The idea of conserved (or rejected) species names was voted down at Stockholm in 1950, at Paris in 1954, and at Montreal in 1959.

Rejection of Names Not Listed in the Index Kewensis. A more practical proposal is rejection of name combinations for species published before 1900 and not listed in the Index Kewensis or its supplements covering the period up to 1950 or 1955. This would eliminate resurrection of obscure unused names of the past, overlooked because they did not appear in the Index Kewensis. This proposal, if adopted, might be helpful in a small number of cases.

All botanists agree upon the existence of a problem, but the solutions proposed so far are not practical (see Smith, 1949). Fortunately, very thorough generic monographs gradually are bringing stability to nomenclature through study of plant groups from a world-wide rather than a local viewpoint, thus reducing inconsistencies in naming and the necessity for future upsets.

NOMENCLATURAL SHIFTS REFLECTING PROBLEMS OF CLASSIFICATION

The occasional shifts in names applied to well-known (or other) species are due not only to problems of nomenclature but also to questions of classification. An example is found in the changes of opinion concerning classification of the royal ferns of eastern North America and of Eurasia. This has required shifting back and forth for the American plants between *Osmunda regalis* L. and *Osmunda regalis* L. var. *spectabilis* (Willd.) A. Gray. A small wild barley or farmer's foxtail introduced and now abundant in parts of North America is known as *Hordeum murinum* L., *Hordeum leporinum* Link, or *Hordeum murinum* L. var. *leporinum* (Link) Arcang., according to the opinion of different botanical authors concerning the status of the proposed species of *Hordeum*. Another example is classification of the redwoods discussed above. After thorough investigation of characters appearing at all stages in the life histories of the redwoods, Buchholz (1939) presented overwhelming evidence for recognition of two genera, the coast redwood remaining as *Sequoia*, the big tree being transferred to *Sequoiadendron*. Under

Sequoiadendron there is no obstacle to use of the specific epithet *gigantea* (*-us, -um*) (see above) and *Sequoia gigantea* (Lindl.) Decn. (in 1855) becomes *Sequoiadendron giganteum* (Lindl.) Buchholz (in 1939). But *Sequoia gigantea* is illegitimate because the coast redwood (*Sequoia sempervirens* (Lamb.) Endl.) (priority from 1824) had been named unnecessarily *Sequoia gigantea* by Endlicher in 1847. The epithet *gigantea* is legitimate, except under *Sequoia*, for the big tree because it was published first as *Wellingtonia gigantea* Lindl. in 1853, and priority dates from that year. In this instance, reclassification eliminates the necessity for use of the combination (*Sequoia gigantea*), proposed by many for conservation, but it reinstates the epithet *gigantea* (under *Sequoiadendron*).

PROBLEM FOR SOLUTION

The following lists of names have been applied to three units of classification. Answer the questions following the lists.

LIST A

Ranunculus Cymbalaria Pursh, Fl. Amer. Sept. 2: 392. 1814
Ranunculus nanus Fisch. in DC. Prodr. 1: 33. 1824, as syn.
Ranunculus Cymbalariae var. *americanus* DC. Prodr. 1: 33. 1824
Ranunculus saxifragaefolius Stephan. ex Steudl. Nom. ed. 2. 435. 1841, as syn.
Oxygraphis Cymbalaria Prantl. In Engl. Bot. Jahrb. 9: 263. 1888
Cyrtorhyncha Cymbalaria Britt. Mem. Torrey Club 5: 161. 1894
Halerpestes Cymbalaria Greene, Pittonia 4: 208. 1900
Ranunculus Cymbalaria forma *hebecaulis* Fern. Rhodora 16: 162. 1914.

LIST B

Ranunculus kamchaticus DC. Syst. 1: 302. 1818
Ficaria glacialis Fisch. ex DC. Syst. 1: 305. 1818, not *Ranunculus glacialis* L. in 1753
Oxygraphis glacialis Bunge, Mem. Acad. Sci. St. Petersb. 2: 557. 1835

LIST C

Ranunculus Chamissonis Schlecht. Animad. Ranunc. 1: 12. 1820
Ranunculus glacialis L. subsp. *Chamissonis* Hult. Fl. Alaska and Yukon, Lunds. Univ. Årssk. II. 40 (1): 753. *f*.3. 1944
Ranunculus glacialis L. var. *Chamissonis* L. Benson, Amer. Midl. Nat. 40 (1): 226. 1948

Assuming there are no other taxa in the group, give the proper name combination and author's name reference for each taxon, taking into account the following assumptions:

1. In your research you have found Lists A, B, and C to be really a single taxon of the rank of species classified in the genus *Ranunculus*.
2. A, B, and C are three species of *Ranunculus*.
3. A, B, and C are three varieties composing a single species of *Ranunculus*.
4. A is one species of *Ranunculus*; B and C are varieties composing another.

In *all cases* below assume that in 1800 the name combination *Ranunculus Cymbalaria* was applied to a species different from A, B, or C.

5. In your research you have found A, B, and C to be really phases of a single taxon of species rank classified in the genus *Ranunculus*.
6. A, B, and C are three species of *Ranunculus*.
7. A, B, and C are three varieties composing a single species of *Ranunculus*.
8. A is one species of *Ranunculus*; B and C are varieties composing another.
9. The three units, A–C, are classified as varieties of *Ranunculus glacialis* L. 1753, none being typical var. *glacialis*.
10. The three units, A–C, are classified as species of *Oxygraphis*.
11. The three units are classified as varieties composing a single species of *Halerpestes*.

SUGGESTED READING

DANDY, J. E., J. S. L. GILMOUR, T. A. SPRAGUE, and E. M. WAKEFIELD. 1952. Opposition to conservation of specific names; support of rejection of some names.

LITTLE, ELBERT L., JR. 1957. Conservation of some specific names; rejection of obscure or ineffectively published specific names; rejection of specific names not listed in the Index Kewensis. (Cf. A. A. BULLOCK, 1959.)

RICKETT, H. W. 1952. Inasmuch as the trend is away from strict priority and toward conservation based upon usage of names, the author proposes criteria of satisfactory typification for choice among competing names.

——, and W. H. CAMP. 1955. The effective use of the type method is proposed as the best solution to the problem of stability of names.

SMITH, A. C. 1949. Neither conservation nor rejection of specific names is considered practical; normal taxonomic procedures are slowly solving the problems underlying changes of names for species.

STAFLEU, F. A. 1956. History and discussion of the problem of conserved names.

Part IV

DESCRIPTION AND DOCUMENTATION

chapter 14

Keys and Descriptions

When plants have been classified and named, it is still necessary to provide means for other persons to identify them. This is accomplished through keys and descriptions.

KEYS

The following is an example of a key to a small group of species of the genus *Acacia* occurring in and near the deserts of the southwestern United States. The spiny species are illustrated in Fig. 14–1.

KEY TO THE SPECIES

1. Flowers in cylindroidal spikes or in heads which have a tendency to be racemose; filaments of the stamens white or tinged with pink or lavender or else creamy yellow, not a bright nearly golden yellow; stem *not* with a pair of stout, rigid spines at each node, *either* with a pair of weak, more or less flexible spines at each node *or* with prickles irregularly disposed or with *no* spines or prickles; petals separate.

    2. Inflorescence composed of cylindroidal spikes 2–4 cm. long and 10–12 mm. in diameter; stem with a pair of weak spines at each node or with irregularly disposed prickles; pods 9–19 mm. broad; seeds broader than long.

        3. Prickles disposed irregularly on the stem, similar to rose prickles or to a cat's claws, broad at the bases and curved above, about 3–5 mm. long; spines none; flowers creamy yellow; pods mostly 6–13 cm. long, 10–19 mm. broad, often constricted between the seeds; primary leaflets in 2–3 pairs; secondary leaflets in 4–6 pairs, each leaflet oblong-obovate, 3.5–7 mm. long, 1–3.5 mm. broad. . .

        1. *Acacia Greggii*

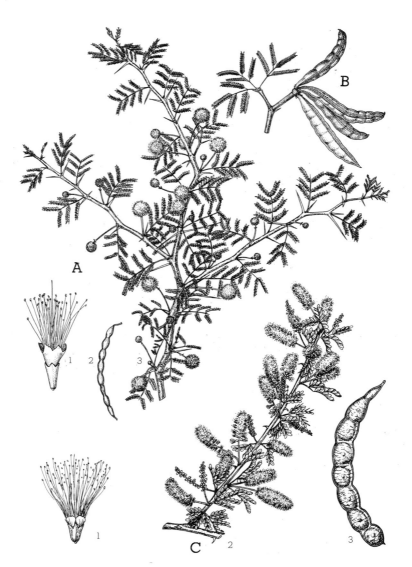

Fig. 14–1. Native spiny acacias of the deserts of the United States: (A) white thorn (*Acacia constricta*)—(1) flower, (2) fruit (a legume or pod), (3) leafy branch, showing the bipinnate leaves, globular ball-like heads of flowers, and pairs of spines at the joints (nodes) of the branches; (B) huisache (*Acacia Farnesiana*) twig with leaves and fruits; (C) cat-claw (*Acacia Greggii*)—(1) flower, (2) leafy branch, showing the bipinnate leaves, the elongated spikes of flowers, and the irregularly arranged prickles, (3) fruit, containing seeds which are broader than long. (By Lucretia Breazeale Hamilton for Lyman Benson and Robert A. Darrow, *The Trees and Shrubs of the Southwestern Deserts*. Ed. 1, 149, 1945; Ed. 2, 155, 1954. Courtesy of the University of Arizona and University of New Mexico presses. Used by permission.)

3. Prickles none, the stipules forming two slender, weak spines at each node of the stem; flowers white; pods 5–8.5 cm. long, 9–12 mm. broad, not constricted between the seeds; primary leaflets in usually 5–10 pairs; secondary leaflets in about 20–30 pairs, each oblong but with an acute tip, about 2–3 mm. long, approximately 1 mm. broad. . . . . .2. *Acacia millefolia*

2. Inflorescence composed of heads which have a tendency to be racemose; stems with neither spines nor prickles; pods 7–9 or 10 mm. broad, not constricted between the seeds; seeds markedly longer than broad. . . . . .3. *Acacia angustissima*

1. Flowers in essentially hemispheroidal heads; filaments of the stamens a bright nearly golden yellow; stem with a pair of stout rigid spines at each node; petals coalescent; seeds longer than broad.

2′. Pod flattened, constricted between the seeds, not woody, splitting promptly, the seeds in one row; common. . . . . .4. *Acacia constricta*

2′. Pod cylindroidal, not constricted, woody, splitting tardily, the seeds in 2 rows; rare in California and Arizona, common in the tropics. . . . . . .
5. *Acacia Farnesiana*

In writing keys, the taxonomist pays attention to the following technical points:

1. *Inclusion of All the Relatively Stable Distinguishing Characters.* The real distinction of taxa is by groups of associated characters, not by individual characters. Not all characters are of infallible occurrence, and not all are available at every season of the year or in all pressed specimens. Inclusion of all the significant features makes the keys longer and sometimes slightly cumbersome, but, if some stable characters are omitted, too often the characters retained break down and the key becomes impossible to follow. Unless only a few plants are covered, this weakness nearly always appears in "simplified" keys and especially in simple "artificial" keys based upon characters chosen arbitrarily regardless of plant relationships.

2. *Statement of Measurements.* Use of comparative terms alone is vague. Examples include "long" vs. "short," "narrow" vs. "broad," and (as in one case) "tall" vs. "taller." A range of measurements, such as "4–6 dm." vs. "8–12 dm." is more definite and meaningful.

3. *Employment of Only Two Opposed Leads.* Some keys are written with more than two leads at a given level, but often a third lead is overlooked, and to distinguish between two leads is simpler than to search among several.

4. *Selection of the Same Noun To Begin Each Pair of Opposed Leads.* The following are examples: flowers vs. flowers, inflorescence vs. inflorescence, prickles vs. prickles, fruit vs. fruit. The same practice is recommended for each additional subject within the lead. Nouns should come first; modifiers should follow. This organization facilitates rapid scanning of the key.

DESCRIPTIONS AND STATEMENTS OF DISTRIBUTION

Descriptions must be adequate, that is, they must cover all important points, but characters should be selected to include only the relevant ones. Descriptions may be criticized for any of several faults. Some are inaccurate and carelessly constructed; others are accurate but have characters that are not well selected to set off the group from its immediate relatives; others are painstakingly accurate but so detailed that the reader is left with the task of determining what is significant and what is not. This is a problem for which he is ill equipped, having perhaps only a single specimen before him. There are numerous definitions of intelligence, and probably no definition is adequate, but a thought-provoking one is the following: "Intelligence is the ability to recognize the significant elements in a situation." Recognition of the significant elements or significant characters to be described is surely the test of a plant describer. The amount of detail to be included varies according to the type of publication, ranging from more in a monograph to less in a manual.

Casual inspection of most manuals reveals striking inconsistencies in the way the species of each genus, the varieties of each species, or the genera of each family are described. Often, it is impossible to determine whether the characters described for one species exist at all in its nearest relatives, and the author seems to have described the characters of each species just as they came to mind. He may describe the stems of one and omit them for the next; he may give the leaf shape for one and not mention its margin, and do the reverse for the nearest relative. Obviously a standard practice should be formulated by an author to cover the *variable* characters of the members of each plant group. Characters which do not vary should be described for the group as a whole but not for its individual elements. For example, it would be folly to include the entry "stamens 6" under each genus and species of the lily family, for this is practically a family character; the exceptions are rare and readily emphasized when they do occur.

The following is an example of an ordinary description of a genus and one of its species as it might appear in a manual of the flora of a region. The example does not necessarily represent a standard form to be followed. Practice in arrangement, wording, and punctuation varies.

1. *Acacia.* ACACIA

Trees or shrubs. Spines or prickles often present; spines, when present, developed from stipules and occurring at the nodes; prickles, when present, arranged irregularly. Primary leaflets in 1 or 2 or commonly 3—many pairs; secondary leaflets commonly numerous, sometimes in as few as 5 or 6 pairs. Corolla choripetalous (apopetalous) or sympetalous; *stamens more than 10 (usually 20–100), distinct; anthers minute,* (in the species of this region) *about 0.2 mm. square.* Legume flat or turgid, linear, *the margins not prominent.* (Note: semicolons may be substituted for the periods.)

1. ACACIA GREGGII A. Gray. CATCLAW. Large shrubs or small trees up to 7 m. high; *prickles resembling the claws of a cat,* dark brown or gray, *broadbased, curved,* 3–5 mm. long; *primary leaflets in 2–3 pairs; secondary leaflets in 4–6 pairs, cuneate-oblong, 3.5–7 mm. long, 1–3.5 mm. broad,* glabrous; stipules thin, scalelike, deciduous; *flowers pale yellow, in cylindroidal spikes 3.7–5 cm. long and about 12 mm. in diameter;* calyx green, 2 mm. long; petals green, with narrow creamy margins, distinct, 3 mm. long; stamens about 50, *the filaments pale yellow,* about 6 mm. long; *legume ribbon-like, somewhat twisted, usually 6–12.5 cm. long, about 1.2 cm. broad,* often constricted between the seeds; *seed dark, biconvex, nearly circular but a little broader than long, about 7–8 mm. long, 8–10 mm. broad.*

Each segment of the description begins with a noun, the subject; the modifiers are separated by commas; there are usually no verbs but they may be represented by participles. Key characters may be emphasized by italics.

Measurements in modern scientific work are in the metric system, although the English system may be used for a popular work or for popular sections of a basically scientific book.

Description of the geographical range and the ecological requirements of each species (or variety) and of its association with other taxa and its distributional range is important. A statement for *Acacia Greggii* follows.

Along washes and on mesas in chiefly the Sonoran and Chihuahuan deserts and the Desert Grassland from sea level to 5,000 feet elevation. California in the eastern Mojave Desert and southward to the Colorado Desert; southernmost Nevada and the southwestern corner of Utah to the deserts of Arizona; New Mexico from Albuquerque southward; western Texas; northwestern Mexico [this may be more or less detailed according to the type of publication].

One logical geographical sequence corresponds on a map to progression on a printed page, that is, from west to east and north to south. Some authors follow the sequence in Gray's *Manual,* that is, east to west and north to south, following the gradual expansion of the United States westward and southward during the lifetime of Asa Gray. The history of civilization or settlement of other continents of course does not necessarily duplicate that of North America.

Ranunculus acris L.

Hirsute   _terrestrial_   _perennials_ ;
(pubescence)   (habitat)   (duration)

roots _stout but not tuberous, 0.5–1 mm. in diameter_ ;

stems _several_ , _erect_ ,
                                        (habit)

not rooting, _5–10_ ~~cm.~~ dm. long, _1.5–3_ mm. in diameter,

unbranched in the first 2–3 dm., fistulous ,
      (ramification)   (solid or fistulous)

glabrous or sparsely hirsute , basal leaf blades _simple_ ,
      (pubescence)   (complexity)

pentagonal in outline , _4–8_ ~~mm.~~ cm. long.
      (shape)

_5–10_ ~~mm.~~ cm. broad, _deeply 3-parted and the lateral segments_
                                (lobing)

again lobed, appearing 5-parted , proximally _deeply cordate_ ,
                                      (shape)

distally _rounded in outline_ , _appressed-pubescent_ , the
          (shape)   (pubescence)

petioles _5–17_ ~~mm.~~ cm. long, _hirsute_ , the stipular leaf
                        (pubescence)

bases _3–5_ ~~mm.~~ cm. long; cauline leaves _alternate_ ,
                                   (arrangement)

the bracts _of 3 linear divisions_ ,

sessile .
~~petioled~~ ; pedicels _1.5_ ~~mm.~~ cm. long in flower, _4–12_ ~~mm.~~ cm. long in

fruit, _densely pubescent_ ; sepals _5_ , _greenish_ ,
       (pubescence)   (number)   (color)

spreading , _ovate_ , _4–7_ mm. long, _about 3_ mm. broad,
    (habit)   (shape)

densely pubescent dorsally , _one-third_ the length of the
         (pubescence)

petals, _promptly deciduous_ ; petals _5_ , _bright yellow_ ,
      (when deciduous)   (number)   (color and appearance)

Fig. 14–2. A form useful in

The following illustrates descriptions of two of the five varieties of *Dalea Fremontii* Torr.:

a. Var. FREMONTII. FREMONT DALEA. Leaflets 3–5, oblong, about 6 mm. long, 1–3 mm. broad, free from the rachis, with appressed pubescence, the pubescence sparse; calyx not strongly ribbed; legume about 8–12 mm. long.

Hills and sandy plains of the Sagebrush Desert and the Mojavean Desert at 4,500–7,000 feet elevation. Nevada and Utah; California in Owens Valley north of Bishop.

b. Var. SAUNDERSII (Parish) Munz. INDIGO BUSH. Leaflets mostly 7–9, elliptic-lanceolate to lanceolate or oblong, 6-13 mm. long, 2.5–3.5 or 4 mm. broad, free from the rachis, sparsely appressed-pubescent, the rachis often densely so; calyx not markedly ribbed; legume 8–12 mm. long.

Desert slopes and washes primarily in the Mojavean Desert at 2,000–6,000 feet elevation. California from the Owens River Valley southward to the Mojave Desert and as far eastward as Victorville and the Death Valley region.

Descriptions of related species (for example, those treated in the monograph of a genus) should cover the same characters in a uniform sequence. The following form was set up for writing rough drafts of descriptions, to insure uniformity in treatment of the species of *Ranunculus*. The form saves time and facilitates writing. Since the genus has many species, the description of each one must be longer than for the few species of the genus *Acacia* occurring in a restricted area, but not longer than would be necessary in a treatment of the entire genus *Acacia*, which also is large (for the species described in Fig. 14–2, see Figs. 1–6, 4–11).

obovate-cuneate , __8-14__ mm. long, __6-10__ mm. broad, the
    (shape)

nectary scale *glabrous, free laterally, 1.2 mm. long, truncate* ;

stamens __40-80__ ; achenes __25-40__ in a *globose* head
   (number)   (number)   (shape)

about 6 mm. long and __6__ mm. in diameter, each achene

obovoid, discoid , __2-2.5__ mm. long, __1.8__ mm. dorsoventrally,
  (shape)

__0.5__ mm. laterally, *smooth* , *glabrous* , the margin
              (surface)   (pubescence)

conspicuous , *keeled* , the achene beak *deltoid basally* ,

__0.3-0.6__ mm. long, *recurved* ; receptacle *pyriform* ,
         (curvature)   (shape)

__1-2__ mm. long in flower, __2-5__ mm. long in fruit, *glabrous* .
                                       (pubescence)

writing descriptions of taxa.

NEW TAXA

When new species or other taxa are described or new name combinations are published, the name commonly appears in **boldface
type** to facilitate indexing of proposed scientific names. In addition
to the usual description in a modern language (which is optional),
a Latin diagnosis is required, and a type specimen must be designated (see pp. 353, 357). The relationships of the new entity and
its distinctions from its near relatives should be set forth, and sufficient herbarium specimens should be cited to enable others to check
the identity of the newly discovered plant.

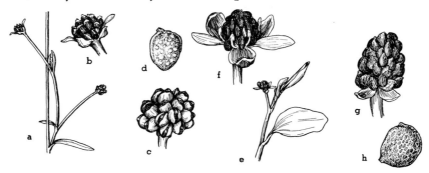

Fig. 14–3. *Ranunculus alveolatus* Carter: (a–d) (for comparison) *Ranunculus
pusillus,* a related species with which this plant has been confused—(a) upper
portion of the plant showing the sessile, linear-lanceolate leaves, (b) flower,
(c) hemispherical fruiting head, (d) papillate achene; (e–h) *Ranunculus alveolatus*
—(e) upper portion of the plant, showing the petiolate, ovate leaves, (f) flower,
(g) fruiting head, (h) alveolate achene. (From Annetta Carter, American Journal
of Botany 26: 556, *Fig. 1,* 1939. Used by permission.)

The following is an example of the description of a proposed
new species (Fig. 14–3) American Journal of Botany 26: 555–557.
1939; quoted by permission):

Ranunculus alveolatus Carter, sp. nov. Glabrous to sparsely pubescent
semi-aquatic annual; roots filiform, numerous; stems many-branched from near
the bases, semi-decumbent to erect, rooting adventitiously at the lower nodes,
12–30 cm. long and 1–1.5 mm. in diameter, fistulous; leaves alternate, the
blades simple, ovate to ovate-lanceolate, 6–20 mm. long, 4–12 mm. broad,
entire to slighty dentate, petioles of lower cauline leaves 30–85 mm. long,
petioles of upper cauline leaves 6–35 mm. long; stipular leaf-bases membranous-margined, non-ciliate or slightly ciliate at the apices, 4–6 mm. long, conspicuous; pedicels 5–10 mm. long in flower and 10–40 mm. long in fruit; sepals
3, membranous-margined at the bases, broadly to obtusely ovate, 2–2.5 mm.
long, 1–1.5 mm. broad, glabrous, persistent; petals 2–3, yellow, clawed, each

blade ovate, 2–2.5 mm. long, 1 mm. broad, the nectary-scale a glabrous pocket, truncate; stamens 4–5, 1.25–1.5 mm. long; achenes 15–25 in a slightly elongated head 3–5 mm. long by 3–4 mm. in diameter, each achene oval, flattened, 1.5 mm. long, 1.25 mm. dorsoventrally, and 0.5 mm. laterally, the surface alveolate, the margin obscure, the achene-beak obsolete; receptacle conical to narrowly ovate, 1 mm. long in flower and 2–3.5 mm. long, 1.25–1.5 mm. in diameter in fruit, glabrous.

Herba annua amphibia, glabra vel sparse pubescens; radices filiformes; caules 12–30 cm. longi, 1–1.5 mm. diametro, fistulosi, semidecumbentes vel erecti, ad basim versus multiramosi, ramis e nodis inferioribus radicantibus; folia alterna laminis ovatis ovato-lanceolatis integerrimis vel paullo dentatis; foliorum inferiorum petioli 30–85 mm. longis, superiorum 6–35 mm. longis; laminae 6–20 mm. longae, 4–12 mm. latae; stipulae 4.6 mm. longae, conspicue membranaceo-marginatae eciliatae vel sparse ciliatae; pedicelli per anthesin 5–10 mm. longi, fructiferi 10–40 mm. longi; sepala 3, late obtuseque ovata, basi membranaceo-marginata 2–2.5 mm. longa, 1–1.5 mm. lata; petala 2–3, lutea unguiculata 2–2.5 mm. longa, laminis ovatis 1 mm. latis, squamulis nectariferis truncatis; stamina 4–5; carpellorum capitulum ovoideum, 3–5 mm. longum, 3–4 mm. latum; achenia ovalia complanata 1.5 mm. longa, diametro dorsoventraliter 1.25 mm., lateraliter 0.5 mm.; pericarpio alveolato, rostro obsoleto; receptaculum in fructu 2–2.5 mm. longum, 1.25–1.5 mm. latum.

Margins of ponds and marshy areas along small streams; Sierra Nevada foothills from Calaveras County to Placer County, California.

The type specimen was collected between Fair Oaks and Folsom, 1½ miles southeast of Orangevale, Sacramento County, April 25, 1937, *Annetta Carter 1244 (Herbarium of the University of California No. 604080)*.

The following material from Dudley Herbarium, Stanford University, *SU*, and the Herbarium of the University of California, *UC*, has been examined. Placer County: Roseville, *J. W. Congdon*, April 2, 1894, *SU*. Sacramento County: Folsom, *Katherine Brandegee*, May 8, 1907, *UC*, in part; between Fair Oaks and Folsom, 1½ miles southeast of Orangevale, *Annetta Carter 821*, May 12, 1935, *U.C.* Calaveras County: 7.5 miles west of San Andreas, *John Thomas Howell 4707*, April 13, 1930, *SU, UC*.

The relationships [insofar as they are expressed by comparison of diagnostic characters] of the two [including *R. oresterus*] new species to other members of the section *Flammula* occurring in North America north of Mexico are shown by the following [slightly revised] key:

1. Perennials; achenes 1.2–2.5 mm. long, the beaks 0.3–1.5 mm. long or in one species 0.1–0.2 mm. long; petals 5–10, conspicuous and usually large, longer than the sepals, except in one species. . . . . Subsection 1. FLAMMULAE

    2. Achenes nearly beakless, the beaks, if present, 0.1–0.2 mm. long, the styles stout. . . . . .1. *R. Flammula*

    2. Achenes distinctly beaked, the beaks 0.3–1.5 mm. or rarely only 0.2 mm. long.

        3. Cauline leaves lanceolate, oblanceolate, or linear.

            4. Roots glabrous in their mature portions; petals exceeding the sepals.

                5. Leaves not dentate, sometimes serrulate or wavy-margined, usually entire.

6. Stems rooting at at least the lower nodes.

    7. Achene beaks 0.3–0.5, rarely 0.7 mm. long; stems mostly less than 2.5 mm. in diameter....1. *R. Flammula* vars.

    7. Achene beaks 1 mm. long; stems mostly 5–10 mm. in diameter.........................2. *R. ambigens.*

6. Stems never rooting adventitiously.........3. *R. alismaefolius.*

    5. Leaves (at least the basal) dentate.....5. *R. hydrocharoides, var.*

4. Roots densely pubescent their whole length; petals 5, not exceeding the sepals, narrowly oblong, 3 mm. long, 1–1.5 mm. broad; leaves entire; stems not rooting adventitiously....4. **R. oresterus**

3. Cauline leaves ovate or ovate-lanceolate.

    4′. Stems rooting at at least the lower nodes; flowers never in cymes having opposite branches.

        5′. Roots with no thickened storage parts.

            6′. Stems not fistulous or inflated, 1–1.5 mm. thick; cauline petioles sheathing the stem..............1. *R. Flammula* var.

            6′. Stems usually fistulous, 1–5 mm. thick, cauline petioles not sheathing the stem.................5. *R. hydrocharoides.*

        5′. Roots each with a light-colored, fusiform storage thickening at the base..........................6. *R. Gormanii.*

    4′. Stems never rooting; flowers usually in cymes having opposite branches; roots each with a light-colored fusiform storage thickening at the base............................7. *R. Populago.*

1. Annuals; achenes 0.6–1 or rarely 1.5 mm. long, the beaks 0.1–0.2 mm. long...Subsection 2. Pusilli.

    2′. Petals 5–9, large and conspicuous, about twice as long as the sepals; styles in anthesis 0.5 mm. long, filiform, deciduous in fruit; head of achenes hemispherical or ovoid......................8. *R. oblongifolius.*

    2′. Petals 1–3, minute and inconspicuous, shorter than or equal to the sepals; styles in anthesis 0.1–0.2 mm. long.

        3′. Sepals 5; upper cauline leaves linear to lanceolate or oblanceolate or very narrowly elliptic, sessile; achenes oblong-obovate, 0.6–1 mm. long, smooth, reticulate, or papillate, the units of the reticulate pattern perhaps 0.03 mm. in diameter when visible.....9. *R. pusillus.*

        3′. Sepals 3; upper cauline leaves ovate, petioled; achenes obovate, about 1.5 mm. long, reticulate, the units of the pattern about 0.1 mm. in diameter...........................10. **R. alveolatus.**

ILLUSTRATION

Scientific illustration is of first importance as a supplement to description. This subject is discussed on pages 439–445.

chapter 15

Documentation

THE HERBARIUM AS A RECORD

The herbarium includes a record of the plants described and discussed in technical botanical books and papers. Nearly every large collection is the basis for botanical literature, which is documented by reference to individual plant specimens according to collector and field number, or sometimes according to the herbarium number stamped on the sheet. Specimens, if they are complete, may indicate beyond doubt the plant under discussion; they are a connecting link between the living organism and what is written about it. Every seriously prepared plant manual, flora, or monograph is based on herbarium specimens, which are available for study by properly qualified persons. Specimens are not only evidence of what has been described but are also the basis for statements concerning geographical distribution, variation within the species, and distinctions or interrelationships of taxa. The herbarium is a permanent record of what is in the living flora or (too seldom) of which plants have been studied experimentally.

Any modern manual or flora, for example, those of Abrams (1923, 1944, 1951, 1960), Coulter and Nelson (1909), Davis (1952), Deam (1940), Fernald (1950 and earlier editions), Gleason (1952), Harrington (1954), Jepson (1909– , 1923–1925), Jones (1945, 1950), Kearney and Peebles (1942, 1951), Louis-Marie (1931); Marie-Victorin (1935, 1947), Munz (1935), Munz and Keck (1959), Peck (1941), Piper and Beattie (1915), St. John (1937, 1956), Small (1933), Stevens (1950), or Weber (1953), would be uncertain in its application and incapable of ready correction or confirmation if the author had not deposited specimens in the herbarium at which he worked. Often he has supplied identification labels for specimens there and in other herbaria.

TYPE SPECIMENS

The epithet designating each species or variety is based on a type specimen in a particular herbarium. Certain herbaria are rich in type collections, and some, for example, the herbarium of Linnaeus at the Linnaean Society in London, may be composed largely of types. (Fig. 12–1.) Consultation of the two Linnaean herbaria (London and Stockholm) adds meaning to the works of Linnaeus, and his books would be difficult to interpret without the plant specimens. In the instances in which Linnaeus preserved no specimen, the meaning of his brief descriptions often is obscure.

The following is an example of discussion of the type collections which fall within a species. This should include the type of every epithet applied, because, whether it is the basis for the accepted name or not, each is as imporant as any other. All must be checked by any student of the species. Methods of presentation of data vary from author to author. References for illustration of styles will be given in Chapter 16.

Ranunculus canus Benth. var. *canus*

(1) R. *canus* Benth. Pl. Hartw. 294. 1848.
R. *occidentalis* Nutt. var. *canus* A. Gray, Proc. Amer. Acad. 8: 374. 1872.
R. *californicus* Benth. var. *canus* Brew. & Wats. Bot. Calif. 1:8. 1876.

"In pascuis humidis vallis Sacramento ubi terram late obtegit." *Hartweg 1626 (239)* in 1847. Jepson (Erythea 5: 54. 1897) quotes the following from Hartweg: "On April the 13, I left [the junction of the Yuba and Feather rivers] with Mr. L. for his farm, seventy miles higher up the valley. . . . Crossing Feather River, which here is eighty yards broad, and of considerable depth, our course lay five and twenty miles along that river, through a beautiful wood of evergreen and deciduous oaks. . . . Leaving Feather River we struck across a prairie for twenty miles; here immense fields of Eschscholtzia crocea, E. californica and Ranunculus No. 239, presented themselves, each species growing by itself." The junction of the Yuba and Feather rivers is at the present town of Marysville; Oroville is 26 miles up the Feather River; Chico is 21 miles northwest of Oroville. The country between Oroville and Chico is grassland. The type station for *Ranunculus canus*, therefore, must be between Oroville and Chico. (Fig. 15–1). The species has been collected on the plains and foothills between the towns in recent years. (Figs. 15–2, 3). Type *K*[1] (Royal Botanic Gardens, Kew, England) (Fig. 15–1), photograph *DS*, isotypes *NY*, *GH*, photograph *Pom*.

[1] Standard symbols for herbaria are discussed on pages 407–409.

Fig. 15–1. Type specimen of *Ranunculus canus* Benth., collected in the Sacramento Valley of California between Oroville and Chico by Hartweg in 1847 (Herbarium of the Royal Botanic Gardens, Kew, England) (see text). (Photographs courtesy of Ira L. Wiggins, Dudley Herbarium, Stanford University.)

Fig. 15–2. A specially collected topotype (specimen from the same place as the type, i.e., holotype), *Ranunculus canus* Benth. (cf. Figs. 15–1, 15–3).

Fig. 15–3. A topotype, *Ranunculus canus* Benth. Note the differences in the leaves of this plant, the other topotype (Fig. 15–2), and the holotype (Fig. 15–1). A topotype has no official status. Often it is useful, but it should be checked with the holotype in order that it may not be misleading.

(2) *R. canus* var. *Blankinshipii* Rob. in A. Gray, Syn. Fl. N. Amer. 1: 35.
1895.
R. *Blankinshipii* Heller, Muhlenbergia 1: 40. 1904.

"Capay, Yolo County, Calif., J. W. Blankinship. 15 April, 1893." Type *GH*,
photographs *DS* and *Pom;* isotype, *UC 118180* [Fig. 15–4 (1)].

(3) *R. longilobus* Heller, Muhlenbergia 2: 36. 1905.

"The type is [Heller] no. 7912, collected May 31, 1905 on hills about one
mile back from Middle Creek Station near Keswick, Shasta County, California,
growing in damp ground near a little stream." This plant is intermediate in
vegetative characters between *Ranunculus occidentalis* vars. *Eisenii* and
ultramontanus, and both the type collection and a specially collected topotype
(*Heller 13930*) show on some specimen sheets fruit of the *Ranunculus canus*
type and on others of the *Ranunculus occidentalis* var. *Eisenii* type. While
Ranunculus longilobus is placed in synonymy under *Ranunculus canus*, the
type is not identical with that species. The Middle Creek Station plants seem
to represent a local variable population displaying recombination of characters
of *Ranunculus canus* and *Ranunculus occidentalis* vars. *Eisenii* and *ultramontanus*. Probably the population is not sufficiently homogeneous and consistently
differentiated to be considered a variety. This point might be determined by
intensive field work at and near the type locality. Herbarium specimens are
inadequate for such a study. Type specimen, *CAS 57722 and 57723* [Fig.
15–4 (2), (3)] (see note on season's collecting, Muhlenbergia 2: 1. 1905, the
types having been deposited at the California Academy of Sciences); older
fruit like that of *Ranunculus canus*, the younger giving the erroneous impres-
sion of being that of *Ranunculus occidentalis* var. *Eisenii;* isotypes *NY* (fruit of
canus), *US 611014* (fruit of *Eisenii*), *DS 95764* [Fig. 15–5 (left)] (fruit of
Eisenii), *GH* [Fig. 15–5 (right)] (fruit of *Eisenii*), *PA 51849* (fruit of *canus);*
and topotypes collected at Keswick, *Heller 13930* (fruit of *canus*), *NY, DS,
UC, RM, Wash, GH* (fruit rather small), *Mo, Pom.*

The material above is adapted to a monographic study. For a
flora only a brief note might be included, for a manual little or
nothing.

CITATION OF SPECIMENS

At the beginning of the paragraph concerning the type of *Ranunculus canus*, there is a reference to *"Hartweg 1626,"* a specimen collected by Hartweg and bearing that number. Recent collectors
make this a serial number, but this was not so in Hartweg's time
(1847). Another system applied to his specimens is indicated by
"(239)." Heller 7912 and *13930* are precise number references because in his later years Heller followed meticulously the modern
serial numbering system, though, like that of many collectors,
Heller's earlier numbering was less systematic. Such symbols as *DS*
(Dudley Herbarium, Stanford University), *NY* (New York Botanical
Garden), *GH* (Gray Herbarium, Harvard University) and *Pom*

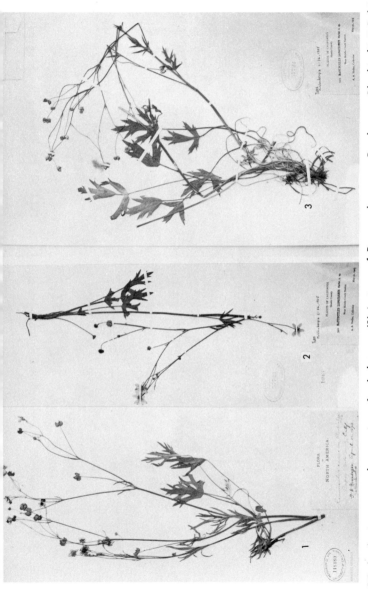

Fig. 15–4. An isotype and a portion of a holotype: (1) isotype of *Ranunculus canus* Benth. var. *Blankinshipii* Robinson, a specimen collected by the same man at the same place and at the same time as the holotype, which is in the Gray Herbarium of Harvard University, the plants intergrading with *Ranunculus canus* and *Ranunculus occidentalis* var. *Eisenii*; (2) most of one specimen sheet of the type of *Ranunculus longilobus* Heller; (3) the other sheet of the two composing the holotype of *Ranunculus longilobus* Heller. The described specimens are from a hybrid swarm, but nearer *Ranunculus canus* than *Ranunculus occidentalis* vars. *Eisenii* and *ultramontanus*, characters of which appear in the hybrid population (for isotypes, see Fig. 15–5).

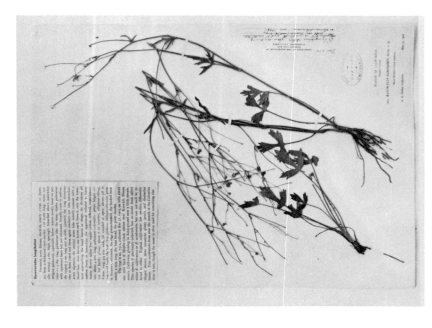

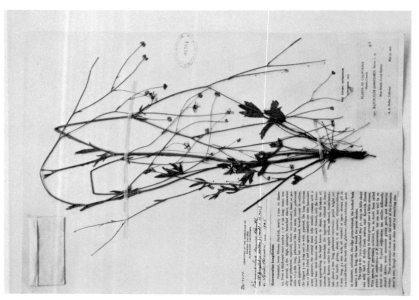

Fig. 15–5. Two isotypes of *Ranunculus longilobus* Heller [cf. Fig. 15–4 (2), (3), showing the holotype].

(Pomona College) refer to the institutional herbarium in which the specimen is deposited. A series of symbols may represent a specimen duplicated in several herbaria. For standard symbols for the herbaria of the world, see Lanjouw and Stafleu (1952, 1954, 1956, 1959).

All the *specimens examined,* certain geographically critical or otherwise *significant specimens,* or a selection of *representative specimens* may be cited for a species or variety. Various styles of citation are illustrated in the references listed in Chapter 18.

Part V
TREATISES AND MONOGRAPHS

chapter 16

Starting a Treatise
or a Monograph

In pure science, ***detection of the existence of problems*** is the most important task and the most difficult. In applied science the problems usually are obvious—there is an insect pest to be killed, an apparent soil deficiency to be analyzed, a disease-resistant strain of a crop plant to be developed, or some other practical problem to be solved. In pure science, the research worker must find his own problems, then solve them. Problems are everywhere, but few can see them.

The choice of a plant group to be studied taxonomically should be made, in the light of suggestions and advice, by the individual who is to prepare the treatise or monograph. Originality and achievement in pure science depend upon satisfaction of curiosity, for the greatest joy of research is in discovering the answer to a problem uncovered by one's own inquisitiveness. At first, interest in a particular genus may develop either from its beauty, its precision in flower organization, its peculiar mode of pollination, its unusual ecological tolerances, its occurrence on the farm at home or in a familiar city garden or park, or from the chance identification of several species or the difficulty, perhaps because of intergradation through hybridizing, of separation of the species by the key in the local manual. Any of several genera may be of nearly equal interest, and the choice among them may depend upon practical factors. For example, a specialist may have research already well under way or just completed in one genus, another group may have too few local species for satisfactory field study, or still another group may have a life cycle too long for experimental investigation in the time available.

Starting a taxonomic monograph is dependent upon finding the classification problems existing in a group of plants. Problems are abundant in every genus, but they are elusive, and the beginner of monographic work needs something specific to do, so that gradually he may ferret out the points requiring investigation. The following methods of approach are suggested.

A preliminary distributional study may be begun by mapping the occurrence of each species and variety in the genus or in smaller groups or related species. In order to map the species, the identity of each herbarium specimen and living plant must be checked with the existing literature, especially with the keys in earlier technical papers or in regional manuals. Checking identifications with more than one key to the plants of the same area nearly always brings inconsistencies to light, and these discrepancies usually overlie classification problems. Mapping the distribution reveals correlation of certain character combinations with particular geographical areas, altitudes in the mountains, or special habitats. Zones of inconsistency may be evident where the ranges of plants with different character combinations overlap. Ultimately new lines of classification emerge. The process may be slow and sometimes discouraging, but ultimate satisfaction is greater because the job is not easy.

Because most classification problems are detected through inconsistencies of the characters of field populations or difficulties in the use of keys, herbarium and field studies of association of characters are the usual beginning of taxonomic research on a group of plants. In the herbarium new preliminary keys should be constructed, and the geographical distribution of the species should be mapped. In the field numerous populations should be analyzed for combinations of characters in many individuals. For this purpose the methods of numerical analysis described in Chapter 3 are particularly helpful.

As the study progresses, other herbaria should be consulted, and the herbarium and field research should be supplemented by data from other fields, as is described in Chapters 4 to 7. As a classification system emerges, the technical literature, especially that connected with the application of epithets to the species and varieties, should be investigated. Once classification is completed, attention shifts to problems of nomenclature, then to those of description and documentation.

Any stage in preparation of a monograph may be difficult and discouraging, but the greatest difficulty is in getting started. Part of the trouble may be lack of a clear objective. Before the project is begun much thought should be given to the question of just what is being attempted, and this should be discussed with the major professor, other faculty members, and other students. Once the objective is clear, an over-all plan of attack can be formulated. From time to time, as ramifications of the main problem become clear and as side problems appear, replanning may become desirable. It is necessary to have the vision to see clearly the goal ahead and, despite occasional discouragement, to have the tenacity to continue toward it.

A GRAPHIC METHOD FOR EXPRESSING RELATIONSHIPS BASED UPON GROUP CORRELATIONS OF INDEXES OF DIVERGENCE

The following is an application of the principles of synthesis and expression of phylogenetic data presented on pages 273–277. This material [1] presents a method designed for starting evaluation of the evolutionary pattern of a group of plants to be monographed.

1. Study in detail and compare at least twenty (more if possible) of the characters of the taxa under investigation to determine their total variation.

2. Determine the generalized or primitive condition of each character by studying its distribution among the taxa and by systematic comparisons among organisms of near relationship, and by comparison with the various specialized conditions. A character found in most of all of a number of related taxa is probably inherited essentially unchanged from a common ancestor and should therefore be counted as primitive.

3. For each character studied, assign the value 0 to the generalized or primitive conditions and 1 to the specialized condition. For immediate conditions, 0.5 may be used. For unusually extreme expressions of the advanced condition, 1.5 may be assigned.

4. In the form of a table, list all of the taxa involved, and for each member of the study give the character divergence values [Table 16–1].

5. To determine the total divergence index of each taxon, add the individual divergence values of each character together.

6. Determine mutual groupings of characters between taxa, and arrange these in sequence according to these groupings.

7. Plot these data on a concentric chart or graph, the radii to be determined by the mutual groupings of characters, and the distance to be determined by the divergence of each taxon [Fig. 16–1].

8. Where divergences in character combinations occur, plot the hypothetic common ancestor (i.e., the typological ground-plan) as possessing the common characters of all derivatives, but at the level [at which] . . . its advancement index places it [Fig. 16–1: the circles represent postulated ancestors].

[1] Quoted from an information sheet supplied through the courtesy of Warren H. Wagner, Jr., Department of Botany, University of Michigan, and used by permission.

TABLE 16–1

Index of Divergence

Characters	Species					
	purpurea	*flava*	*alba*	*rosea*	*rubra*	*nigra*
A		1			1	1
B						1
C			1	1	1	1
D				1	1	1
E				1		
F		1				
G	1	1				
H	1	1				
I	1					
J					1	
Adv. Ind.	3	4	1	3	4	4

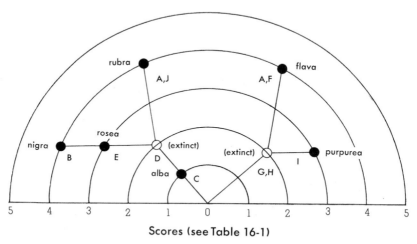

Scores (see Table 16-1)

Fig. 16–1. Graphic representation of the data in Table 16–1. The six species of a hypothetical genus are arranged according to their total scores in the table. The characters appearing in each species are indicated by the letters used in the table. For example, characters C, D, A, and J appear in the species *rubra*, C, D, and E in *rosea*, and C, D, E, and B in *nigra*. The hypothetical ancestor of the group would be at zero in the diagram.

The method outlined above and on pages 273–277 emphasizes the characters which run through groups of organisms, either showing no modification or considerable modification of detail from one group to another, but in all cases retaining a common basic plan. An example is the common higher-vertebrate plan of reptiles, birds, and mammals, which includes presence of four limbs attached to a body which contains a heart, arteries, veins, lungs, a digestive tract, and other recurring structures. These are present in one form or another throughout the group, but each displays considerable modification in detail in accordance with specialization of the particular organism. Possession of the whole complex certainly is a common primitive feature of the group—one retained through countless generations during which great divergence has occurred among the members of the taxon. The individual types of specialization may represent many lines of evolution.

Nevertheless, another situation must be kept in mind. In many groups of organisms relatively rare characters may be the primitive ones retained from pre-existing plants or animals. For example, the unsealed conduplicate carpel (p. 329; Figs.10–7, 10–8), the scale-leaf type of stamen (p. 329; Figs. 10–9, 10–10), or the monocolpate gymnosperm or monocotyledon type of pollen grain (p. 331; Fig. 10–11) is a rare feature in the order Ranales and many times more rare, therefore, in the Dicotyledoneae. Similarly, the trimerous flower and the pattern of numerous, ultimately separating carpels of *Platystemon* (p. 319; Fig. 10–3) are rare in the Papaverales. Nevertheless, each is very likely a primitive feature retained from the ancestors of the group in question, though now present in only a few members of the order. The difficulty is that full application of the method of analysis must be based upon the extinct as well as the living members of the line of development and that many of these have left no fossil record or only a fragmentary one related to characters of the hard parts of the organism. Thus, the method is a useful one, but its results must be treated with caution, as must those of all other methods of analysis.

chapter
17

Materials and Methods
of Research

USE OF THE HERBARIUM

Arrangements of Specimens. Most large herbaria are arranged
according to the system of classification favored by the staff when
the herbarium was started or in the period of its most rapid development. For example, the herbarium of the Royal Botanic Gardens
at Kew, England, is arranged according to the Bentham and Hooker
system, which originated there. The Linnaean herbarium in London
follows the Sexual System of classification published by Linnaeus.
Most herbaria in North America are arranged, for at least the flowering plants, according to Engler and Prantl, whose system of classification is the basis for organization of most recent manuals and
floras, for example, of *Gray's Manual of Botany* (Fernald, 1950), of
*The New Britton and Brown Illustrated Flora of the Northeastern
United States and Adjacent Canada* (Gleason, 1952), and of *A
Manual of the Flowering Plants of California* (Jepson, 1923–1925).
In some instances the gymnosperms, pteridophytes, and other non-
flowering plants are arranged also according to Engler and Prantl,
but the arrangement may follow other systems.

Arrangement according to a particular author or group of authors
sometimes is carried only as far as the family, the genera being arranged alphabetically or according to some other system. Most frequently in the flowering plants and gymnosperms, taxa of this rank
are organized according to Engler and Prantl, but the exact sequence is that appearing in *Genera Siphonogarum ad Systema*

418

Englerianum Conscripta (Dalla Torre and Harms, 1900–1907). The genera were numbered by these authors, and frequently each generic folder is marked by the Dalla Torre number. This is the key to finding the position of the genus in the herbarium, and it is secured by checking the index of *Genera Siphonogarum*. The names of synonyms appear in the index in a slightly different typography from that used for recognized genera.

Most frequently the species within a genus are arranged alphabetically, but they may be grouped according to subgenera or sections or filed in the sequence of a particular book or other publication. Unless permission for rearrangement has been obtained, the sequence should be maintained when the specimens are studied. Commonly there is no special order of the sheets within a folder, but this point should be checked with the staff of each herbarium.

In many herbaria, colored folders indicate geographical divisions of species. For example, a herbarium in New York City may have special colored folders for plants collected in or near the metropolitan area or these plants may be segregated into a local herbarium apart from the rest of the collection. Some herbaria have elaborate folder systems, for example, with one color for the state within which the herbarium is located or for some other local area of special interest, and others for the United States, for the rest of North America, and for each other continent.

Handling Specimens. Herbarium paper is somewhat flexible, and care must be taken to avoid bending the sheets and consequently injuring the mounted specimens. At first, the herbarium sheets should be picked up with two hands, but, once the proper method has been learned through experience, one hand usually is sufficient.

Practices in use of herbaria differ, and the director or curator of each herbarium should be questioned concerning special methods of handling specimens. For example, in many herbaria, turning specimen sheets upside down or as if they were the pages of a book is considered a dangerous practice because it places extra strain on the plants and tends to dislodge fragments.

Fragments often are important parts of specimens, and in many herbaria standard practice includes mounting a paper fragment folder on every herbarium sheet. If any part of the specimen is loose, it should be placed immediately in the folder or mounted in its original position, provided its origin is clearly from the sheet upon which it reposed.

When specimens are replaced in the species or genus folder, care should be taken that the pile is straight and that one specimen sheet is not pushed across another in straightening the pile.

Visiting Herbaria. The specimens in a single herbarium may be sufficient for an undergraduate project, but they are not adequate for a graduate monographic study, and those in a number of herbaria should be inspected. In most instances, these will include the larger herbaria known to have specimens representing the plant populations in the area studied or to have specimens such as types that are significant because of study by earlier authors. If, for example, the group under investigation occurs only in the southeastern United States, it will be represented best in the larger herbaria of the southeastern states and in the major institutions of the northern Atlantic Coast (such as Gray Herbarium of Harvard University, New York Botanical Garden, Academy of Natural Sciences of Philadelphia, and United States National Herbarium), as well as in a few institutions in other areas. For a thorough study, all these herbaria should be investigated.

Locations of herbaria and a summary of the collections within them have been published by Lanjouw and Stafleu (1952, 1954, 1956, 1959) in their *Index Herbariorum,* Part I. This includes a listing of herbaria open to scientists that has been arranged according to cities of the world. It gives the addresses of the herbaria, their status in relation to institutions or governments, time of founding, number of specimens, scope, and general activities. The names of directors, curators, and other staff members are given also, and often there is a brief statement concerning policies with respect to loan of specimens. Part II is an index of collectors, and as far as possible, of the herbaria in which their collections are deposited.

When a herbarium is to be visited, advance arrangements should be made in order to determine what visiting time will be convenient for the director and staff. This avoids, for example, the awkwardness of arriving at ten o'clock on a Saturday morning and finding that the herbarium is not open on Saturday, or at least that it will close on Saturday afternoon, unless some member of the staff makes a special effort to be there. Most frequently, herbaria are closed in the evening, although in some instances they may be open to individuals by special arrangement. The privilege of evening, Saturday, or Sunday use may be offered, but ordinarily it should not be requested. The best plan is to visit during regular weekday hours when some member of the staff will be on duty as a matter of course.

Literature must be used in connection with specimens. Usually this may be arranged through the herbarium staff, who may give or obtain permission for the use of books housed in the herbarium or in the botany, biology, or main library.

Loans of Specimens. Travel to all the herbaria to be inspected often is not practical, and some specimens must be borrowed. This should be postponed ordinarily until late in the study, when the resources locally available have been nearly exhausted. This avoids a long loan period or the complications arising if the project is not carried out.

The loan policy of most herbaria permits lending to institutions and not to individuals. This restriction on loans is made because (1) institutions go on, but individuals may die, move away, or lose interest and (2) lending to a private individual at his home involves greater danger of fire or other loss of specimens than does lending to an institution. Thus ordinarily an undergraduate student working on a paper, or a graduate who is preparing a treatise or monograph as a thesis for an advanced degree, may not borrow specimens directly. However, the major professor, department head, or director of the herbarium of his college or university may make arrangements, if the project warrants them, for an interinstitutional loan of specimens. Sometimes this is at the expense of the college or university, but usually the student is expected to bear the expense, and this point should be understood in advance.

Clerical work in selecting specimens should be reduced in every way possible. The individual requesting the loan for the student should be given a typewritten list (and a carbon copy) of the species and varieties for which specimens are desired. This should be arranged alphabetically and should include synonyms under which specimens may be filed. Geographical restrictions require extra work, and, if possible, they should be avoided. If they are necessary they should follow simple lines paralleling (as determined by inquiry) the segregations by folders in the lending herbarium.

When specimens arrive they should be checked carefully for transit, insect, or other damage, and all injury to specimens should be reported when the loan slip is signed and returned.

When specimens are sent on loan, most institutions number them lightly in pencil, applying a consecutive number series which is of great value in checking to be certain that every specimen is returned. This arrangement should be noted when the specimens are received, and it should be checked to be sure that no numbers have been skipped or duplicated.

When specimens are borrowed, they are to be studied at the institution and housed in a fire-resistant laboratory or herbarium building, never taken home or to a dormitory. They should be stored in insectproof and fire-resistant cases or other containers and provided with insect repellant. Fumigation upon arrival is a wise routine precaution.

Dissection of specimens should be undertaken only with permission, and the dissections and any fragments should be added to the original sheets.

Returning Specimens. Insofar as the lending institution is concerned, the value of making specimen loans is partly in securing the identifications resulting from a special study. When the study is complete and borrowed plants are ready to be returned, an identification label should be pasted neatly in place on each sheet. This should give the determination of the genus, species, and author reference, and (where necessary) the variety (or subspecies) and the references connected with it. The label should bear also the name of the person who makes the identification and the date or at least the year in which the determination was made.

The specimens of a large herbarium constitute a body of raw data for study, and usually only a relatively small percentage of specimens bear the names to be selected finally by a monographer. Previous identifications usually have been haphazard, having been supplied for one or a few specimens at a time by the collector or some other individual. These have been made according to a variety of local manuals, and often the name applied is a synonym of the one to be chosen. In many cases it is incorrect. However, among the representatives of some species there will be a large number of correctly identified specimens. Correct identifications may be confirmed by use of a rubber stamp with very small letters stating, for example, "Verified by John Jones at Ohio State University in 1958." Since in the course of time other identifications may be added by later authors, this stamp should be placed in a position where it will be associated clearly with the confirmed identification, for example, near the one on the original label or near a later identification on a special label. It should not be placed in a remote part of the herbarium sheet or where it may be confused with another identification added in the future.

In general, additions should *not* be made on the original label. Professional workers sometimes make minor exceptions to this, but the practice should not be adopted by beginners. Ordinarily, writing directly on the herbarium sheet should be avoided even though the practice is relatively common. The full name of the identifier should be written clearly; initials may mean nothing to future workers.

Except by agreement, when specimens are returned they should be arranged by number in the order in which they were received. Unless there is special permission to do otherwise, all specimens in any loan should be returned at the same time.

The original mode of shipment of specimens should be duplicated when they are returned. Customarily the expense of transportation both ways is borne by the borrower, and, if more than a few specimens are sent, ordinarily it is by collect express to the borrower and express prepaid back to the lender. However, for an unusually large shipment, some institutions use freight instead, packing the specimens very carefully in heavy wooden boxes which would be expensive to send by express but which afford special protection.

The details of packing are highly important because the specimens are valuable and irreplaceable. Notes should record the methods of tying in bundles, of wrapping the bundles, and of padding between them. The exact materials used for shipment should be retained in the original cartons or boxes so that the shipping method may be duplicated. Specimens should always be insured heavily for the return shipment, for at least the amount of insurance taken out when they were sent on loan. In an actual case of loss, herbarium specimens may not be considered as having commercial value, but insurance is likely to promote more careful handling or tracing. The specimens should be tied carefully in relatively thin individual bundles, just as they were in the earlier shipment. Cardboard sheets on the tops and bottoms of the bundles must be stiff and wider than herbarium sheets, and ribbons or strings must not cut into the edges of the sheets. Usually cloth tape instead of string is used for tying the bundles, because the tape does not cut. The bundles should be tied tightly—not tightly enough to injure the specimens but so firmly that there is no danger of shifting of the specimens during shipment. Any tendency to twist or rub within the bundle or to move (especially sidewise) may partly destroy the specimens. Usually an unprinted newspaper sheet is placed on top of each specimen as a cushion. As the bundles are wrapped, the director or curator of the herbarium, or some other person with experience in shipping of specimens, should be consulted to be sure that no precautions have been overlooked.

Duplicate Specimens. In some instances herbarium specimens have been duplicated needlessly. When these are discovered in the course of writing a monograph, they may be called to the attention of the supervising major professor, who may wish to request that they become available for his institution on the basis of exchange.

The professor may confer by letter or in person with the director
of the institution lending the specimens and work out a basis for
transfer of ownership. Sometimes they are offered as a gift as a
courtesy in appreciation of the identification of specimens. Ordinarily, however, duplicate specimens are returned with the loan
for inspection by the director of the institution to which they belong, in order that he may determine whether retaining them is
necessary.

FIELD STUDY AND COLLECTION OF SPECIMENS

Selection of Material for Specimens. Research specimens require, as nearly as possible, a complete representation of the characters of the plant and of the natural population to which it belongs. If the plants are not too large, an entire individual should
be included on the herbarium sheet; otherwise the specimen should
be made up, if possible, entirely from the parts of one individual.
If more than one is represented, the parts derived from each should
be indicated. Ideally, the specimen should represent all the character combinations which can be detected, and there should be
enough material from each individual to permit dissections of flowers, fruits, or other parts.

Recording Data. Specimen labels are prepared from data recorded first in a field book at the time of pressing of the specimen.
The serial number given to each collection appears also on the margin of the folded newspaper sheet in which the plant is pressed. In
the field book, a paragraph records the data for any given locality
in which specimens are procured on a particular date. The serial
numbers applying to the plants collected at this spot are listed beneath the data. A blank line opposite each number is used to enter
the name and author references for each plant. These are written
at the time of identification. Thus, the data necessary for typing or
writing the labels are recorded in the field book, and the labels may
be prepared without the necessity of having the specimens present.
   Full data should be recorded in the field book, except that some
items such as county names readily provided by a map may not be
necessary. The points ordinarily significant in taxonomic research
are included, for example, on the printed label appearing in Fig.
3–25, but these may be supplemented by notes recording ecological
data or the frequency of occurence of certain characters or character
combinations in the population. These may be in the form of
numerical analyses such as those in Chapter 3. Characters some-

times lost in pressing the plant should be noted. These include flower color or the color of individual parts; glaucescence; height of a tree and the diameter of its trunk; or odor or taste of flowers, fruits, or bark. Recording should not be carried to extremes so that the specimen labels are cluttered with insignificant data. Nevertheless, any characters which may be of importance in classification, ecological, or other study should be included.

A good photograph of the plant, especially of a tree or shrub, may record data supplementing a specimen. A photograph is not a satisfactory substitute for the pressed plant, because the data recorded are incomplete and dissection is impossible. Nevertheless, it is an excellent addition to the specimen because it may record not only the characters of the plant as a whole but also ecological features of the habitat.

The field number is of particular importance in research because it is used as a means of reference to collections. For example *Fernald 12577, GH*, refers to a particular sheet in the Gray Herbarium of Harvard University. Fernald, like other American collectors, used a serial numbering system which ran through year after year. Thus the number is not duplicated in the Gray Herbarium, and if it appears in another herbarium it is because duplicate specimens are distributed to other institutions. Each of these specimens, as far as Fernald could determine, portrayed the same character combinations as the specimen retained at Harvard University. Thus, if Fernald or another author cited the number *12577* in a published paper or book, the plant to which he referred or its equivalent may be seen in each of several institutional herbaria. Although any of several systems of numbering may be satisfactory as far as an individual is concerned, employment of the standard serial numbering system is important for the sake of precision in reference to specimens.

LIVING MATERIALS FOR EXPERIMENTAL STUDY

Many botanists and students help each other in securing living materials for study, and the major professor should be consulted about this. Seeds, cuttings, and other structures may be requested from individuals who can obtain them readily. Care must be taken that the request is reasonable and that the plants grow near the institution from which they are requested, for some states are large. For example, some parts of Texas are farther from other parts of Texas than they are from Chicago.

CYTOLOGICAL INVESTIGATION AS PART OF A
MONOGRAPHIC STUDY

Methods are developed in conjunction with courses and according to the special procedures recommended by the major professor and other faculty members associated with him. The following techniques, however, are particularly good for beginning the study of chromosomes. By use of them, once the necessary solutions and equipment have been brought together, chromosomes may be seen with only a small amount of actual time spent in preparation.

The "smear" and "squash" techniques for rapid examination of cells to determine chromosome numbers have replaced study of microtome sections of meristematic regions of plants. The simplicity of these techniques saves much time, but use of them is restricted to study of favorable tissues, such as microspore mother cells ("pollen mother cells"), which may be separated readily from others which surround them, or of meristematic areas, in which the cells have been separated by removal of the substances which bind them together. An advantage of anther smears is the presence of the reduced number of chromosomes, which makes counting easier, but the characteristics of individual chromosomes seen in mitosis do not appear in the prophase of meiosis. Squashes and smears guarantee the presence of whole chromosomes instead of fragments which may result from passing a microtome knife through a cell.

Selection of Material. Meiosis occurs when flower buds are very small. For example, in species of *Ranunculus* with full-blown flowers 2 or 3 cm. in diameter the meiotic process occurs when the buds are only 1 or 2 mm. in diameter. The size of the bud must be determined for each species by trial and error. This is true also of the time of day for the reduction divisions, but a common period is between 11:00 A.M. and 2:30 P.M.

Killing and Fixing. SOLUTION. Three parts of absolute alcohol to 1 of glacial acetic acid. This is completely anhydrous (see below).

The anthers are immersed directly in a small vial of the killing and fixing fluid. They are accompanied by a slip of paper with an identifying number, normally the serial field number used for the herbarium specimen. This number is written in pencil or typewritten to avoid the effect of the fluids upon ink. The material to be placed in the fluid depends upon the size of the bud. As little foreign matter as possible should be preserved, because the accompanying water should not be added to the anhydrous fluid and because the effective use of the smear technique requires reduction of extraneous materials to a minimum when the slide is prepared. Very small buds may be preserved whole, provided the perianth is spread widely and the anthers are exposed to quick action by the preservative. Buds large enough for dissection in the field should be opened and the anthers plunged quickly into the killing fluid. If the young stamens are very large, they should be cut into segments, provided this can be done without squeezing out and losing the microspore mother cells.

After a minimum of 12 hours or a period of up to two or three weeks, the anthers are removed from the killing and fixing fluid. They may be stored in 70% alcohol.

Staining. SOLUTION. Various methods of preparing iron acetocarmine have been published by Belling (e.g., 1921, 1926), and others have proposed modifications. The following is an example: Mix 90 cc. of glacial acetic acid with 110 cc. of distilled water. Heat to boiling, and, after removal from the flame, add about 1 gram of certified carmine dye. Cool in a refrigerator and then decant. Add a few drops of an aqueous solution of ferric acetate. The amount of the iron salt can be excessive, and caution is necessary. Too much will precipitate the dye. On standing, the color should be a dark wine red. Storage should be in a tightly closed bottle.

Only new slides and cover glasses should be used, and these should be cleaned thoroughly by immersion for some time in the mixture of concentrated sulfuric acid and potassium dichromate used by chemists for cleaning glassware. After being rinsed in running water, they should be cleaned with alcohol to which a little ammonia has been added, then rinsed again and dried. The cloth used for drying should be completely free from lint, for every fiber adds one more distracting factor when the slide is prepared and ready for study.

A drop of iron acetocarmine is placed on a slide under a dissecting microscope, and an anther, an anther segment, or a small bud is placed in the drop of stain. If the bud is so small as to have been preserved whole, an anther is dissected from it with needles. The single anther (or a segment of one) is then pressed lightly with a narrow scalpel blade or the side of a dissecting needle until the contents are seen to pass outward into the stain. Then the remains of the anther are removed, and a cover glass is placed over the extruded contents, that is, the microspore mother cells. Better results are obtained, however, if before the microspore mother cells are covered the fluid is removed with absorbent paper and then replaced with fresh iron acetocarmine. The excess dye beyond that necessary to form a thin film under the cover glass should be removed with absorbent paper.

The slide should be heated slightly over an alcohol lamp (*not* over a Bunsen burner) after the cover slip has been added. Heating should be for only an instant, and the solution of iron acetocarmine should not be allowed to boil. The process should be repeated four or five times.

At this time—only a few minutes after the anther has been placed in the dye—a preliminary view of the chromosomes is possible. The material may be either retained for completion of staining and ultimate preservation, or discarded in favor of trying another anther. Flower buds having large numbers of stamens may present various stages of maturity and different stages of meiosis. The most favorable stages for counting chromosomes range from diakinesis (diaphase) on to the second meiotic division. Most frequently the first preparations to be made are disappointing in that meiosis may be over and pollen grains with thick walls may have been formed. If so, younger anthers should be selected, and this may require younger flower buds, especially if the flowers being studied have only a single cycle of anthers.

If the anthers are all from flower buds too old for meiosis and no younger buds are available, selection may take another direction. The division of the microspore nucleus preceding formation of a tube cell and a generative cell may be studied (see below). Also, mature pollen grains may be germinated, usually in a sugar solution, and the division of the generative cell giving rise to the two male nuclei may be found.

When suitable specimens of chromosomes appear in the stain, the cover glass should be sealed in place for several days until the staining process is completed. Various substances have been used for sealing. These include paraffin with a low melting point or a mixture of equal parts of gum mastic (obtainable at drugstores) and paraffin or Parowax heated and mixed together. More recently, plastic materials such as nail polish have been used. The material is applied with a warm metal instrument such as a broad needle.

Permanent Mounts. McClintock's Method (1929). After staining has been completed, the sealing material is removed carefully by scraping with a razor blade, the cover glass being retained in place. The slide and the cover glass (still in position) are placed in 10% acetic acid. The cover glass is lifted off by one corner with the acid of a scalpel. Both the slide and the cover glass are run through a series of liquids in slotted dishes, as follows:

1. One part absolute alcohol, one part glacial acetic acid
2. Three parts absolute alcohol, one part glacial acetic acid
3. Nine parts absolute alcohol, one part glacial acetic acid
4. Absolute alcohol
5. Seven parts absolute alcohol, one part xylene (xylol)
6. Balsam—added to the slide and the cover glass quickly placed in its original position on the slide (as shown by traces of the sealing material and other debris)

Pure xylene preferably may be used before mounting in balsam, provided experience shows that the microspore mother cells are not discolored or shrunken by it.

BEEKS' METHOD (1955). This involves use of Hoyer's mounting medium, which is composed of the following:

  50 cc. distilled water
  30 grams gum arabic
200 grams chloral hydrate
  16 cc. glycerine

The gum arabic is dissolved completely in water, and then the chloral hydrate is added, each process requiring about 24 hours. Glycerine is added and mixed well. Water is added to the medium occasionally, because evaporation of water causes too high a concentration of solutes.

Two schedules for squash techniques (flattening the anthers by pressure) are suggested, as follows:

1. SQUASH AND MOUNT

1. After staining, place the cover glass over the anther. Before squashing the anther, heat the slide, using a steam bath, a microscope lamp, or a warming plate instead of an alcohol-lamp flame.
2. Squash the anther, then place a ring of sealing medium around the cover glass (use 10 grams of gelatine to 100 cc. of 50% glacial acetic acid).
3. If permanent mounting is desired, float the cover glass off with 50% glacial acetic acid after staining is complete. The slide and cover glass should be immersed in distilled water until the excess stain has diffused away (in approximately one minute).
4. After removal from water and wiping away of the excess moisture except from the stained area, add a small drop of Hoyer's medium in the center of the area of cells.

5. Replace the cover glass and heat it and the slide over steam until the medium has spread to the edge of the cover glass. Press gently on the cover glass to remove the excess of Hoyer's medium.
6. Harden the medium by placing the slide on a warming plate set for 26° C. A weight on the cover slip to decrease the depth of the field is recommended.

2. PERMANENT SQUASH

1. Crush the anthers and apply a small drop of stain made with slightly less iron than usual. The stain must not be exposed to the air long enough for precipitation of the dye.
2. Add a small drop of Hoyer's medium to the solution from the tip of a thin needle. Do not disturb the surface of the slide. The Hoyer's medium will spread over the cells and flatten them.
3. Place the cover slip over the stain and heat over steam or a microscope lamp until the medium flattens. This requires only a few seconds. Wipe away the water which has condensed on the slide.
4. Invert the slide on filter paper, and fold the paper over the slide. Steady the slide with one hand, and apply the "squash" with the other. The force necessary varies inversely with the size of the cells. Pressure should be released slowly in order to avoid tearing the cell membranes.
5. If, under the microscope, the cells are seen not to be spread properly, the slide may be placed over the steam bath for 3 or 4 seconds and the squashing repeated.
6. Place the slide on a warming plate as in item 6 under "Squash and Mount."

Hoyer's medium has the advantage of permitting removal of the cover glass over a steam bath and destaining or restaining. If there are trapped air bubbles, these may be **removed** by inverting the slide over steam.

Special Treatment for Microspores and Root Tips. The internal divisions of the microspore or of the meristematic cells of root tips may be studied by the smear technique, if after killing they are treated as follows (Warmke, 1935):

1. Place the material in a solution consisting of one part 95% alcohol and one part concentrated hydrochloric acid. This dissolves the pectic substances of the wall of a microspore, causing "the heavy exine wall to split and fall away, like the shell of a nut," or the middle lamellas between other cells to separate. The addition of a little pressure may be necessary to help this process along (see below). Remove after five or ten minutes.
2. Transfer the root tips to Carnoy's fluid (with chloroform). This hardens the cells, which will have been softened in the first stage.

3. Remove the material from Carnoy's fluid, and place it on a slide in a drop of iron acetocarmine as with anthers. Gentle pressure with a flat instrument (such as the side of a scalpel) on the top of the cover glass is necessary to separate the cells of root tips.

Microscopic Study. The preliminary study above requires use of a binocular dissecting microscope and an ordinary student-type compound microscope. Final study of the chromosomes requires a binocular oil-immersion microscope of higher power, magnifying 1,000 to 1,200 times.

REFERENCES FOR METHODS OF STUDYING CHROMOSOMES

BEEKS, RICHARD M. 1955. *Improvements in the squash technique for plant chromosomes.* Aliso 3: 131–134.

BELLING, JOHN. 1921. *On counting chromosomes in pollen-mother cells.* American Naturalist 55: 573–574.

———. 1926. *The iron-aceto-carmin method of fixing and staining chromosomes.* Biological Bulletin 50: 160–162.

BRADLEY, MURIEL V.* 1948. *A method for making aceto-carmine squashes permanent without removal of the cover slip.* Stain Technology 23: 41–44.

DARLINGTON, C. D., and L. F. LA COUR. 1950. *The handling of chromosomes.* George Allen & Unwin Ltd., London.

JOHANSEN, DONALD A. 1940. *Plant microtechnique.* McGraw-Hill Book Co., Inc., New York. Standard textbook of methods, including those of cytological technique.

McCLINTOCK, BARBARA. 1929. *A method for making aceto-carmin smears permanent.* Stain Technology 4: 53–56.

PFEIFFER, HANS H. 1953. *Rapid chromosome methods.* Taxon 2: 86–87.

TRAUB, HAMILTON P. 1953. *Rapid chromosome methods for the taxonomist.* Taxon 2: 28–29.

WARMKE, HARRY E. 1935. *A permanent root tip smear method.* Stain Technology 10: 101–103.

TAXONOMIC LITERATURE

The literature concerned with a particular genus appears in books and periodicals. The books to be consulted are numerous; many are regional and local floras and manuals developed for identification of genera, species, and varieties.

Location of other pertinent literature is primarily through the use of abstracting and indexing journals. The most useful reference work for the biological sciences in general is *Biological Abstracts,* a forerunner of which was *Botanical Abstracts.* Nearly every significant biological paper appears in condensed form as an abstract, which usually is adequate to indicate whether the original warrants further investigation. The index to each volume of *Biological Abstracts* is arranged by both author and subject, the subjects including the names of genera. Thus, checking the major literature concerned directly with a particular genus is relatively simple.

The nomenclature of genera and species occurring in North America is indexed in the following two basic works:

The *Index Kewensis* (Hooker and Jackson *et al.*, 1885–   ) includes references to the original publication of the name of each genus and species proposed or modified in rank or taxonomic position since the official start of botanical nomenclature in 1753. It is applicable to the world as a whole. The two original volumes covered all publications known to have been made until the year 1885. Supplements published at five- or ten-year intervals since that time bring the published list of genera and species up to date. Unfortunately, the names of taxa of infraspecific rank are not included.

The *Gray Herbarium Card Index* (Gray Herbarium, 1885–   ) is a catalog of North and South American genera, species, and infraspecific taxa published since 1885.

The use of these great reference works facilitates finding the original publication of the name of the taxon, the original description, and whatever data may be available for use in determining the type specimen and its location.

Another highly useful work is the *Bibliographic Index to North American Botany* (Watson, 1878).

The books in the following list are particularly helpful in determining the full titles of works referred to by abbreviation in the *Index Kewensis* and the *Gray Herbarium Card Index:*

ANONYMOUS. 1885–   . *Gray Herbarium shelf list.* Offset copies of book cards, arranged by subject.

ANONYMOUS. 1903–1940. *Catalog of books, manuscripts, maps, and drawings in the British Museum (Natural History)* 1–8 (6–8, supplementary). London.

CHRISTENSEN, CARL. 1906; supplements, 1913, 1917, 1934. *Index filicum.* Copenhagen.

PRITZEL, GEORG AUGUST. 1872. *Thesaurus literaturae botanicae.* Books listed by author and subject. Index of authors. This is a standard work relating to the older botanical literature.

REHDER, ALFRED. 1911–1918. *The Bradley bibliography: A guide to the woody plants of the world published before the beginning of the twentieth century* 1–5. Cambridge, Mass.

TUCKER, ETHELYN MARIA. 1914–1933. *Catalog of the Library of the Arnold Arboretum of Harvard University.* Cambridge, Mass.

The following are other sources useful in consulting the literature:

1. Bibliographies of Other Workers. These appear in many papers published in journals. Familiarity with bibliographies of this type, it is assumed will result from looking up papers cited at the close of earlier chapters of this book. Some taxonomic books such as *A Flora of California* (Jepson, 1909–   ), *Arizona Flora* (Kearney and Peebles, 1951), and *Plant Taxonomy* (Lawrence, 1951) include bibliographic references for each family and many genera of flowering plants.

2. *Library Stacks.* The books in the stacks of most college and university libraries are arranged by subject matter according to either the Library of Congress system or the Dewey decimal system. Consultation of the taxonomic works on the shelf and of those in the sections concerned with the genus or other special subject under investigation affords an opportunity not only to find books arranged by subject but also to check them quickly for usefulness.

3. *Volume Indexes of Journals.* Certain journals publish primarily (though not necessarily exclusively) taxonomic literature. Examples of these are *Brittonia, Rhodora,* and *Madroño.* These and certain other journals should be consulted volume by volume through their indexes for references to the genus under study.

An introduction to most of the general journals as well as to those which deal primarily with related fields such as ecology or evolution has been given through the citations of suggested reading in the earlier chapters. The following lists present examples of general, regional, or specialized journals dealing exclusively or at least significantly with botanical taxonomy:

Publications of Botanical or Natural-Historical Societies:

American Fern Journal (American Fern Society)
American Journal of Botany (Botanical Society of America)
Brittonia (American Society of Plant Taxonomists)
Bulletin of the Torrey Botanical Club
Cactus and Succulent Journal (Cactus and Succulent Society of America)
Canadian Field-Naturalist (Ottawa Field-Naturalists' Club)
Castanea (Southern Appalachian Botanical Club)
Journal of the Elisha Mitchell Society
Journal of the Washington Academy of Sciences
Madroño (California Botanical Society)
Proceedings of the Biological Society of Washington
Rhodora (New England Botanical Club)
Taxon (International Association for Plant Taxonomy and Nomenclature)

Publications of Institutions:

Aliso (Rancho Santa Ana Botanic Garden)
American Midland Naturalist (University of Notre Dame)
Annals of the Missouri Botanical Garden
Asa Gray Bulletin (University of Michigan and Michigan Botanical Club)

Contributions from the Dudley Herbarium of Stanford University
Contributions from the Gray Herbarium of Harvard University
Field and Laboratory (Southern Methodist University)
Fieldiana (Chicago Natural History Museum)
Gentes Herbarum (Bailey Hortorium, Cornell University)
Journal of the Arnold Arboretum of Harvard University
Le Naturaliste Canadien (University of Montreal)
Memoirs of the New York Botanical Garden
Proceedings of the California Academy of Sciences
University of California Publications. Botany

Privately Owned Journals:

Leaflets of Western Botany
Phytologia

4. Libraries of Other Institutions. Arrangements for use of other libraries should be made through the major professor or the department head. Other institutions often have books and periodicals not available locally, and library visits are as important as herbarium trips.

INTERLIBRARY LOANS. Books not available in one library commonly may be borrowed from another for a limited time—usually one or two weeks. The major professor should be consulted concerning the institutional method of obtaining books on interlibrary loan and the expenses involved.

chapter 18

Presentation of the Results
of Research

The methods and principles presented in the preceding chapters are necessary for preparation of a taxonomic research paper. Their full expression is in a technical treatise or a monograph on a special plant group, for example, a genus. Such a study should include

1. a review and evaluation of the history and literature of the subject;
2. a summary of plants examined in the herbarium and in the field;
3. a summary of observational and experimental methods employed;
4. a discussion of the results of cytological, experimental, and other special studies;
5. an explanation of special or unusual diagnostic characters and a discussion of any new or unusual features of the investigation or its presentation; and
6. a list of acknowledgements.

The body of a generic monograph includes a description of the genus, keys to its subgenera or sections (or both), descriptions of these taxa, keys to the species in each subdivision of the genus, and descriptions and discussions of the species and their subdivisions.

PREPARING THE MANUSCRIPT

Style. The papers in the list below are representative monographic publications of several authors whose practices differ in detail. Each paper should be studied for methods of treating genera, subgenera, sections, species, and infraspecific taxa. The form of each paper and the details of typography and punctuation should be noted. These are intricate, and full appreciation of them will be achieved only through writing a treatise or a monograph after the papers have been studied. The major professor should be asked for suggestions.

The following are examples of treatises and monographs:

BABCOCK, ERNEST BROWN. 1947. *The genus* Crepis. University of California Publications. Botany. 21–22: 1–1030.

BENSON, LYMAN. 1948, 1954. *A treatise on the North American Ranunculi.* American Midland Naturalist 40: 1–261. Supplement 52: 328–369.

CHAMBERS, KENTON L. 1955. *A biosystematic study of the annual species of Microseris.* Contributions from the Dudley Herbarium, Stanford University 4:207–312.

CONSTANCE, LINCOLN. 1941. *The genus* Nemophila. University of California Publications. Botany. 19: 341–398.

DAVIDSON, JOHN F. 1950. *The genus* Polemonium (Tournefort) L. University of California Publications. Botany. 23:209–282.

GOODSPEED, T. H. 1954. *The genus* Nicotiana. Chronica Botanica 16: 1–536.

GRANT, VERNE, *et al.* 1950– . *Genetic and taxonomic studies in* Gilia. See Suggested Reading, Chapter 7.

HARDIN, JAMES W. 1957. *A revision of the American Hippocastanaceae—I and II.* Brittonia 9: 145–171, 173–195.

LEWIS, HARLAN, and MARGARET ENSIGN LEWIS. 1955. *The genus* Clarkia. University of California Publications. Botany. 20: 241–392.

MCVAUGH, ROGERS. 1951, 1952. *A revision of the North American black cherries* (Prunus serotina Ehrh., *and relatives*). Brittonia 7: 279–315. Suggested phylogeny of *Prunus serotina* and other wide-ranging phylads in North America. Brittonia 7: 317–346.

OWNBEY, MARION, and HANNAH C. AASE. 1955. *Cytotaxonomic studies in Allium.* I. The *Allium canadense* alliance. Research Studies of the State College of Washington. Monographic Supplement No. 1. 1–106.

ROLLINS, REED C. 1941. *Monographic study of* Arabis *in western North America.* Contributions from the Gray Herbarium (138); Rhodora 43: 289–325, 348–411, 425–481.

SHERFF, EARL EDWARD. 1954. *Revision of the genus* Cheirodendron Nutt. *for the Hawaiian Islands.* Fieldiana. Botany. 29: 1–45.

THOMPSON, HENRY J. 1953. *The biosystematics of* Dodecatheon. Contributions from the Dudley Herbarium, Stanford University 4: 73–154.

WOODSON, ROBERT E., JR. 1930–1951. *Studies in the Apocynaceae.* (For example papers I, IV, and VIII in this series) Annals of the Missouri Botanical Garden 17: 1–212; 20: 605–790; 22:153–306; 23: 169–438; 38: 119–206.

———. 1954. *The North American species of* Asclepias. Annals of the Missouri Botanical Garden 41: 1–211.

The principles laid down in freshman English composition take on a new meaning because of an immediate need for them. The style of writing should be clear, simple, and direct, and sentences should be neither overly long nor choppy. The use of modifiers should be held to a minimum. As Mark Twain said of the adjective, "When in doubt, strike it out!" A statement usually is stronger without it.

Organization. The papers appearing in the *American Journal of Botany* are good models for over-all organization of scientific articles.

The introduction to a treatise or a monograph should be prepared similarly.

The fundamental point in organization is selection of what is to be included and what is to be omitted. Every sentence must be relevant to the subject under discussion and a contribution to understanding the main topic.

Each section of the introduction should begin with a topic paragraph setting forth what is to be discussed. Each paragraph should begin with a topic sentence. The introduction as a whole should end with a summary.

Generalization. The most common fault in the early stages of research is too ready generalization. Conclusions must be warranted by the facts. Even in the most advanced stages of investigation there may be gaps in the evidence, and conclusions should be tentative and with due acknowledgement of deficiencies in the data. Additional factors may change the conclusions.

Consistency of Practice. Consistency in the construction and organization of the manuscript is of first importance, and this consistency extends to minor matters such as abbreviations or recurrent types of punctuation. Abbreviations may follow the pattern adopted by a publication, for example, the *American Journal of Botany,* the *Bulletin of the Torrey Botanical Club, Brittonia, Rhodora,* or *Madroño,* or a book containing many abbreviated references, such as *An Illustrated Flora of the Pacific States* (Abrams 1923, 1944, 1951, 1960). Recently the American Institute of Biological Sciences sponsored a codification of citations of literature (Riker *et al.,* 1952). Accepted abbreviations for titles of journals may be found in *Biological Abstracts,* in the *World List of Scientific Periodicals,* and in a paper prepared for botany, especially for plant taxonomy (Schwarten and Rickett, 1958).

Quotations. References to the literature and quotations must be accurate down to the last detail, including indication for each quoted word of the kind of type (Roman, *italics,* or **boldface**) used in the original (see "Typography" below). Additional material inserted for clarification of a quotation is placed in square brackets; omitted parts are indicated by series of dots (ellipsis marks). Use three ellipses to indicate omission of a word or words within a sentence; use four ellipses where the omission continues to the end of the sentence.

Form of the Manuscript. Institutions have specified requirements concerning the form of typewritten theses, but these are

subject to modification according to the demands of the special field
of research. Essentially, a thesis should be also a manuscript for
technical publication. For this purpose any of the monographic
styles illustrated by the references at the beginning of this chapter
may be followed, or some combination or modification of them may
be adopted in accordance with suggestions and individual judgment.
All manuscripts submitted for typesetting must be double-spaced,
and this is standard thesis practice as well.

Typography. The following printer's markings should be used
in preparing manuscripts:

Roman—no marking, e.g., Helianthus

Italics—single straight underline, e.g., Helianthus (used for all generic
and infrageneric names and epithets)

SMALL CAPITALS—double straight underline, e.g., HELIANTHUS

LARGE CAPITALS—triple straight underline, e.g., HELIANTHUS

LARGE AND SMALL CAPITALS—triple underline for the initials, double
for the rest, e.g., HELIANTHUS

Boldface—wavy underline, e.g., Helianthus (since most typewriters
do not have a wavy underline, a broken underline may be used)

BOLDFACE SMALL CAPITALS—two straight underlines and one wavy
underline, e.g., HELIANTHUS

BOLDFACE LARGE CAPITALS—three straight underlines and one
wavy underline, e.g., HELIANTHUS

Latin Terms of Reference. Certain Latin terms are used for brief
statements and as standard means of reference to other portions of
the paper or to other works. The following is a list of the more
commonly used Latin words or abbreviations:

cf., *confer*—compare
e.g., *exempli gratia*—for example
et al., *et alii*—and others
et seq., *et sequentes*—and the following, or the pages following
i.e., *id est*—that is
ibid., *ibidem*—in the same place (the same reference)
loc. cit., *loco citato*—in the place cited
op. cit., *opere citato*—in the work cited
sic—thus (used to indicate an error in the original version of quoted
matter)
viz., *videlicet*—namely

Bibliography. Many page references appear in the main portion of a taxonomic paper. Most indicate the original publications of the scientific names of taxa. The form of citation varies, and a consistent practice should be adopted after consulting the monographic studies listed at the beginning of this chapter. Ordinarily these page references are not repeated in a bibliography at the end of a published taxonomic paper. However, in a thesis they may be included in a full bibliography. For this purpose each reference appears without abbreviation and with the title of the paper and its first and last page number.

For publication, the literature cited in the monograph's introduction should be summarized as a short bibliography following the introduction. The form used in the *American Journal of Botany* is recommended as is the means of referring from the text to the bibliography.

Special Features of Taxonomic Papers. The introduction should include a list of the herbaria in which specimens have been investigated, arranged alphabetically according to the standard herbarium symbols in the *Index Herbariorum* (Lanjouw and Stafleu, 1959–). Regardless of individual style, the following items usually appear under the discussion of each species or infraspecific taxon:

1. the accepted name and its author reference(s);
2. a list of synonyms with references to the places of publication;
3. a description of the taxon including, if it is new, a Latin description;
4. a statement of geographical distribution;
5. citation of specimens examined or those considered significant;
6. data concerning the type collections upon which the published scientific names were based;
7. discussion of relationships, intergradation with other taxa, experimental or cytological studies, ecological data, paleobotanical data, etc.

The names of newly described taxa appear in boldface type to facilitate preparation of indexes such as the *Index Kewensis* and the *Gray Herbarium Card Index* (see Chapters 12 and 17), or of such publications as *Biological Abstracts*.

ILLUSTRATIONS

Photographs. Illustration by photographs requires good equipment. Securing a good close-up photograph may call for a reflex-type camera, that is, one having a ground-glass screen upon which the object may be viewed through the lens before the picture is taken. For work at a fixed distance, precision may be attained with more difficulty by use of portrait lenses. Equipment is discussed in books on photography.

The *exposure* times for the film and the *composition* of the picture are even more important than equipment.

The *exposure* should be checked with a meter, and one exposure should be made exactly as the meter indicates. If the subject will be difficult to rephotograph, exposures should be made also at slightly less and slightly greater lens openings than indicated by the meter reading. Often the exposure reading for an outdoor picture should be taken through the incident light attachment instead of according to light reflected from the object. The attachment is a translucent shield used for measuring directly the intensity of the light from the sun. Except insofar as a reflection from clouds may have greater intensity, this represents the maximum lighting in the picture. If the exposure is correct for the highlighted parts, the others usually will be in proportion and therefore correct also. The light reflected from an 18% reflectance gray card commonly indicates the correct exposure.

The *composition* of the picture is worked out according to the object to be emphasized. Whatever is of primary importance should form the center of the picture, and all else should contribute to it. This may be accomplished partly by "framing" the picture with objects which tend to emphasize the central point [Figs. 18–1, 18–2]. Additional emphasis may be given by arranging the lines formed by trunks or branches of trees, mountain ridges, canyons, sky lines, shadows, and the edges of clouds to converge on the center [Fig. 18–1 (1), (2), (3)]. The effect may be increased by greater illumination of the main subject than of the areas at the edges of the picture.

Sharply defined objects and their shadows (Fig. 18–2) give depth or perspective. In a photograph of a landscape, as in one illustrating a vegetation type, clearly distinguishable minor subjects or variations in texture should occur at a series of distances from the camera. In the same way, cumulus clouds add to the effect of depth. A uniform sky tends to flatten out the picture and to make it dull and uninteresting. When clouds are lacking the monotony may be broken by objects such as the silhouettes of tree branches and dangling leaves.

Drawings. The ability to make good illustrations is developed by hard work and patience. Scientific drawing is not difficult, because the lines represent realistic boundaries rather than artistic impressions. Sharp, clear pen lines are made with India ink and are reproduced in periodicals or books as zinc etchings. Illustrators use a wide variety of pens, but for scientific purposes the crow-quill type often is used. It is made in varying degrees of fineness.

Fig. 18–1. Composition of a picture: (1) dark dot on a blank field; (2) emphasis of the dot by lines converging on the central object; (3) sketch of a saguaro (giant cactus) emphasized by converging lines of a canyon and other objects; (4) sketch of a saguaro emphasized by the converging outlines of a hill.

A high-quality paper such as two- or three-ply kid should be used. If the drawings are to be saved for possible reuse the paper should be an all-rag linen type.

Drawings usually are prepared on a large scale with the expectation of reduction to about half-size. Although making the original drawing large is easier for the artist, some journals do not approve of the practice; the editor should be consulted. A glossy reduced reproduction usually will be accepted, if it introduces no errors.

Published illustrations exemplify various techniques of shading or stippling to give the illusion of depth (Fig. 18–3). A lighter area

Fig. 18–2. Two photographs of the same trees: (1) the illusion of depth provided by the shadow in the foreground; (2) nearer view emphasizing the trees more strongly, but with some loss of depth because of the nearly blank foreground.

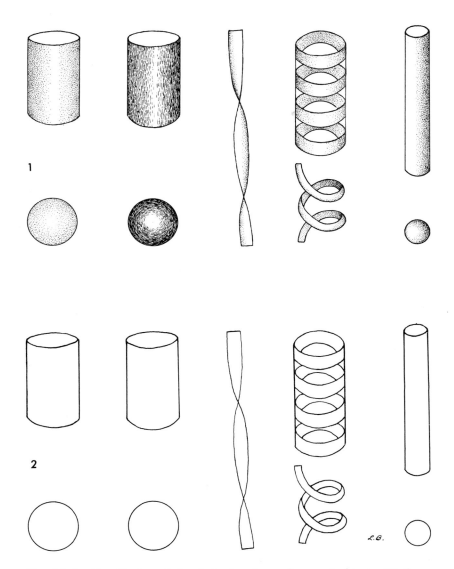

Fig. 18–3. The illusion of depth in drawings of curved objects: (1) figures with shading or stippling; (2) the same figures without shading or stippling.

usually is interpreted as nearer the eye and a darker area as farther away. Practice with several techniques is suggested.

The steadiness of the human hand is correlated in part with an ability to see clearly the position in which the point of the pen is being placed. For this reason stippling and shading may be done under a reading glass which magnifies the drawing to about twice its actual size. In this way, dots may be placed with precision instead of by guess, and drawing of intricate details is facilitated. For more or less mechanical stippling of large surfaces, prepared sheets of printed dots may be purchased.

When drawings are reproduced, the original effect may be altered by reduction in size. The dots made in close stippling may run together, forming a uniform or blotchy mass. To avoid this difficulty, the dots should be placed well apart and distributed uniformly. Examination with a reducing glass will give some indication of the effect of reduction.

White ink or white poster paint (tempera coloring) is used to eliminate drawing errors, but the white material (e.g., Craftint Super White 37) used for catalog numbering on the spines of library books is better. Under magnification, the white fluid may be applied with a pen or a fine brush to areas with too many dots or to lines which are out of position or which overlap others. These fluids may be applied with a camel's-hair brush, and the resulting white surface may be used for redrawing. The zinc-etching process does not reproduce the difference between this area and the surrounding paper.

When the drawing is completed the penciled guidelines should be scrubbed off with a soft eraser, Artgum, or rubber cement (see below). Pencil lines are said not to show in zinc etchings, but this is not always so.

Grouping of Illustrations. Although a single photograph or drawing makes the best plate, most journals require grouping of illustrations because publication is less expensive. Engravers charge three-fourths as much for a half page or smaller illustration as for a full page. Photographs and line drawings are not grouped together, because the processes of reproducing are different and because the appearance is not attractive.

The arrangement of illustrations should be attractive; their appearance is important in even a technical paper. For example, photographs should not be cut along irregular jagged lines. They should be kept as rectangles, and there should be sufficient space between them to make them distinct units after reduction.

Illustrations should be arranged so that they are in balance and attractive. The photographs on a page should harmonize with each other, that is, one should not outweigh or clash with the others. Generally, if there are slight differences, the "heavier" (usually darker) picture(s) should be on the lower part of the page. Photographs and related drawings are mounted with rubber cement, which is sold in bookstores. Both the back of the photograph or drawing and the paper 'background are coated with the cement, which is applied with a stick or a glass rod, then spread out into a film with paper cleansing tissue. When both surfaces have been exposed to the air for a brief period, they are brought together. On contact they adhere firmly. The excess rubber cement around the edges or on the surface of the photograph or drawing should be rubbed off with cleansing tissue. Even when rubber cement is dry it rubs off, leaving the paper cleaner than it was before.[1] Boundaries between adjoining pieces of paper either do not show in zinc etchings or are faint and readily routed out.

PUBLICATION

The Choice of a Journal. Taxonomic papers usually appear in taxonomic journals or in those devoted to botany in general. Reaching a large audience is desirable, but some papers may be of interest to only a special group. This group may be all taxonomists, those in a particular region, or those with an interest in only certain plants, such as the cactus or the orchid family, the ferns, or the conifers. Papers emphasizing more strongly the evolutionary aspect of the subject (for example, the mechanism of speciation) should be submitted to journals in that field. Those which combine several methods of investigation as applied to taxonomy may be of general interest, and submission to a general journal may be best.

Even general journals have a tendency to become specialized, sometimes by chance, sometimes because several more restricted journals tend to take away the publication of papers in individual fields, leaving only one or two fields as a residue. One journal, originally intended to embrace all the natural sciences, has a disproportionately large number of papers in biochemistry, probably because through some chance the biochemists started sending their papers there. Botanical morphological papers have tended to be unduly prominent in the general botanical journals because there has been no special medium for their publication.

[1] Smudges and even pencil marks can be taken off by applying rubber cement, allowing it to dry, and rubbing it off with cleansing tissue.

There is an abundance of outlets for journal publication of good short taxonomic papers requiring not more than 8 to 20 pages of print. Publication of long papers such as treatises and monographs is difficult and is almost restricted to journals sponsored by institutions such as universities, well-supported academies of sciences, and botanical gardens. Institutional publications usually accept only the papers of members of the staff or their students. A journal published by a botanical or natural-historical society may accept a monograph for publication as a series of papers. Publication in parts is not altogether satisfactory, but for many individuals it is the only method available.

If the journal is published for a society, membership is the usual requisite for the privilege of publication. Most scientific societies are open to anyone, but membership in a few is invitational. The botanical staff of the institution where the paper is prepared can supply information on this point.

Submitting the Manuscript. Ordinarily the paper is sent to the editor of the journal, but it may be submitted through another member of the editorial board. The manuscript is expected to conform to the following points:

1. It must be typewritten so that it is readily legible; this requires typing with a new black ribbon. The universal requirement of double-spacing includes not only the main text but also the bibliography or references to literature cited, the footnotes, the quotations, and the legends of illustrations. Many publishers also require a carbon copy to send to at least one prepublication reviewer (as discussed below).

2. Headings, abbreviations, and other details must conform approximately to practice in recent issues of the journal. Consistency is important in the publication as well as within the individual paper.

3. Illustrations must conform to the requirements of the journal.

4. The length of the manuscript must be within the maximum permitted by the journal. The cost of publishing beyond the allowance is charged to the author. An estimate of length is made by translating the number of typed pages into the number of printed pages on the basis of a count of the number of characters (letters and punctuation marks) and blank spaces per line. This should be multiplied by the number of lines per page. For the printed page of the *American Journal of Botany* the product is about 6,000, for the *Bulletin of the Torrey Botanical Club* about 3,000. A similar count should be made for representative pages of the typed manuscript. Dividing the number of characters and spaces per page of

the manuscript into the number for a printed page of the journal yields the approximate number of typed pages per printed page.

Some journals include on the inside of the cover of each issue specific instructions to those who submit manuscripts and illustrations for publication. An excellent example of this is to be found in the *American Journal of Botany.*

Prepublication Review and Criticism. Most technical journals submit manuscripts for prepublication review by individuals other than the editor. The paper or its carbon copy is sent to an editorial board member or to a specialist in the field, with a request for evaluation, criticism, and corrections. These are sent to the editor, who sends the manuscript and the suggestions to the author. The author is not forced to accept the recommendations of the anonymous reviewer, but he is expected to have good reasons for not doing so. The review system was devised to improve the quality of the papers accepted for publication. This is advantageous to both the journal and the author, whose reputation is enhanced by publication of a better paper. The advice of several experienced individuals should be sought before a reviewer's suggestion is rejected. Furthermore, if the point is trivial it usually should be accepted; argument should be saved for issues worthy of it.

The revised manuscript is resubmitted to the editor for final consideration for publication. If it has been improved, acceptance is likely.

PROOFREADING

Galley Proof. The first printed version of the paper is on elongated strips of "galley" proof to be divided into pages by the printer when proofreading is finished. The galley proof is sent to the author to be checked for typographical errors and for correspondence with the original manuscript. It should be read several times, and usually should be read aloud (including the punctuation) at least once by one person while another checks the manuscript.

After type has been set, alteration is expensive and changes are chargeable to the author. The editor assumes the submitted manuscript to be free from errors and in the form the author intended. Sometimes slight changes in wording may be allowed if new information has become available while the manuscript has been awaiting publication, but this depends upon the policy of the editor and the journal. If a slight change is needed, letters and spaces should be counted carefully and the new wording arranged to necessitate the least possible resetting of type. Any change requires substitution of a full line, and altering a word near the beginning of a paragraph may require resetting several lines, unless the new line is exactly the same length as the old.

Proofreading Symbols. The following marks are used by print-ers, editors, proofreaders, and authors to indicate corrections and changes in proofs:

Delete. This symbol varies with the habits of the individual, and often it becomes a scrawl.

\#   Insert space.

Close up, i.e., eliminate extra space.

¶   Start a new paragraph.

No ¶   Run into a single paragraph.

[Move to the left.

]   Move to the right.

Move up.

Move down.

Indent the indicated distance.

Indent 1 em.

Double-space.

∧   Insert matter added in the margin.

Insert comma.

;/:   Insert semicolon or colon.

Insert period.

Insert apostrophe.

Insert quotation marks.

=/   Insert hyphen.

Transpose. one only/ I /and you/

The following are common abbreviations used in proof correction:

tr—transpose

stet—let it stand (i.e., matter which has been crossed out is to be kept as it was originally)

rom—Roman (ordinary) type

ital—*italics*

bf—**boldface**

caps—capital letters; correction marked thus: b̳

sc—small capital letters; correction marked thus: b̲

c & sc—large capital initials with small capitals following

lc—lower case type (i.e., small letters rather than capitals); correction marked thus: B

The following paragraph is an extreme example of one corrected in proof:

⁋ starting a monograph is dependant upon

finding the classification problems existing in a group of abundant are in Every

genus but they are elusive, and the beginner

ginner of monographic work something

specific to do so thatgradually he may

ferret out the points requiring investiga-

tion.

The following methods of approachare

suggested

⁋ Semistatistical devices like those illustrated in

The author's corrections should be in a different color from those added previously.

Ordinarily, when the proofs are returned to the editor an order is placed for reprints of the paper for distribution to other workers in the field and to friends. These reprints are furnished to the author at cost, and the charge diminishes rapidly beyond the minimum number. A price list is sent with the galley proof.

When the proofs are returned many journals request an abstract for publication in *Biological Abstracts.* The method of preparation is described on a printed sheet sent with the proof.

Ordinarily, page proof of a technical paper is not sent to the author.

Some journals give the dates of submission of the papers published in each issue, and the length of the waiting period for appearance of the final product can be estimated accordingly.

The Style Manual for Biological Journals (1960) prepared by the Committee on Form and Style of the Conference of Biological Editors (American Institute of Biological Sciences, 200 P Street, N W, Washington 6, D.C.) has been adopted by a large number of publications. It should be consulted, and ordinarily followed, in preparation of papers for publication.

The following are examples of other manuals for preparation of theses and technical papers:

ANONYMOUS. 1934. *The Wistar Institute style brief.* A guide for authors from the experience of editor and publisher. Philadelphia.

CAMPBELL, W. G. 1954. *Form and style in thesis writing.* Houghton-Mifflin, Boston.

HUBBELL, GEORGE SHELTON. 1941. *Writing documented papers.* Barnes & Noble, New York.

NELSON, J. RALEIGH. 1940. *Writing the technical report.* McGraw-Hill, New York.

SCHWARTEN, LAZELLA, and HAROLD WILLIAM RICKETT. 1958. *Abbreviations of titles of serials cited by botanists.* Bulletin of the Torrey Botanical Club 85: 277–300.

SEYFRIED, JOHN EDWARD. 1933. *Preparing and printing a manuscript.* University of New Mexico Bulletin. Education Series 7(1). University of New Mexico Press, Albuquerque.

———. 1935. *Principles and mechanics of research with emphasis on term reports and theses.* University of New Mexico Bulletin. Education Series 9(1). University of New Mexico Press, Albuquerque.

TRELEASE, SAM F., and EMMA SAREPTA YULE. 1936. *Preparation of scientific and technical papers.* Ed. 3. Williams & Wilkins, Baltimore.

TURABIAN, KATE L. 1955. *A manual for writers of term papers, theses, and dissertations.* University of Chicago Press, Chicago. Guide for typewritten reports and research. Format, footnotes, quotations, bibliography, illustrations, tables, abbreviations.

UNIVERSITY OF CHICAGO STAFF. 1944. *A manual of style.* Ed. 2. University of Chicago Press, Chicago. Informative on printing, publishing, preparation of copy, editing. Glossaries of terms and symbols, specimens of type, hints to authors.

VASSAR COLLEGE. 1933. *Form manual for the preparation of papers.* Vassar College, Poughkeepsie, New York.

WILLIAMS, CECIL B., and ALLAN H. STEVENSON. 1951. *A research manual with bibliographic guide to college studies and interests.* Ed. 2. Harper & Bros., New York.

WOOD, GEORGE MCLANE. 1935. *Suggestions to authors of papers submitted for publication by the United States Geological Survey, with directions to typists.* Government Printing Office, Washington.

References

Note: The following list does not necessarily duplicate the lists of reference material on special subjects given in the text rather than at the ends of the chapters. It completes the reading lists at the ends of the chapters, documents the references given by author and year in the text, and lists some of the other publications important in the field of study. Inasmuch as the book is intended for undergraduate and beginning graduate student use, the bibliography is not designed to be complete. Publications received from November 1, 1960, to July 1, 1961, are included only in the References section and not in the reading lists at the ends of the chapters. Papers received after July 1, 1961, are not included.

ABBE, ERNST, and DONALD B. LAWRENCE. 1940. *The use of outline maps on herbarium labels.* Science 92: 181–182.

ABRAMS, LEROY. 1923, 1944, 1951, 1960. *An illustrated flora of the Pacific States, Washington, Oregon, and California.* 4 vols. (vol. 4 by ROXANNA S. FERRIS). Stanford University Press, Stanford, Calif.

ADAMS, CHARLES C. 1902. *Postglacial origin and migration of the life of the northeastern United States.* Journal of Geography 1: 300–310, 352–357.

ADDISON, GEORGE, and ROSENDO TAVARES. 1952. *Hybridization and grafting in species of* Theobroma *which occur in Amazonia.* Evolution 6: 380–386.

ALLARD, H. A. 1932. *A progeny study of the so-called oak species,* Quercus Saulii, *with notes on other probable hybrids found in or near the District of Columbia.* Bulletin of the Torrey Botanical Club 59: 207–277.

———. 1942. *The hybrid oak,* Quercus Rudkinii, *at Arlington, Virginia.* Rhodora 44: 262–266.

———. 1949. *An analysis of seedling progeny of an individual of* Quercus Saulii *compared with a typical individual of the white oak* (Quercus alba) *and a typical rock chestnut oak* (Quercus montana [Prinus]). Castanea 14: 107–117.

ALSTON, R. E., and H. S. IRWIN. 1961. *The comparative extent of variation of free amino acids and certain "secondary" substances among* Cassia *species.* American Journal of Botany 48: 35–39.

———, and B. L. TURNER. 1959. *Applications of paper chromatography to systematics: Recombination of parental biochemical components in a* Baptisia *hybrid population.* Nature 184: 285–286.

AMADON, DEAN. 1947. *Ecology and the evolution of some Hawaiian birds.* Evolution 1: 63–77. Review by ERNST MAYR. Evolution 5: 86. 1951.

ANDERSON, EDGAR. 1937. *Cytology in relation to taxonomy.* Botanical Review 3: 335–350.

———. 1948. *Hybridization of the habitat.* Evolution 2: 1–9.

ANDERSON, EDGAR. 1949. *Introgressive hybridization.* John Wiley & Sons, Inc., New York. Review by CARL HUBBS. Evolution 4: 100–101. 1950.

———. 1951. *Concordant versus discordant variation in relation to introgression.* Evolution 5: 133–141.

———. 1952. *Plants, man and life.* Little, Brown & Co., Boston. Review by G. LEDYARD STEBBINS, JR. *The evolution of cultivated plants and weeds.* Evolution 6: 445–448.

———. 1953. *Introgressive hybridization.* Biological Reviews 28: 280–307.

———. 1957. *An experimental investigation of judgments concerning genera and species.* Evolution 11: 260–262.

———, and BURTON R. ANDERSON. 1954. *Introgression of* Salvia apiana *and* Salvia mellifera. Annals of the Missouri Botanical Garden 41: 329–338.

———, and L. HUBRICHT. 1938. *The evidence for introgressive hybridization.* American Journal of Botany 25: 396–402.

———, and G. LEDYARD STEBBINS, JR. 1954. *Hybridization as an evolutionary stimulus.* Evolution 8: 378–388.

ANONYMOUS. 1867. *Laws of botanical nomenclature adopted by the International Botanical Congress held at Paris in August, 1867.*

ANONYMOUS. 1907. *American code of botanical nomenclature.* Bulletin of the Torrey Botanical Club. 34: 167–178.

ANONYMOUS. 1954. *Nomina generica conservanda.* Taxon 3: 155–156. (Adopted at Paris in 1954.) See Taxon 3: 112–123, 1954, for more information.

ANONYMOUS. 1958. *International code of nomenclature for cultivated plants.* Regnum Vegetabile 10. International Bureau for Plant Taxonomy and Nomenclature, Utrecht.

ANONYMOUS. 1961. *The mathematical assessment of taxonomic similarity, including the use of computors.* Taxon 10: 97–101.

AVERY, AMOS G., SOPHIE SATINA, and JACOB RIETSEMA. 1959. *Blakeslee: the genus* Datura. The Ronald Press Co., New York.

AXELROD, DANIEL I. 1944. *The Sonoma flora.* Carnegie Institution of Washington Publication (553): 167–206.

———. 1948. *Climate and evolution in western North America during middle Pliocene time.* Evolution 2: 127–144.

———. 1956. *Mio-Pliocene floras from west-central Nevada.* University of California Publications in Geological Sciences 33: 1–322.

———. 1957. *Late Tertiary floras and the Sierra Nevadan uplift.* Bulletin of the Geological Society of America. 68: 19–45.

———. 1958. *Evolution of the Madro-Tertiary Geoflora.* Botanical Review 24: 433–509.

———. 1959. *Late Cenozoic evolution of the Sierran bigtree forest.* Evolution 13: 9–23.

BABCOCK, E. G. 1947. *The genus* Crepis. University of California Publications in Botany 21: 1–197; 22: 1–1030.

———, G. L. STEBBINS, JR., and J. A. JENKINS. 1942. *Genetic evolutionary processes in* Crepis. American Naturalist 76: 337–363.

BAILEY, IRVING W. 1944a. *The comparative anatomy of the Winteraceae III. Wood.* Journal of the Arnold Arboretum 25: 97–103 (see also under BAILEY and NAST, 1943a, 1943b, 1945).

———. 1944b. *The development of vessels in angiosperms and its significance in morphological research.* American Journal of Botany 31: 421–428.

———. 1949. *Origin of the angiosperms: Need for a broadened outlook.* Journal of the Arnold Arboretum 30: 64–70.

———. 1951. *The use and abuse of anatomical data in the study of phylogeny and classification.* Phytomorphology 1: 67–69.

———. 1953a. *Evolution of the tracheary tissue of land plants.* American Journal of Botany 40: 4–8.

————. 1953b. *The anatomical approach to the study of genera.* Chronica Botanica 14: 121–125.

————, and CHARLOTTE G. NAST. 1943a, 1943b, 1945. *The comparative morphology of the Winteraceae.* Journal of the Arnold Arboretum I. *Pollen and stamens* 24: 340–346; II. *Carpels* 24: 472–481; III. (See under BAILEY, 1944a); VII. *Summary and conclusions* 26: 37–47.

————, CHARLOTTE G. NAST, and A. C. SMITH. 1943. *The family Himantandraceae.* Journal of the Arnold Arboretum 24: 190–206.

————, and A. C. SMITH. 1942. *Degeneriaceae: A new family of flowering plants from Fiji.* Journal of the Arnold Arboretum 23: 356–365.

————, and B. G. L. SWAMY. 1951. *The conduplicate carpel of dicotyledons and its initial trends of specialization.* American Journal of Botany 38: 373–379.

————, and W. W. TUPPER. 1918. *Size variation in tracheary cells.* I. *A comparison between secondary xylems of vascular cryptogams, gymnosperms and angiosperms.* Proceedings of the American Academy of Arts and Sciences 54: 149–204.

BAKER, H. G. 1952. *The ecospecies: Prelude to discussion.* Evolution 6: 61–68.

————. 1959. *The contribution of autecological and gene-ecological studies to our knowledge of the past migrations of plants.* American Naturalist 93: 209–211.

BARGHOORN, E. S., JR. 1940, 1941a, 1941b. *The ontogenetic development and phylogenetic specialization of rays in the xylem of dicotyledons.* American Journal of Botany. I. *The primitive ray structure.* 27: 918–928. II. *Modification of the multiseriate and uniseriate rays.* 28: 273–282. III. *The elimination of rays.* Bulletin of the Torrey Botanical Club 68: 317–325.

BAUM, WERNER. 1954. *Systematic serology of the family Cucurbitaceae, with special reference to the genus* Cucurbita. Serological Museum Bulletin 13: 5–8.

BEEKS, RICHARD M. 1955. *Improvements in the squash technique for plant chromosomes.* Aliso 3: 131–134.

BELL, C. RITCHIE. 1959. *Taxonomy: One kind, or many?* ASB Bulletin 6: 39–40.

BENSON, LYMAN. 1936. *Pacific States Ranunculi.* I, II. American Journal of Botany 23: 26–33, 169–176.

————. 1939. *Notes on taxonomic techniques.* Torreya 39: 73–75.

————. 1940a. *Taxonomic contributions.* American Journal of Botany 27: 186–190.

————. 1940b. *The North American subdivisions of* Ranunculus. American Journal of Botany 27: 799–807.

————. 1941a. *Taxonomic studies.* I. *A revision of the semaphore grasses: The genus* Pleuropogon. American Journal of Botany 28: 358–360, 362.

————. 1941b. *The mesquites and screw-beans of the United States.* American Journal of Botany 28: 748–754.

————. 1941–1942. *North American Ranunculi.* I–V. Bulletin of the Torrey Botanical Club. 68: 157–172, 477–490, 649–659; 69: 298–316, 373–386.

————. 1942a. *Notes on the flora of Arizona.* Torreya 42: 9–11.

————. 1942b. *The relationship of* Ranunculus *to the North American floras.* American Journal of Botany 29: 491–500.

————. 1943. *The goal and methods of systematic botany.* Cactus and Succulent Journal 15: 99–111.

————. 1948a. *The identity of* Ranunculus uncinatus. American Midland Naturalist 39: 761.

————. 1948b. *A Treatise on the North American Ranunculi.* American Midland Naturalist 40: 1–261.

————. 1950a. *The cacti of Arizona.* Ed. 2. University of Arizona Press, Tucson; University of New Mexico Press, Albuquerque (see BENSON, THORNBER, and NICHOL, 1940).

————. 1950b. *Permanent plant records.* Cactus and Succulent Journal 22: 115–122.

————. 1953. *Relationships of the Ranunculi of the Continental Divide and of the Pacific and eastern forests of North America.* Proceedings of the Seventh International Botanical Congress, Stockholm, 1950. 862–863.

BENSON, LYMAN. 1954. *Supplement to a treatise on the North American Ranunculi.* American Midland Naturalist 52: 328–369.

———. 1955. *The Ranunculi of the Alaskan Arctic Coastal Plain and the Brooks Range.* American Midland Naturalist 53: 242–255.

———. 1957. *Plant classification.* D. C. Heath & Co., Boston.

———. 1959. *Typification of* Prosopis odorata *Torr. & Frem. (Leguminosae).* Madroño 14: 53–54.

———, and ANNETTA M. CARTER. 1939. *Two new species of* Ranunculus § *Flammula.* American Journal of Botany. 26: 555–557.

———, and ROBERT A. DARROW. 1945, 1954. *A manual of southwestern desert trees and shrubs.* University of Arizona Biological Science Bulletin 6: 1–411. Title of ed. 2 changed to *The trees and shrubs of the southwestern deserts,* published by the University of Arizona Press, Tucson, and the University of New Mexico Press, Albuquerque.

———, J. J. THORNBER, and A. A. NICHOL. 1940. *The cacti of Arizona.* Ed. 1. University of Arizona Press, Tucson (see BENSON, 1950a).

BLAIR, W. FRANK. 1950. *Ecological factors in speciation of* Peromyscus. Evolution 4: 253–275.

BONNER, JAMES. 1960. *Thoughts about biology.* AIBS Bulletin 10: 17 (See DOBZHANSKY, 1961; HERRE, 1960).

BRADLEY, MURIEL V. 1948. *A method for making aceto-carmine squashes permanent without removal of the cover slip.* Stain Technology 23: 41–44.

BRIQUET, JOHN. 1935. *International rules of botanical nomenclature.* Gustave Fischer, Jena.

BRITTON, NATHANIEL LORD. 1882. *On a hybrid oak near Keyport, New Jersey.* Bulletin of the Torrey Botanical Club 9: 12–15.

———, and ADDISON BROWN. 1896–1898, 1913–1914. *An illustrated flora of the northeastern United States, Canada, and the British possessions from Newfoundland to the parallel of the southern boundary of Virginia and from the Atlantic Ocean westward to the 102nd meridian.* Eds. 1, 2. Charles Scribner's Sons, New York.

BROUWER, W., and A. STÄHLIN. 1955. *Handbuch der Samenkunde.* Frankfurt am Main.

BROWN, META S. 1951. *The spontaneous occurrence of amphiploidy in species hybrids of* Gossypium. Evolution 5: 25–41. 1951.

BRYAN, E. H., JR. 1954. *The Hawaiian chain.* Bishop Museum, Honolulu.

BUCHHOLZ, J. T. 1939. *The generic segregation of the sequoias.* American Journal of Botany 26: 535–538.

BUEHRER, T. F., and LYMAN BENSON. 1945. *Rubber content of native plants of the southwestern desert.* University of Arizona Agricultural Experiment Station Bulletin 108.

BULLOCK, A. A. 1959. *Notes on some nomenclatural proposals before the Montreal (1959) Congress.* Taxon 8: 111–113.

BURMA, BENJAMIN H. 1949a. *The species concept: A semantic review.* Evolution 3: 369–370.

———. 1949b. *Postscriptum.* Evolution 3: 372–373.

———. 1954. *Reality, existence, and classification: A discussion of the species problem.* Madroño 12: 193–209.

BUXBAUM, FRANZ. 1951. *Grundlagen und Methoden einer Erneuerung der Systematik der höheren Pflanzen.* Springer-Verlag, Vienna.

CAMP, W. H. 1947. *Distribution patterns in modern plants and the problems of ancient dispersals.* Ecological Monographs 17: 123–126, 159–183.

———. 1951. *Biosystematy.* Brittonia 7: 113–127.

———. 1953. *The herbarium in modern systematics.* American Naturalist 77:322–344.

———, and CHARLES GILLY. 1943. *The structure and origin of species.* Brittonia 4: 323–385.

CANRIGHT, JAMES E. 1952. *The comparative morphology and relationships of the Magnoliaceae. I. Trends of specialization in the stamens.* American Journal of Botany 39: 484–497.

———. 1953. *The comparative morphology and relationships of the Magnoliaceae. II. Significance of the pollen.* Phytomorphology 3: 355–365.

CARLQUIST, SHERWIN. 1957. *The genus* Fitchia *(Compositae).* University of California Publications in Botany 29:1–144.

———. 1958. *Structure and ontogeny of glandular trichomes of* Madinae *(Compositae).* American Journal of Botany 45: 675–682.

———. 1959a. *The leaf of* Calycadenia *and its glandular appendages.* American Journal of Botany 46: 70–80.

———. 1959b. *Glandular structures of* Holocarpha *and their ontogeny.* American Journal of Botany 46: 300–308.

———. 1961a. *Wood anatomy of Inuleae (Compositae).* Aliso 5: 21–37.

———. 1961b. *Pollen morphology of Rapateaceae.* Aliso 5: 39–66.

CAVE, MARION S. 1953. *Cytology and embryology in the delimitation of genera.* Chronica Botanica 14: 140–153.

CHALK, L. 1937. *The phylogenetic value of certain anatomical features of dicotyledonous woods.* Annals of Botany II. 1: 410–428.

———. 1944. *The taxonomic value of wood anatomy.* Proceedings of the Linnaean Society, London 155: 214–218.

CHAMBERS, KENTON L. 1955. *A biosystematic study of the annual species of* Microseris. Contributions from the Dudley Herbarium, Stanford University 4: 207–312.

CHANEY, RALPH W. 1925. *A comparative study of the Bridge Creek flora and the modern redwood forest.* Carnegie Institution of Washington Publication 349: 1–22.

———. 1936. *The succession and distribution of Cenozoic floras around the North Pacific Basin.* Essays in geobotany in honor of W. A. SETCHELL, edited by T. H. GOODSPEED. 55–85.

———. 1938. *Paleocological interpretation of Cenozoic plants in western North America.* Botanical Review 4: 371–396.

———. 1940. *Tertiary forests and continental history.* Bulletin of the Geological Society of America 51: 469–488.

———. 1944. *A fossil cactus from the Eocene of Utah.* American Journal of Botany 31: 507–528.

———. 1947. *Tertiary centers and migration routes.* Ecological Monographs 17: 139–148.

———. 1948. *The bearing of* Metasequoia *on problems of Tertiary paleobotany.* Proceedings of the National Academy of Sciences 34: 503–515.

———. 1949. *Evolutionary trends in the angiosperms.* Paper No. 10 in *Genetics, paleontology, and evolution,* edited by GLENN L. JEPSON, ERNST MAYR, and GEORGE GAYLORD SIMPSON. Princeton University Press, Princeton, N.J. Pp. 190–201.

———. 1951. *A revision of fossil* Sequoia *and* Taxodium *in western North America based upon the recent discovery of* Metasequoia. Transactions of the American Philosophical Society 40: 171–263.

———, CARLTON CONDIT, and DANIEL I. AXELROD. 1944. *Pliocene floras of California and Oregon.* Carnegie Institution of Washington Publication 553.

———, and HERBERT L. MASON. 1930. *A Pleistocene flora from Santa Cruz Island, California.* Carnegie Institution of Washington Publication 415: 1–24.

CHEADLE, VERNON I. 1942. *The rôle of anatomy in phylogenetic studies of the Monocotyledoneae.* Chronica Botanica 7: 253–254.

———. 1943. *The origin and certain trends of specialization of the vessel in the Monocotyledoneae.* American Journal of Botany 30: 11–17.

———. 1953. *Independent origin of vessels in the monocotyledons and dicotyledons.* Phytomorphology 3: 23–44.

CLARKSON, QUENTIN D. 1959. *Field studies of natural hybridization in the Oregon species of* Iris L. *subsection* Californicae *Diels.* Madroño 15: 115–122.

CLAUSEN, JENS. 1951. *Stages in the evolution of plant species.* Cornell University Press, Ithaca, N.Y. Review by G. LEDYARD STEBBINS, JR. Evolution 6: 131–133. 1952.

———. 1952. *New bluegrasses by combining and rearranging genomes of contrasting* Poa *species.* 6th International Grassland Conference, Proceedings 216–221.

———. 1954a. *The ecological race as a variable biotype compound in dynamic balance with its environment.* IUBS Symposium on Genetics of Population Structure, Pavia, Italy 105–113.

———. 1954b. *Partial apomixis as an equilibrium system in evolution.* Caryologia. Supplementary vol., 469–479.

———. 1960. *A simple method for the sampling of natural populations.* Scottish Plant Breeding Station Report 69–75.

———, and WILLIAM M. HIESEY. 1958a. *Phenotypic expression of genotypes in contrasting environments.* Scottish Plant Breeding Station Report. 41–51.

———, and WILLIAM M. HIESEY. 1958b. *Experimental studies on the nature of species.* IV. *Genetic structure of ecological races.* Carnegie Institution of Washington Publication 615: 1–312.

———, and WILLIAM M. HIESEY. 1960. *The balance between coherence and variation in evolution.* Proceedings of the National Academy of Sciences 46: 494–506.

———, WILLIAM M. HIESEY, and MALCOLM A. NOBS. 1958. Poa *investigations.* Carnegie Institution of Washington Year Book 57: 272–278.

———, DAVID D. KECK, and WILLIAM M. HIESEY. 1939. *The concept of species based on experiment.* American Journal of Botany 26: 103–106.

———, DAVID D. KECK, and WILLIAM M. HIESEY. 1940. *Experimental studies on the nature of species.* I. *Effects of varied climates on western North American plants.* Carnegie Institution of Washington Publication 520: 1–452.

———, DAVID D. KECK, and WILLIAM M. HIESEY. 1941. *Experimental taxonomy.* Carnegie Institution of Washington Yearbook 40: 160–170.

———, DAVID D. KECK, and WILLIAM M. HIESEY. 1945a. *Experimental studies on the nature of species.* II. *Plant evolution through amphiploidy and autoploidy, with examples from the Madiinae.* Carnegie Institution of Washington Publication 564: 1–174.

———, DAVID D. KECK, and WILLIAM M. HIESEY. 1945b. *Experimental taxonomy.* Carnegie Institution of Washington Yearbook 44: 71–83.

———, DAVID D. KECK, and WILLIAM M. HIESEY. 1947. *Heredity of geographically and ecologically isolated races.* American Naturalist 81: 114–133.

———, DAVID D. KECK, and WILLIAM M. HIESEY. 1948. *Experimental studies on the nature of species.* III. *Environmental responses of climatic races of* Achillea. Carnegie Institution of Washington Publication 581: 1–129.

———, DAVID D. KECK, and WILLIAM M. HIESEY. 1958. *The function and evolution of ecotypes, ecospecies, and other natural entities.* Uppsala Universitets Årsskift 1958(6): 139–143.

CLAUSEN, ROBERT T. 1941. *On the use of the terms "subspecies" and "variety."* Rhodora 43: 157–167.

———. 1959. Sedum. *of the trans-Mexican volcanic belt: An exposition of taxonomic methods.* Comstock Publishing Associates, Cornell University Press, Ithaca, N. Y.

CLEMENTS, F. E., E. V. MARTIN, and F. L. LONG. 1950. *Adaptation and origin in the plant world: The role of environment in evolution.* Chronica Botanica, Waltham, Mass. Review by GERALD OWNBEY. Ecology 33: 431–433. 1952.

COLBERT, EDWIN H. 1948. *Evolution of the horned dinosaurs.* Evolution 2: 145–163.

COLE, DONALD B. 1956. *A revision of the* Rosa californica *complex.* American Midland Naturalist 55: 211–224.

CONSTANCE, LINCOLN. 1951. *The versatile taxonomist.* Brittonia 7: 225–231.

———. 1953. *The role of plant ecology in biosystematics.* Ecology 34: 642–648.

————. 1955. *The systematics of the angiosperms*. In *A century of progress in the natural sciences*. California Academy of Sciences, San Francisco. Pp. 405–483.

————. 1956. *Plant taxonomy in an age of experiment*. American Journal of Botany 44: 88–92.

COONEN, L. P. 1939. *The chromosomes of* Ranunculus. American Journal of Botany 26: 49–58.

COOPERRIDER, MIWAKO. 1957. *Introgressive hybridization between* Quercus marilandica *and* Q. velutina *in Iowa*. American Journal of Botany 44: 804–810.

CORE, EARL L. 1955. *Plant taxonomy*. Prentice-Hall, Inc., Englewood Cliffs, N.J.

COULTER, JOHN MERLE, and AVEN NELSON. 1909. *New manual of botany of the central Rocky Mountains*. American Book Co., New York.

COX, HIDEN T. 1948a, 1948b. *Studies in the comparative anatomy of the Ericales*. American Midland Naturalist. I. *Ericaceae: Sub-family Rhododendroideae* 39: 220–245. II. *Ericaceae: Sub-family Arbutoideae* 40: 493–516.

CRAMPTON, BEECHER. 1954. *Morphological and ecological considerations in classification of* Navarretia. Madroño 12: 225–238.

————. 1959. *The grass genera* Orcuttia *and* Neostapfia: *A study in habitat and morphological specialization*. Madroño 15: 97–110.

CRONQUIST, ARTHUR. Compositae in C. LEO HITCHCOCK, ARTHUR CRONQUIST, MARION OWNBEY, and J. W. THOMPSON. 1955. *Vascular plants of the Pacific Northwest*. Vol. 5. University of Washington, Seattle. Pp. 1–3.

————. 1957. *Outline of a new system of families and orders of dicotyledons*. Bulletin du Jardin Botanique de l'État, Brussels 27: 13–40.

DALLA TORRE, C. G., and H. HARMS. 1900–1907. *Genera Siphonogarum ad systema Englerianum conscripta*. Leipzig.

DANDY, J. E., J. S. L. GILMOUR, T. A. SPRAGUE, and E. M. WAKEFIELD. 1952. *Committee to deal with urgent nomenclatural needs*. Memorandum by the British members. Taxon 1: 78–80.

DARLINGTON, C. D., and L. F. LA COUR. 1950. *The handling of chromosomes*. George Allen & Unwin, London.

DAVIDSON, JOHN F. 1947. *The polygonal graph for simultaneous portrayal of several variables in population analysis*. Madroño 9: 105–110.

————. 1952. *The use of taxonomy in ecology*. Ecology 33: 297–298.

————. 1954. *A dephlogisticated species concept*. Madroño 12: 246–251.

————, and T. L. THOMPSON. 1956. *Phytoserology vs. genealogy in* Zea Mays. Madroño 13: 252–259.

DAVIS, RAY J. 1952. *Flora of Idaho*. William C. Brown Co., Dubuque, Iowa.

DAVIS, W. T. 1892. *Interesting oaks recently discovered on Staten Island*. Bulletin of the Torrey Botanical Club 19: 301–303.

DEAM, CHARLES C. 1940. *Flora of Indiana*. Buford Printing Company, Indianapolis. (Distributed by the State Forester, Indianapolis.)

DEAN, DONALD S. 1959. *Distribution of tetraploid and diploid* Tradescantia ohiensis *in Michigan and adjoining areas*. American Midland Naturalist 61: 204–209.

DOBZHANSKY, THEODOSIUS. 1937, 1941, 1951. *Genetics and the origin of species*. Eds. 1–3. Columbia University Press, New York.

————. 1961. *Taxonomy, Molecular Biology, and the peck order*. Evolution 15: 263–264 (see BONNER, 1960; HERRE, 1960).

DORF, ERLING. 1957. *The earth's changing climates*. Weatherwise 10: 54–59.

————. 1959. *Climatic changes of the past and present*. Contributions from the Museum of Paleontology, University of Michigan 13: 181–210.

DUFFIELD, J. W. 1940. *Chromosome counts in* Quercus. American Journal of Botany 27: 787–788.

DUNBAR, CARL O. 1950. *The species concept: Further discussion*. Evolution 4: 175–176.

DUNN, DAVID B. 1956. *The breeding systems of* Lupinus, *group* Micranthi. American Midland Naturalist 55: 443–472.

EINSET, JOHN. 1951. *Apomixis in American polyploid blackberries.* American Journal of Botany 38: 768–772.

ELIAS, MAXIM K. 1950. *Paleontologic versus neontologic species and genera.* Evolution 4: 176–177.

ELLIOT, F. C. 1949. Bromus inermis *and* B. pumpellianus *in North America.* Evolution 3: 142–149.

ELLIOTT, RUTH F., and MALCOLM A. NOBS. 1959. *Germination studies on* Mimulus *at controlled temperatures.* Annual Report of the Director of the Department of Plant Biology. Carnegie Institution of Washington Year Book 58: 353–354.

ENGELMANN, GEORGE. 1876–1877. *About the oaks of the United States: Hybrid oaks.* Transactions of the St. Louis Academy of Sciences 4: 398–400, 539–543.

EPLING, CARL. 1939. *An approach to classification.* Scientific Monthly 46: 360–367.

————. 1947a. *Natural hybridization of* Salvia apiana *and* S. mellifera. Evolution 1: 69–78.

————. 1947b. *Actual and potential gene flow in natural populations.* American Naturalist 81: 104–113.

————, and W. CATLIN. 1950. *The relation of taxonomic method to an explanation of organic evolution.* Heredity 4: 313–325.

————, and HARLAN LEWIS. 1952. *Increase in the adaptive range of the genus* Delphinium. Evolution 6: 253–267 (see also LEWIS and EPLING, 1954).

————, HARLAN LEWIS, and FRANCIS M. BALL. 1960. *The breeding group and seed storage: A study in population dynamics.* Evolution 14: 238–255.

ERDTMAN, G. 1952. *Pollen morphology and plant taxonomy: Angiosperms.* Vol. 1 of *An introduction to palynology.* The Ronald Press Co. (A Chronica Botanica Publication), New York.

FAEGRI, KNUT. 1935. *The species problem.* Nature 136: 954.

————. 1937. *Some fundamental problems of taxonomy and phylogenetics.* Botanical Review 3: 400–423.

FAIRBROTHERS, DAVID E., and MARION A. JOHNSON. 1959. *The precipitin reaction as an indicator of relationship in the subfamily Festucoideae of the Family Poaceae* (Gramineae). 9th International Botanical Congress Proceedings 2: 110–111.

FASSETT, NORMAN C., and BARBARA CALHOUN. 1952. *Introgression between* Typha latifolia *and* T. augustifolia. Evolution 6: 367–369.

————, and JONATHAN D. SAUER. 1950. *Studies in the weed genus* Phytolacca. I. *Hybridizing species in northeastern Colombia.* Evolution 4: 332–339 (see also SAUER, 1951).

FERNALD, MERRITT LYNDON. 1925. *Persistence of plants in unglaciated areas of boreal America.* Memoirs of the American Academy of Arts and Sciences 15: 241–342.

————. 1936. *Minor forms and transfers.* Rhodora 38: 233–236.

————. 1940. *Some spermatophytes of eastern North America.* Rhodora 42: 239–276.

————. 1950. *Gray's manual of botany.* Ed. 8. American Book Co., New York.

FOSBERG, F. RAYMOND. 1942. *Subspecies and variety.* Rhodora 44: 153–157.

FOSTER, ADRIANCE S. *Practical plant anatomy.* Ed. 2. D. Van Nostrand Co., Inc., New York.

FRAENKEL, G. S. 1959. *The raison d'être of secondary plant substances.* Science 129: 1466–1470.

FROILAND, SVEN G. 1952. *The biological status of* Betula Andrewsii A. Nels. Evolution 6: 268–282.

FROST, F. H. 1930a, 1930b, 1931. *Specialization in secondary xylem of dicotyledons.* Botanical Gazette. I. *Origin of vessel* 89: 67–94. II. *Evolution of end wall of vessel segment* 90: 198–212. III. *Specialization of lateral wall of vessel segment* 91: 88–96.

FRYER, GEOFFREY. 1959. *Some aspects of evolution in Lake Nyasa.* Evolution 13: 440–451.

GELL, P. G. H., J. G. HAWKES, and S. T. C. WRIGHT. 1960. *The application of immunological methods to the taxonomy of species within the genus* Solanum. Proceedings of the Royal Society 151: 364–383.

GENTRY, HOWARD SCOTT. 1950. *Taxonomy and evolution of* Vaseyanthus. Madroño 10: 142–155.

GIBBS, R. DARNLEY. 1945. *Comparative chemistry as an aid to the solution of problems in systematic botany.* Transactions of the Royal Society of Canada. III. 36(sec. 5): 71–103.

——. 1954. *Comparative chemistry and phylogeny of flowering plants.* Transactions of the Royal Society of Canada. V. 48(sec. 5): 1–47.

GILBERT, S. G. 1940. *Evolutionary significance of ring porosity in woody angiosperms.* Botanical Gazette 102: 105–120.

GILLETT, GEORGE W. 1961. *An experimental study of variation in the* Phacelia sericea *complex.* American Journal of Botany 48: 1–7.

GLEASON, H. A. 1952. *The new Britton and Brown illustrated flora of the northeastern United States and adjacent Canada.* Vols. 1–3. New York Botanical Garden, New York.

GOODSPEED, T. H. 1954. *The genus* Nicotiana. Chronica Botanica 16: 1–536.

GRANICK, ELSA B. 1944. *A karyosystematic study of the genus* Agave. American Journal of Botany 31: 283–298.

GRANT, VERNE. 1949. *Pollination systems as isolating mechanisms.* Evolution 3: 82–97.

——. 1950. *The flower constancy of bees.* Botanical Review 16: 379–398.

——. 1952. *Isolation and hybridization between* Aquilegia formosa *and* A. pubescens. Aliso 2: 341–360.

——. 1953. *The role of hybridization in the evolution of the leafy-stemmed gilias.* Evolution 7: 51–64.

——. 1955. *Cross-fertilization.* In *Encyclopedia Americana* 8: 230–234.

——. 1956a. *The genetic structure of races and species of* Gilia. Advances in Genetics 8: 55–87.

——. 1956b. *The influence of breeding habit on the outcome of natural hybridization in plants.* American Naturalist 90: 319–322.

——. 1956c. *Chromosome repatterning and adaptation.* Advances in Genetics 8: 89–107.

——. 1957. *The species problem in plants.* In *The Species Problem,* edited by ERNST MAYR. AAAS Symposium vol.

——. 1958. *The regulation of recombination in plants.* Cold Spring Harbor Symposia on Quantitative Biology 23: 337–363.

——. 1959. *Natural history of the Phlox family.* International Scholars Forum Vol. 1. The Hague.

——, et al. 1950–1958. *Genetic and taxonomic studies in* Gilia. I–X. Aliso 2: 239–316, 361–374, 375–388; 3: 1–18, 19–34, 35–49, 93–110, 203–288, 289–296, 297–300.

GRAY HERBARIUM OF HARVARD UNIVERSITY. 1885– . *Gray Herbarium card index, being a catalog of American plants published since 1885.* Cambridge, Mass.

GREGUSS, P. 1955. *Identification of living gymnosperms on the basis of xylotomy.* Akadémia Kiado. Budapest.

GRUN, PAUL. 1961. *Early stages in the formation of internal barriers to gene exchange between diploid species of* Solanum. American Journal of Botany 48: 79–89.

GULICK, JOHN THOMAS. 1905. *Evolution, racial and habitudinal.* Carnegie Institution of Washington, Washington, D. C.

GUSTAFSSON, ÅKE. 1946, 1947. *Apomixis in higher plants.* Lunds Universitets Årsskrift. N.F. 42(2): 43(2, 12). Review by G. LEDYARD STEBBINS, JR. Evolution 3: 98–101. 1949.

HÄFLINGER, ERNST. 1943. *Zytologisch-embryologische Untersuchungen pseudogamer Ranunkeln der* Auricomus-*Gruppe.* Berichte der Schweizerischen Botanischen Gesellschaft 53: 317–382.

HAGERUP, O. 1950. *Rain Pollination.* Det Kongelige Danske Videnskabernes Selskab. Biologiske Meddelelser. 18: 1–18.

HALL, HARVEY MONROE. 1926. *The taxonomic treatment of units smaller than species.* Proceedings of the International Congress of Plant Sciences, Ithaca, N.Y. 2: 1461–1468.

———. 1932. *Heredity and environment—as illustrated by transplant studies.* Scientific Monthly 35: 289–302.

———, and FREDERICK E. CLEMENTS. 1923. *The phylogenetic method in taxonomy.* Carnegie Institution of Washington Publication 326.

———, DAVID D. KECK, and WILLIAM M. HEUSI (HIESEY). 1931. *Experimental taxonomy.* Carnegie Institution of Washington Yearbook.

HALL, J. W. 1952. *The comparative anatomy and phylogeny of the Betulaceae.* Botanical Gazette 113: 235–270.

HALL, MARION T. 1952. *A hybrid swarm in* Juniperus. Evolution 6: 347–366.

HALLER, JOHN R. 1959. *Factors affecting the distribution of ponderosa and Jeffrey pines in California.* Madroño 15: 65–71.

HALLIDAY, W. E. D., and A. W. A. BROWN. 1943. *The distribution of some important forest trees in Canada.* Ecology 24: 353–373.

HARLOW, WILLIAM M. 1947. *The identification of the pines of the United States, native and introduced, by needle structure.* New York College of Forestry Technical Publication 32. Syracuse, N.Y.

HARRINGTON, H. D. 1954. *Manual of the plants of Colorado.* Sage Books, Inc., Denver.

HECKARD, LAWRENCE R. 1960. *Taxonomic studies in the* Phacelia magellanica *complex, with special reference to the California members.* University of California Publications. Botany 32: 1–126.

HEDBERG, OLAV. 1946. *Pollen morphology in the genus* Polygonum L. s. lat. *and its taxonomical significance.* Svensk Botaniska Tidskrift 40: 371–404.

———. 1958. *Systematics of today.* Uppsala Universitets Årrskrift 1958(6): 183–195.

HEISER, CHARLES B., JR. 1947. *Hybridization between sunflower species* Helianthus annuus *and* H. petiolaris. Evolution 1: 249–262.

———. 1951. *Hybridization in the annual sunflowers:* Helianthus annuus × H. debilis var. cucumerifolius. Evolution 5: 42–51.

———. 1961. *Morphological and cytological variation in* Helianthus petiolaris *with notes on related species.* Evolution 15: 247–258.

———, and DALE M. SMITH. 1960. *The origin of* Helianthus multiflorus. American Journal of Botany 47: 860–865.

HESLOP-HARRISON, J. 1952. *Statistical methods in taxonomy.* Taxon 1: 53–59, 73–78.

———. 1953. *New concepts in flowering plant taxonomy.* William Heinemann, Ltd., London.

HERRE, ALBERT W. 1960. (Letter to the editor.) AIBS Bulletin 10: 5–6 (see BONNER, 1960; DOBZHANSKY, 1961).

HIESEY, WILLIAM M. 1953. *Growth and development of species and hybrids of* Poa *under controlled temperatures.* American Journal of Botany 40: 205–221.

———, HAROLD W. MILNER, and MALCOLM A. NOBS. 1959a. *Working principles for a physiological approach to the study of climatic races.* Carnegie Institution of Washington Year Book 58: 344–346.

———, HAROLD W. MILNER, and MALCOLM A. NOBS. 1959b. *Controlled cabinets for plant growth.* Carnegie Institution of Washington Year Book 58: 350–351.

HITCHCOCK, C. LEO. 1952. *A revision of the North American species of* Lathyrus. University of Washington Publications in Biology 15: 1–104.

————, ARTHUR CRONQUIST, MARION OWNBEY, and J. W. THOMPSON. 1955, 1959. *Vascular plants of the Pacific Northwest.* Vols. 4, 5. University of Washington Press, Seattle.

HOOKER, JOSEPH DALTON, and B. DAYDON JACKSON (and their successors). 1885– . *Index kewensis: An enumeration of the genera and species of flowering plants.* London.

HOPKINS, DAVID M. 1959. *Cenozoic history of the Bering land bridge.* Science 129: 1519–1528.

HOWELL, JOHN THOMAS. 1946. *Notes on the grass family in Marin County, California.* Leaflets of Western Botany 4: 243–247.

HULTÉN, ERIC. 1937. *Outline of the history of Arctic and boreal biota during the Quaternary period.* Bokförlags aktiebolaget Thule, Stockholm.

————. 1958. *The amphi-Atlantic plants.* Kungl. Vetenskapsakademiens Handlingar. Fjärde Serien. Band. 7. Nr. 1.

HUTCHINSON, JOHN. 1926, 1934. *The families of flowering plants, arranged according to a new system based on their probable phylogeny.* Vol. I. *Dicotyledons.* Vol. II. *Monocotyledons.* Macmillan & Co., Ltd., London.

ILTIS, HUGH H., and WINSLOW M. SHAUGHNESSY. 1960. *Preliminary reports on the flora of Wisconsin.* No. 43. *Primulaceae: Primrose family.* Wisconsin Academy of Sciences, Arts, and Letters 49: 113–135.

INGER, ROBERT F. 1958. *Comments on the definition of genera.* Evolution 12: 370–384.

INGLES, LLOYD G., and NORMAND J. BIGLIONE. 1952. *The contiguity of the ranges of two subspecies of pocket gophers.* Evolution 6: 204–207.

JEPSON, WILLIS LYNN. 1909– . *A flora of California.* 3 vols. issued in parts; vols. 1, 3 incomplete. University of California Press, Berkeley, Calif.

————. 1923–1925. *A manual of the flowering plants of California.* University of California Press, Berkeley.

JOHANSEN, DONALD A. 1940. *Plant microtechnique.* McGraw-Hill Book Co., Inc., New York.

————. 1953. *Morphological criteria for the specific validity of* Pinus Jeffreyi. Madroño 12: 92–95.

JOHNSON, M. A. 1954. *The precipitin reaction as an index of relationship in the Magnoliaceae.* Serological Museum Bulletin 13: 1–5.

JONES, GEORGE NEVILLE. 1945, 1950. *Flora of Illinois.* University of Notre Dame Press, Notre Dame, Indiana.

JUST, THEODOR. 1951. *Citation of specimens in cytotaxonomic literature.* Evolution 5: 280–281.

KARPECHENKO, G. D. 1927. *Polyploid hybrids of* Raphanus sativus *L.* × Brassica oleracea *L.* Bulletin of Applied Botany 17: 305–408.

————. 1928. *Polyploid hybrids of* Raphanus sativus *L.* × Brassica oleracea *L.* Zeitschrift für induktiv Abstammungs- und Vererbungs-Lehre 48: 1–65.

KEARNEY, THOMAS H., and ROBERT H. PEEBLES. 1942. *The flowering plants and ferns of Arizona.* U.S. Department of Agriculture Miscellaneous Publication 423. Government Printing Office, Washington, D.C.

————, and ROBERT H. PEEBLES. 1951. *Arizona flora.* University of California Press, Berkeley.

KECK, DAVID D. 1951. *Systematic botany.* Science 113: 3 (preliminary pages).

————. 1957. *Trends in systematic botany.* Survey of Biological Progress 3: 47–107. Academic Press, Inc., New York.

KOHSHOO, T. N. 1959. *Polyploidy in gymnosperms.* Evolution 13: 24–39.

KRIBS, D. A. 1935. *Salient lines of structural specialization in the wood rays of dicotyledons.* Botanical Gazette 96: 547–557.

————. 1937. *Salient lines of structural specialization in the wood parenchyma of dicotyledons.* Bulletin of the Torrey Botanical Club 64: 177–186.

KRUCKEBERG, ARTHUR R. 1951. *Intraspecific variability in the response of certain native plant species to serpentine soil.* American Journal of Botany 38: 408–419.

KRUCKEBERG, ARTHUR R. 1954. *The ecology of serpentine soils: A symposium.* III. *Plant species in relation to serpentine soils.* Ecology 35: 267–274.

———. 1956. *Notes on the* Phacelia magellanica *complex in the Pacific Northwest.* Madroño 13: 209–221.

———. 1957. *Variation in fertility of hybrids between isolated populations of the serpentine species,* Streptanthus glandulosus *Hook.* Evolution 11: 185–211.

KURTZ, EDWIN B., JR. 1960. *Biochemistry of adaptation in plants to environment.* American Naturalist 94: 237–243.

LANJOUW, J. 1952, 1956. *International code of botanical nomenclature.* Adopted by the 7th International Botanical Congress, Stockholm, July, 1950. Adopted by the 8th International Botanical Congress, Paris, July, 1954. Regnum Vegetabile 6, 8, Utrecht. (Text for 1956 duplicated in English, French, German, and Spanish.)

———, and F. A. STAFLEU. 1952, 1954, 1956, 1959. *Index herbariorum.* (Regnum Vegetabile) Eds. 1–4. International Bureau for Plant Taxonomy and Nomenclature, Utrecht.

LAWRENCE, GEORGE H. M. 1951. *Plant taxonomy.* The Macmillan Co., New York.

LEACH, DAVID G. 1959. *The re-creation of a species.* The Garden Journal. New York Botanical Garden. 9: 3–4.

LEISER, ANDREW T. 1957. Rhododendron occidentale *on alkaline soil.* Rhododendron and Camelia Year Book 48–51.

LEWIS, HARLAN. 1951. *The origin of supernumerary chromosomes in natural populations of* Clarkia elegans. Evolution 5: 142–157.

———. 1953a. *The mechanism of evolution in* Clarkia. Evolution 7: 1–20.

———. 1953b. *Chromosome phylogeny and habitat preference of* Clarkia. Evolution 7: 102–109.

———. 1955. *Specific and infraspecific categories in plants.* Proceedings of the 16th Annual Biology Colloquium. Oregon State College, Office of Publications, Corvallis.

———. 1957. *Genetics and cytology in relation to taxonomy.* Taxon 6: 42–46.

———. 1961. *Experimental sympatric populations of* Clarkia. American Naturalist 95: 155–168.

———, and CARL EPLING. 1954. *A taxonomic study of some Californian delphiniums.* Brittonia 8: 1–22 (see also EPLING and LEWIS, 1952).

———, and CARL EPLING. 1959. Delphinium gypsophilum: *A diploid species of hybrid origin.* Evolution 13: 511–525.

———, and MARGARET ENSIGN LEWIS. 1955. *The genus* Clarkia. University of California Publications in Botany 20: 241–392.

———, and PETER H. RAVEN. 1958a. Clarkia franciscana: *A new species from central California.* Brittonia 10: 7–13.

———, and PETER H. RAVEN. 1958b. *Rapid evolution in* Clarkia. Evolution 12: 319–336.

———, PETER H. RAVEN, C. S. VENKATESH, and HALE L. WEDBERG. 1958. *Observations of meiotic chromosomes in the Onagraceae.* Aliso 4: 73–86.

———, and MARGARET R. ROBERTS. 1956. *The origin of* Clarkia lingulata. Evolution 10: 126–138.

LEWIS, WALTER H. 1959. *A monograph of the genus* Rosa *in North America.* I. R. acicularis. Brittonia 11: 1–24.

LEWTON, FREDERICK L. 1925. *The value of certain anatomical characters in classifying the Hibisceae.* Journal of the Washington Academy of Sciences 15: 165–172.

LINNAEUS, CAROLUS (CARL VON LINNÉ). 1753. *Species plantarum.* Ed. 1.

———. 1754, 1764. *Genera plantarum.* Eds. 5, 6.

LITTLE, ELBERT L., JR. 1957. *Three proposals toward stabilization of botanical nomenclature.* Taxon 6: 188–194. See BULLOCK, 1959.

LONG, ROBERT W. 1960. *Biosystematics of two perennial species of* Helianthus (*Compositae*). I. *Crossing relationships and transplant studies.* American Journal of Botany 47: 729–735.

————. 1961. *Biosystematics of two perennial species of* Helianthus *(Compositae).* II. *Natural populations and taxonomy.* Brittonia 13: 129–141.

LOUIS-MARIE, PÈRE. 1931. *Flore-manuel de la Province de Québec.* Institut Agricole d'Oka, Contribution 23. Montreal.

LÖVE, ÁSKELL. 1954. *The taxonomical evaluation of types with different chromosome numbers.* Proceedings of the 7th International Botanical Congress, Stockholm, 1950. 283–284.

MACDOUGAL, D. T. 1907. *Hybridization of wild plants.* Botanical Gazette 43: 45–58.

MCKELVEY, SUSAN D., and KARL SAX. 1933. *Taxonomic and cytological relationships of* Yucca *and* Agave. Journal of the Arnold Arboretum 14: 76–81.

MCMILLAN, CALVIN. 1953. *Variation in seedlings of* Cupressus Abramsiana *Wolf.* Madroño 12: 28–30.

————. 1959. *Survival of transplanted* Cupressus *in the pygmy forests of Mendocino County, California.* Madroño 15: 1–4.

MCVAUGH, ROGERS. 1952. *Suggested phylogeny of* Prunus serotina *and other wide-ranging phylads in North America.* Brittonia 7: 317–346.

MARIE-VICTORIN. 1935, 1947. *Flore Laurentienne.* Supplement by ERNEST ROULEAU, 1947. La Salle, Montreal.

MASON, CHARLES T. 1959. *A hybrid among the perennial gentians.* Brittonia 11: 40–43.

MASON, HERBERT L. 1932a. *The Santa Cruz Island Pine.* Madroño 2: 8–10.

————. 1932b. *A phylogenetic series of the California closed-cone pines suggested by the fossil record.* Madroño 2: 49–55.

————. 1934. *The Pleistocene flora of the Tomales formation.* Carnegie Institution of Washington Publication 415: 83–180.

————. 1949. *Evidence for the genetic submergence of* Pinus remorata. Paper No. 19 in *Genetics, paleontology, and evolution,* edited by GLENN L. JEPSEN, ERNST MAYR, and GEORGE GAYLORD SIMPSON. Princeton University Press, Princeton N. J. Pp. 356–362.

————. 1950. *Taxonomy, systematic botany, and bio-systematics.* Madroño 10: 193–208.

————. 1953. *Plant geography in the delimitation of genera.* Chronica Botanica 14: 154–159.

————. 1954. *Migration and evolution in plants.* Madroño 12: 161–169.

MAYR, ERNST. 1947. *Ecological factors in speciation.* Evolution 1: 263–288.

————. 1949a. *The species concept: Semantics vs. semantics.* Evolution 3: 371–372.

————. 1949b. *Comments on evolutionary literature: Species in paleontology.* Evolution 3: 381–382.

————. 1951a. *Comments on evolutionary literature: Speciation in ancient lakes.* (Review of J. L. BROOKS, 1950, *Speciation in ancient lakes.* Quarterly Review of Biology 25: 30–60, 131–176.) Evolution 5: 88.

————. 1951b. *Comments on evolutionary literature: Hybrid swarms in birds.* (Review of C. G. SIBLEY, 1950, *Species formation in the red-eyed towhees of Mexico.* University of California Publications in Zoology 50: 109–194.) Evolution 5: 88.

MEIKLE, R. D. 1957. *What is the subspecies?* Taxon 6: 102–105.

METCALFE, C. R. 1944. *An introduction, with special reference to the anatomy of the leaf and stem.* In symposium, *The taxonomic value of the anatomical structure of the vegetative organs of the dicotyledons.* Proceedings of the Linnaean Society. London. 155: 210–214.

————. 1946. *The systematic anatomy of the vegetative organs of the angiosperms.* Biological Review 21: 159–172.

————, and L. CHALK. 1950. *Anatomy of dicotyledons.* Vol. 2. Oxford University Press, London.

MICHENER, C. D., and R. R. SOKAL. 1957. *A quantitative approach to a problem of classification.* Evolution 11: 130–162.

MILNER, HAROLD W., WILLIAM M. HIESEY, and MALCOLM A. NOBS. 1958. *Physiology of climatic races.* Carnegie Institution of Washington Year Book 57: 266–270.

———, WILLIAM M. HIESEY, and MALCOLM A. NOBS. 1959. *Physiology of climatic races.* Carnegie Institution of Washington Year Book 58: 346–350.

MIROV, N. T. 1938. *Phylogenetic relations of* Pinus Jeffreyi *and* Pinus ponderosa. Madroño 4: 169–171.

———. 1953. *Taxonomy and chemistry of the white pines.* Madroño 12: 81–89.

———. 1954. *Apache pine and its relationship to ponderosa pine.* Madroño 12: 251–252.

MORAN, REID. 1949a. *Why count chromosomes?* Desert Plant Life 21: 21–27.

———. 1949b. *The Agavaceae.* Desert Plant Life 21: 64–69.

MOSELEY, M. F., JR. 1948. *Comparative anatomy and phylogeny of the Casuarinaceae.* Botanical Gazette 110: 231–280.

MULLER, CORNELIUS H. 1952. *Ecological control of hybridization in* Quercus: *a factor in the mechanism of evolution.* Evolution 6: 147–162.

MÜNTZING, A. 1930. *Outlines to a genetic monograph of the genus* Galeopsis. Hereditas 13: 185–341.

———. 1931. *Uber Chromosomenvermehrung in Geleopsis-Kreuzungen und ihre phylogenetische Bedeutung.* Hereditas 14: 153–172.

———. 1932. *Cytogenetic investigations on synthetic* Galeopsis Tetrahit. Hereditas 16: 105–154.

MUNZ, PHILIP A. 1935. *A manual of southern California botany.* J. W. Stacey, Inc., San Francisco.

———, and DAVID D. KECK. 1959. *A California flora.* University of California Press, Berkeley.

———, and J. D. LAUDERMILK. 1949. *A neglected character in western ashes* (Fraxinus). Aliso 2: 49–62.

NAST, CHARLOTTE G., and IRVING W. BAILEY. 1945. *Morphology and relationships of* Trochodendron *and* Tetracentron II. *Inflorescence, flower, and fruit.* Journal of the Arnold Arboretum 27: 186–192.

———, and IRVING W. BAILEY. 1946. *Morphology of* Euptelea *and comparison with* Trochodendron. Journal of the Arnold Arboretum 27: 186–192.

NEW YORK BOTANICAL GARDEN. 1906– . *North American flora.* I. 1–34 (incomplete); II. (1955–).

NILSSON-EHLE, H. 1911. *Kreuzungsuntersuchungen an Hafer und Wiesen.* Lunds Universitets Årrskrift N. F. Avd. 2. 7(6): 3–84.

NOBS, MALCOLM A., and WILLIAM M. HIESEY. 1958. *Performance of* Mimulus *races and their hybrids in contrasting environments.* Carnegie Institution of Washington Year Book 57: 270–272.

———, and WILLIAM M. HIESEY. 1959. *Studies on* Mimulus *transplants.* Carnegie Institution of Washington Year Book 58: 353.

NYGREN, AXEL. 1954. *Apomixis in angiosperms.* II. Botanical Review 20: 577–649. Supplement to STEBBINS, 1941a.

OWNBEY, MARION. 1950. *Natural hybridization and amphiploidy in the genus* Tragopogon. American Journal of Botany 37: 487–499.

———, and HANNAH C. AASE. 1955. *Cytotaxonomic studies in* Allium. I. *The* Allium canadense *alliance.* Research Studies of the State College of Washington. Monographic Supplement 1: 1–106.

PALMER, ERNEST J. 1948. *Hybrid oaks of North America.* Journal of the Arnold Arboretum 29: 1–48.

PARKIN, JOHN. 1928. *The glossy petal in* Ranunculus. Annals of Botany 42: 739–755.

———. 1931, 1935. *The structure of the starch layer in the glossy petal of* Ranunculus. Annals of Botany 47: 201–205. II. *The British species examined.* 49: 283–289.

PEARSON, G. A. 1923. *Natural reproduction of western yellow pine in the Southwest.* U.S. Department of Agriculture Bulletin 1105.

————. 1942. *Herbaceous vegetation as a factor in natural regeneration of ponderosa pine in the Southwest.* Ecological Monographs 12: 315–338.

————. 1950. *Management of ponderosa pine in the Southwest.* U.S. Department of Agriculture Monograph 6: 16–19, 116–117.

PECK, MORTON E. 1941. *A manual of the higher plants of Oregon.* Binfords & Mort, Portland, Ore.

PFEIFFER, HANS H. 1953. *Rapid chromosome methods.* Taxon 2: 86–87.

PICHON, M., and J. STAFLEU. 1955. *Huitième congrès international de botanique section nomenclature.* Taxon 4: 121–127. (Propositions discussed at Paris and the action on them.)

PIPER, CHARLES VANCOUVER, and R. KENT BEATTIE. 1915. *Flora of the northwest coast.* . . . New Era Printing Co., Lancaster, Pa.

PITTENDRIGH, COLIN S. 1948. *The bromeliad-Anopheles-malaria complex in Trinidad.* I. The bromeliad flora. Evolution 2: 58–89.

PORSILD, A. E. 1958. *Geographical distribution of some elements in the flora of Canada.* Geographical Bulletin No. 11. Canadian Government Publication. 57–77.

PORTER, C. L. 1959. *Taxonomy of the flowering plants.* W. H. Freeman & Co., San Francisco.

RAND, A. L. 1948. *Glaciation: An isolating factor in speciation.* Evolution 2: 314–321.

RAUP, HUGH M. 1941. *Botanical problems in boreal America.* Botanical Review 7: 147–218.

RAVEN, PETER H., and HARLAN LEWIS. 1959. *The relationship of clarkias from two continents.* Brittonia 11: 193–205.

REEDER, JOHN R. 1957. *The embryo in grass systematics.* American Journal of Botany 44: 756–768.

RICKETT, HAROLD W. 1947. *The royal botanical expedition to New Spain, 1788–1820.* Chronica Botanica 11: 1–86.

————. 1953. *Expediency vs. priority in nomenclature.* Taxon 2: 117–124.

————, and W. H. CAMP. 1955. *Toward nomenclatural stability.* Taxon 4: 37–40.

————, and F. A. STAFLEU. 1959– . *Nomina generica conservanda et rejicienda spermatophytorum.* Taxon 8: 213–243, 256–274, 282–314; 9: 67–86, 111–124, 153–160, *et seq.*

RIKER, A. J., *et al.* 1952. *Preparing literature citations.* A report prepared by the AIBS (American Institute of Biological Sciences) publications committee. AIBS Bulletin 2: 21–23.

RILEY, HERBERT P. 1938. *A character analysis of colonies of Iris fulva, Iris hexagona var. giganticaerulea, and natural hybrids.* American Journal of Botany 25: 727–738.

————. 1939a. *The problem of species in the Louisiana irises.* Bulletin of the American Iris Society 3–7 (July, 1939).

————. 1939b. *Introgressive hybridization in a natural population of Tradescantia.* Genetics 24: 753–769.

————. 1952. *Ecological barriers.* American Naturalist 86: 23–32.

————, and T. R. BRYANT. 1959. *Preliminary studies in the identification of species by the paper chromatography of fluorescent compounds.* 9th International Botanical Congress Proceedings 2: 73.

————, and T. R. BRYANT. 1961. *The Separation of nine species of the Iridaceae by paper chromatography.* American Journal of Botany 48: 133–137.

ROBERTS, E. A. H., W. WIGHT, and D. J. WOOD. 1958. *Paper chromatography as an aid to the taxonomy of thea camellias.* New Phytologist 57: 211–225.

ROBERTS, MARGARET R., and HARLAN LEWIS. 1955. *Subspeciation in Clarkia biloba.* Evolution 9: 445–454.

ROLLINS, REED C. 1941. *Monographic study of* Arabis *in western North America.* Rhodora 43: 289–325, 348–411, 425–481. (Contributions from the Gray Herbarium No. 138.)

——. 1944. *Evidence for natural hybridity between guayule* (Parthenium argentatum) *and mariola* (Parthenium incanum). American Journal of Botany 31: 93–99.

——. 1945. *Interspecific hybridization in* Parthenium. I. *Crosses between guayule* (P. argentatum) *and mariola* (P. incanum). American Journal of Botany 32: 395–404.

——. 1946. *Interspecific hybridization in* Parthenium. II. *Crosses involving* P. argentatum, P. stramonium, P. tomentosum, *and* P. hysterophorus. American Journal of Botany 33: 21–30.

——. 1949. *Sources of genetic variation in* Parthenium argentatum Gray (Compositae). Evolution 3: 358–368.

——. 1952. *Taxonomy today and tomorrow.* Rhodora 54: 1–19.

——. 1953. *Cytological approaches to the study of genera.* Chronica Botanica 14: 133–139.

——. 1957. *Taxonomy of higher plants.* American Journal of Botany 44: 188–196.

——, and D. G. CATCHESIDE. 1951. *A note on some techniques of obtaining genetic segregation in apomictic strains of the guayule rubber plant.* Genetics 36: 435–440.

ROSENDAHL, CARL OTTO. 1949. See SHERFF, 1949.

ROTHMALER, WERNER. 1950. *Allgemeine Taxonomie und Chorologie der Pflanzen: Grundzuge der speziellen Botanik.* Wilhelm Gronav, Jena.

ROUSSEAU, JACQUES. 1953. *The value of botany as an indicator of unglaciated areas.* Seventh Pacific Science Congress 5: 1–8.

ST. JOHN, HAROLD. 1937, 1956. *Flora of southeastern Washington and of adjacent Idaho.* Student Book Corp., Pullman, Wash.

——. 1946. *Endemism in the Hawaiian flora, and a revision of the Hawaiian species of* Gunnera (Haloragidaceae). *Hawaiian plant studies,* 11. Proceedings of the California Academy of Sciences 25: 377–420.

——. 1958. *Nomenclature of plants: A text for the application by the case method of the International Code of Botanical Nomenclature.* The Ronald Press Co. (A Chronica Botanica Publication), New York.

SAUER, JONATHAN D. 1951. *Studies in variation in the weed genus* Phytolacca. II. *Latitudinally adapted variants within a North American species.* Evolution 5: 273–279 (see also FASSETT and SAUER, 1950).

——. 1957. *Recent migration and evolution of the dioecious amaranths.* Evolution 11: 11–31.

SAVILE, D. B. O. 1961. *The botany of the northwestern Queen Elizabeth Islands.* Canadian Journal of Botany 39: 909–942.

SCOGGAN, H. J. 1950. *The flora of Bic and the Gaspé Peninsula, Quebec.* National Museum of Canada, Ottawa. Review by H. H. BARTLETT. Science 113: 130–131.

SCHWARTEN, LAZELLA, and HAROLD W. RICKETT. 1958. *Abbreviations of the titles of serials cited by botanists.* Bulletin of the Torrey Botanical Club 85: 277–300.

SCHWARZ, O. 1949. *Beitrage zur Kenntnis kritischer Formenkreise im Gebiete der Flora von Thuringen.* Mitteilungen der Thuringischen Botanischen Gesellschaft 1(1): 120–143.

SENN, HAROLD A. 1938. *Experimental data for a revision of the genus* Lathyrus. American Journal of Botany 25: 67–78.

SHERFF, EARLE E., et al. 1949. *Symposium on botanical nomenclature.* American Journal of Botany 36: 1–32.

SHREVE, FORREST. 1917. *The establishment of desert perennials.* Journal of Ecology 5: 210–216.

——. 1925. *Ecological aspects of the deserts of California.* Ecology 6: 93–103.

——. 1942. *The desert vegetation of North America.* Botanical Review 8: 195–246.

————. 1951. *Vegetation of the Sonoran Desert.* Vol. 1 of *Vegetation and flora of the Sonoran Desert* by FORREST SHREVE and IRA L. WIGGINS. Carnegie Institution of Washington Publication 591.

SILLIMAN, FRANCES E., and ROBERT S. LEISNER. 1958. *An analysis of a colony of hybrid oaks.* American Journal of Botany 45: 730–736.

SIMPSON, GEORGE GAYLORD. 1951. *The species concept.* Evolution 5: 285–298.

————. 1961. *Principles of animal taxonomy.* Columbia University Press, New York.

SMALL, JOHN KUNKEL. 1933. *Manual of the southeastern flora.* . . . Science Press, Inc., Lancaster, Pa.

SMITH, ALBERT C. 1949. *A legislated nomenclature for species of plants?* American Journal of Botany 36: 624–626.

————. 1957. *Fifty years of botanical nomenclature.* Brittonia 9: 2–8.

SMITH, C. EARLE. 1954–1956. *A century of botany in America.* Bartonia 28: 1–30, pl. 1–8.

SMITH, JAMES EDWARD. 1819. Ranunculus, *in* A. REES, *The cyclopedia or universal dictionary of arts, sciences, and literature.* 29: (pages not numbered).

SPORNE, K. R. 1956. *The phylogenetic classification of the angiosperms.* Biological Review 31: 1–29.

————. 1959. *On the phylogenetic classification of plants.* American Journal of Botany 46: 385–394.

STAFLEU, F. A. 1956. *Nomenclatural conservation in the phanerogams.* Taxon 5: 85–95.

STEBBINS, G. LEDYARD, JR. 1938. *Cytological characteristics associated with the different growth habits in the dicotyledons.* American Journal of Botany 25: 189–198.

————. 1940. *The significance of polyploidy in plant evolution.* American Naturalist 74: 54–66.

————. 1941a. *Apomixis in angiosperms.* Botanical Review 7: 507–542 (see NYGREN, 1954).

————. 1941b. *Additional evidence for a holarctic dispersal of flowering plants during the Mesozoic era.* Proceedings of the Sixth International Pacific Science Congress 649–660.

————. 1942a. *Polyploid complexes in relation to ecology and the history of floras.* American Naturalist 76: 36–45.

————. 1942b. *The role of isolation in the differentiation of plant species.* Biological Symposia 6: 217–233.

————. 1942c. *The genetic approach to problems of rare and endemic species.* Madroño 6: 241–258.

————. 1947. *Evidence on rates of evolution from the distribution of existing and fossil plant species.* Ecological Monographs 17: 149–158.

————. 1949. *The evolutionary significance of natural and artificial polyploids in the family Gramineae.* Proceedings of the 8th International Congress of Genetics. Hereditas. Supplementary vol. 461–485.

————. 1950. *Variation and evolution in plants.* Columbia University Press, New York. Review by CARL EPLING. Science 112: 764–766. 1950.

————. 1952. *Aridity as a stimulus to plant evolution.* American Naturalist 86: 33–44.

————. 1956a. *Taxonomy and the evolution of genera, with special reference to the family Gramineae.* Evolution 10: 235–245.

————. 1956b. *Cytogenetics and the evolution of the grass family.* American Journal of Botany 43: 890–905.

————. 1958. *Longevity, habitat, and release of genetic variability in the higher plants.* Cold Spring Harbor Symposia on Quantitative Biology 23: 365–378.

————. 1959. *The rôle of hybridization in evolution.* American Philosophical Society, Proceedings 103: 231–251.

————, and E. B. BABCOCK. 1939. *The effect of polyploidy and apomixis on the evolution of species in* Crepis. Journal of Heredity 30: 519–530.

STEBBINS, G. LEDYARD, JR., and K. DALY. 1961. *Changes in the variation pattern of a hybrid population of* Helianthus *over an eight-year period.* Evolution 15: 60–71.

———, and FUNG TING PUN. 1953. *Artificial and natural hybrids in the Gramineae, Tribe Hordeae.* V. *Diploid hybrids of* Agropyron. American Journal of Botany 40: 444–449.

———, and J. A. JENKINS. 1939. *Aposporic development in the North American species of* Crepis. Genetics 21: 191–224.

———, and R. M. LOVE. 1941a. *A cytological study of California forage grasses.* American Journal of Botany 28: 371–382.

———, and R. M. LOVE. 1941b. *An undescribed species of* Stipa *from California.* Madroño 6:137–141.

———, E. B. MATZKE, and C. EPLING. 1947. *Hybridization in a population of* Quercus marilandica *and* Quercus ilicifolia. Evolution 1: 79–88.

———, and H. A. TOGBY. 1944. *The cytogenetics of hybrids in* Bromus. I. *Hybrids within the section* Ceratochloa. American Journal of Botany 31: 1–11.

———, H. A. TOGBY, and JACK R. HARLAN. 1944. *The cytogenetics of hybrids in* Bromus. II. Bromus carinatus *and* Bromus arizonicus. Proceedings of the California Academy of Sciences IV. 25: 307–322.

———, and MARTA S. WALTERS. 1949. *Artificial and natural hybrids in the Gramineae, Tribe Hordeae.* III. *Hybrids involving* Elymus condensatus *and* E. triticoides. American Journal of Botany 36: 291–301.

STEVENS, A. O. 1950. *Handbook of North Dakota plants.* North Dakota Agricultural College. Knight Printing Co., Fargo, North Dakota.

STONE, DONALD E. 1959. *A unique breeding system in the vernal pool mousetails.* Evolution 13: 151–174.

STRAW, RICHARD M. 1955. *Hybridization, homogamy, and sympatric speciation.* Evolution 9: 441–444.

———. 1956. *Floral isolation in* Penstemon. American Naturalist 90: 47–53.

STURTEVANT, A. H. 1948. *Evolution and function of genes.* American Scientist 36: 225–236.

SYMPOSIUM ON BOTANICAL NOMENCLATURE. 1949. American Journal of Botany 36: 1–32 (see SHERFF *et al.*, 1949).

THOMPSON, HENRY J. 1953. *The biosystematics of* Dodecatheon. Contributions from the Dudley Herbarium 4: 73–154.

THORNE, ROBERT F. 1958. *Some guiding principles of angiosperm phylogeny.* Brittonia 10: 72–77.

TIPPO, OSWALD. 1938. *Comparative anatomy of the Moraceae and their presumed allies.* Botanical Gazette 100: 1–99.

———. 1946. *The rôle of wood anatomy in phylogeny.* American Midland Naturalist 36: 362–372.

TRAUB, HAMILTON P. 1953. *Rapid chromosome methods for the taxonomist.* Taxon 2: 28–29.

TRELEASE, WILLIAM F. 1917. *Naming American hybrid oaks.* Proceedings of the American Philosophical Society 56: 44–52.

TUCKER, JOHN M. 1952a. *Evolution of the Californian oak,* Quercus Alvordiana. Evolution 6: 162–180.

———. 1952b. *Taxonomic interrelationships in the* Quercus dumosa *complex.* Madroño 11: 234–251.

———. 1953. *Two new oak hybrids from California.* Madroño 12: 119–127.

———. 1961. *Studies in the* Quercus undulata *complex.* I. *A preliminary statement.* American Journal of Botany 48: 202–208.

———, WALTER P. COTTAM, and RUDY DROBNICK. 1961. *Studies in the* Quercus undulata *complex.* II. *The contribution of* Quercus turbinella. American Journal of Botany 48: 329–339.

———, and HORACE S. HASKELL. 1960. Quercus Dunnii *and* Q. chrysolepsis *in Arizona.* Brittonia 12: 196–219.

————, and CORNELIUS H. MULLER. 1956. *The geographic history of* Quercus ajoensis. Evolution 10: 157–175.

————, and CORNELIUS H. MULLER. 1958. *A reëvaluation of the derivation of* Quercus margaretta *from* Quercus gambelii. Evolution 12: 1–17.

————, and JONATHAN D. SAUER. 1958. *Aberrant* Amaranthus *populations of the* Sacramento–San Joaquin Delta, California. Madroño 14: 252–261.

TURESSON, G. 1922a. *The species and variety as ecological units.* Hereditas 3: 100–113.

————. 1922b. *The genotypical response of the plant species to the habitat.* Hereditas 3: 211–350.

————. 1925. *The plant species in relation to habitat and climate.* Hereditas 6: 147–236.

————. 1927. *Contributions to the genecology of glacial relics.* Hereditas 9: 81–101.

TURNER, B. L., and RALPH ALSTON. 1959. *Segregation and recombination of chemical constituents in a hybrid swarm of* Baptisia laevicaulis × B. viridis *and their taxonomic implications.* American Journal of Botany 46: 678–686.

TURRILL, W. B. 1950. *Character combinations and distribution of the genus* Fritillaria *and allied genera.* Evolution 4: 1–6.

UHL, CHARLES H. 1956. *The Crassulaceae and cytotaxonomy.* Cactus and Succulent Journal 28: 28–30.

————. 1961. *Some cytotaxonomic problems in the Crassulaceae.* Evolution 15: 375–377.

VALENTINE, D. H., and ÁSKELL LÖVE. 1958. *Taxonomic and biosystematic categories.* Brittonia 10: 153–166.

VAN DER PIJL, L. 1960, 1961. *Ecological aspects of flower evolution.* I. *Phyletic evolution.* II. *Zoöphilous flower classes.* Evolution 14: 403–416; 15: 30–43.

VASEY, GEORGE. 1883. *On the hybrid oaks near Washington, D. C.* Bulletin of the Torrey Botanical Club 10: 25–26.

VESTAL, P. A. 1937. *The significance of comparative anatomy in establishing the relationship of the Hypericaceae to the Guttiferae and their allies.* Philippine Journal of Science 64: 199–256.

————. 1940. *Wood anatomy as an aid to classification and phylogeny.* Chronica Botanica 6: 53–54.

VICKERY, ROBERT K., JR. 1959. *Barriers to gene exchange within* Mimulus guttatus (Scrophulariaceae). Evolution 13: 300–310.

————, and C. DWAYNE OGZEWALLA. 1958. *A progress report on a new method for the study of the nature of species.* Utah Academy of Sciences, Proceedings 35: 91–94.

————, and RICHARD L. OLSON. 1956. *Flower color inheritance in the* Mimulus cardinalis *complex.* Journal of Heredity 47: 194–199.

VIOSCA, P. 1935. *The irises of southeastern Louisiana.* Bulletin of the American Iris Society. 3–56.

WAGENER, WILLIS W. 1960. *A comment on cold susceptibility of ponderosa and Jeffrey pines.* Madroño 15: 217–219.

WAGNER, WARREN H., JR. 1954. *Reticulate evolution in Appalachian aspleniums.* Evolution 8: 103–118.

————, and THOMAS DARLING, JR. 1957. *Synthetic and wild* Asplenium Gravesii. Brittonia 9: 56–63.

WARD, GEORGE H. 1953. Artemisia, *section* Serphidium, *in North America: A cytotaxonomic study.* Contributions from the Dudley Herbarium, Stanford University 4: 155–205.

WARMKE, HARRY E. 1935. *A permanent root tip smear method.* Stain Technology 10: 101–103.

WATSON, SERENO. 1878. *Bibliographic index to North American Botany.* Washington, D. C.

WEATHERBY, C. A. 1942. *Subspecies.* Rhodora 44: 157–167.

Weber, William A. 1953. *Handbook of the plants of the Colorado Front Range.* University of Colorado Press, Denver.

Went, F. W. 1948, 1949. *Ecology of desert plants.* I. *Observations on germination in the Joshua Tree National Monument, California.* II. *The effect of rain and temperature on germination and growth.* Ecology 29: 242–253; 30: 1–13.

Whitaker, Thomas W. 1934. *Chromosome constitution in certain monocotyledons.* Journal of the Arnold Arboretum 15: 135–143.

———. 1959. *An interspecific cross in* Cucurbita (C. Lundelliana × C. moschata Duch.). Madroño 15: 4–13.

Wodehouse, Roger P. 1935. *Pollen grains.* McGraw-Hill Book Co., Inc., New York.

———. 1936. *Evolution of pollen grains.* Botanical Review 2: 67–84.

Wolf, Carl B. 1938. *California plant notes* II. Rancho Santa Ana Botanic Garden. Occasional Papers I(2): 44–90.

Woodford, Alfred O. 1924. *The Catalina metamorphic facies of the Franciscan series.* University of California Publications. Geology 15: 49–68.

Wooton, E. O., and Paul C. Standley. 1915. *Flora of New Mexico.* Contributions from the U.S. National Herbarium 19. Government Printing Office, Washington, D.C.

Wunderlich, Rosalie. 1950. *Die Agavaceae Hutchinsons im Lichte ihres Embryologie, ihres Gynözeums-, Staubblatt- und Blattbaues.* Österreichische Botanische Zeitschrift 97: 438–502.

Wynne-Edwards, V. C. 1937. *Isolated Arctic-alpine floras in eastern North America: A discussion of their glacial and recent history.* Transactions of the Royal Society of Canada II(5)31: 1–26.

———. 1939. *Some factors in the isolation of rare alpine plants.* Transactions of the Royal Society of Canada. III(5)33: 35–42.

Zimmerman, Elwood C. 1948. *Insects of Hawaii.* 5 vols. University of Hawaii Press, Honolulu.

———. 1960. *Possible evidence of rapid evolution in Hawaiian moths.* Evolution 14: 137–138.

Zobel, Bruce. 1951. *The natural hybrid between Coulter and Jeffrey pines.* Evolution 5: 405–413.

———. 1953. *Geographic range and intraspecific variation of Coulter pine.* Madroño 12: 1–7.

Index

Page numbers in Roman type (143) indicate that a subject is discussed significantly on the page given. Some subjects, such as taxonomy, evolution, and hybridization, appear throughout the book, and no attempt is made to list all pages upon which they appear. **Boldface type** (**143**) indicates the first page of a major discussion or a critical explanation of a subject. *Italics* (*143*) indicate an illustration. Personal names are indicated only as they appear in the text or in a list of publications at the ends of chapters; names in the list of references on pages 451–470 are not indexed.